The Agricultural
Development of
Venezuela

This volume is No. 5 in the series entitled *Bench Mark Studies on Agricultural Development in Latin America*. The other books in the series are:

THE AGRICULTURAL DEVELOPMENT OF URUGUAY
Problems of Government Policy
by Russell H. Brannon   (1967)

THE AGRICULTURAL DEVELOPMENT OF MEXICO
Its Structure and Growth Since 1950
by Eduardo L. Venezian
William K. Gamble   (1969)

THE AGRICUTURAL DEVELOPMENT OF ARGENTINA
A Policy and Development Perspective
by Darrell F. Fienup
Russell H. Brannon
Frank A. Fender   (1969)

THE AGRICULTURAL DEVELOPMENT OF PERU
by Arthur J. Coutu
Richard A. King   (1969)

THE AGRICULTURAL DEVELOPMENT OF BRAZIL
by G. Edward Schuh, in collaboration
with Eliseu Roberto Alves   (Forthcoming)

PRAEGER SPECIAL STUDIES IN
INTERNATIONAL ECONOMICS AND DEVELOPMENT

The Agricultural Development of Venezuela

Louis E. Heaton

**Foreword by Lowell S. Hardin,
The Ford Foundation**

PRAEGER PUBLISHERS
New York • Washington • London

The purpose of the Praeger Special Studies is to make specialized research monographs in U.S. and international economics and politics available to the academic, business, and government communities. For further information, write to the Special Projects Division, Praeger Publishers, Inc., 111 Fourth Avenue, New York, N.Y. 10003.

PRAEGER PUBLISHERS
111 Fourth Avenue, New York, N.Y. 10003, U.S.A.
5, Cromwell Place, London S.W.7, England

Published in the United States of America in 1969
by Praeger Publishers, Inc.

Library of Congress Catalog Card Number: 68-55006

Printed in the United States of America

FOREWORD

This book is based on one of several agricultural
"bench mark" studies undertaken under Ford Foundation
sponsorship in Latin American countries during 1966
and 1967. The researchers addressed themselves to
questions such as: What changes are taking place in
each country's agricultural output and productivity?
Are levels of per capita food production, human nutrition, and rural living rising? What relationships exist between the performance of the agricultural sector
and the nation's total economic development? Can the
strengths and weaknesses of the agricultural sector
be identified? What are the major impediments to
more rapid rates of advance? Among the means of accelerating agricultural development, which should be
given priority? Subjective judgments necessarily are
involved in the analysis of such questions. The potential for improvement, however, is substantial and
real.

If the potential is great, why has it not been
realized? A partial answer is that much of today's
advanced technology for food and fiber production is
developed to meet the needs of production within a
specific geographical area. Modern agricultural
production techniques developed in temperate zones
generally do not transfer directly to different envi-
ronments. Moreover, it is difficult to project the
rate at which new, well-adapted technology may be developed in a particular country. This, in turn,
complicates attempts to estimate a nation's future
comparative advantage in the production of a crop or
an animal product. Historically, it was presumed that
developing nations had relative advantages in agriculture, compared with industry; these countries were
important exporters of agricultural products, including the food grains. In recent years, however, the

v

net flow of trade in basic food crops has been from
the developed to the less-developed nations.

Public and private investments in production research, educational programs, provision of fertilizer
and other inputs, and infrastructure development compete for scarce resources. In the absence of systematic evaluation and policy guidelines, therefore,
policy decisions concerning resource development and
use may be the product of short-run pressures, rather
than contributions to a rational plan.

This study of Venezuela (and related studies in
the series) indicates that several nations that formerly gave top priority to industrialization now are
re-examining the potential contribution of agriculture to balanced development. Research in agricultural production technology carried on in tropical
and subtropical regions has been greatly stimulated
by the performance of the new Mexican wheat and Phil-
ippine rice varieties. Multidisciplinary teams have
shown that substantial yield increases can be profit-
ably obtained.

Although capacity to advance production technology
is necessary, this capability in itself constitutes
only part of the total effort needed for rapid economic growth. Structural, institutional, policy, and
organizational changes often are equally important.
Work in the policy area, however, is often more con-
troversial and harder to evaluate than is production
research. As this study demonstrates, key questions
in the policy-organization-planning area remain to be
answered. It is at the interface where agriculture,
industry, and public policy meet that the most significant questions are raised.

Lowell S. Hardin
The Ford Foundation
June, 1968

PREFACE AND ACKNOWLEDGMENTS

The preparation of the analysis presented herein, including the gathering of data, was accomplished in Venezuela during the latter part of 1966 and the early months of 1967. Although the author directed the study and performed the task of writing an account of the results, the work was basically a team effort, with several Venezuelan agricultural technicians and organizations taking part. Consequently, acknowledgment is gratefully extended to the following organizations, who made the study possible, and to the several technicians who provided information or counsel with regard to the work:

The Consejo de Bienestar Rural (CBR), or Rural Welfare Council, in Caracas provided its office and staff facilities for executing the study. The Ford Foundation provided the funds for carrying out the study, through a grant to CBR.

The following Venezuelan technicians offered valuable assistance: Juan Guevara and J. A. Jiménez Martucci, who worked as assistants to the author; Arnaldo Ron Pedrique, Haydée Castillo, and Alonso Calatrava, Jr., who were the principal consultants; and the regular CBR staff members--Edgardo Mondolfi, Hugo Estrada, Ricardo Gondelles, Ricardo Araque, José L. Zúñiga, Oswaldo Peraza, Bernardo Herrera Aldana, Bernardo Herrera Klindt, César Jiménez, Evelio Tovar, Martín Rivero, and Irma González. The assistance of Antonio Pons and Cristina Villoria, who managed the study reproduction work, is also acknowledged.

Finally, the counseling of the Ford Foundation representatives, F. F. Hill, Lowell S. Hardin, and Roy W. Crawley, is acknowledged with thanks.

CONTENTS

                                                            Page

FOREWORD BY LOWELL S. HARDIN   v

PREFACE AND ACKNOWLEDGMENTS   vii

LIST OF TABLES   xiv

LIST OF FIGURES   xxiii

GLOSSARY OF ABBREVIATIONS AND TERMS   xxiv

Chapter

1   INTRODUCTION   3

     Purpose of the Study   3
     Principal Objectives of the Study   3
     Scope of the Investigation   4

2   THE ECONOMIC DEVELOPMENT OF VENEZUELA   5

     Recent History of the Venezuelan Economy   5
     Status of Economic Indicators   11
        Gross Territorial Product   11
        National Income   16
        Existing Capital and Annual Investment
           in the Economy   19
        Foreign-Exchange and International
           Reserve Balances   22
        Exports and Imports   24
        Indexes of Product Price Changes   30
        Demographic and Employment Situation   32
        Other Service Facilities of Importance   44
           to the Economy of Venezuela   44
     Projections for 1970 and 1975 for General
           Economic Indicators   45
        Forecasts for Gross Territorial Product   48

Forecasts for Fixed Gross Investment   49
Forecasts for Population Growth   50
Forecasts for Employment or Occupation   51
Observations on Major Obstacles and Problems
        in Future General Economic Development
        of Venezuela   52
Notes   57

3   AGRICULTURE'S ROLE IN THE ECONOMY   59

Contribution to the Gross Territorial   60
        Product
Portion of the Total Population Dependent on
        Agriculture   61
Source and Consumption of Agricultural
        Products in Venezuela   65
Political Influence of the Agricultural
        Sector in Determining Development
        Policies   66
Notes   70

4   PUBLIC ATTITUDE TOWARD AGRICULTURE   71

Review of Recent Laws and Decrees Concerning 72
        Agriculture
Public Investment in Support of Agriculture   75
Private Investment in Development and
        Services for Agriculture   82
Agricultural Education Facilities and
        Support for Agriculture   93
Capital Transfers in and out of Agricul-
        ture and Capital Formation in this
        Sector   94

5   DYNAMICS OF THE AGRICULTURE   97

Land Use on Farms   97
Land Tenancy   99
Size of Farms   103
Agricultural Production and Productivity   110
   Crop Production Data   110
   Livestock and Livestock Production   111
   Fishing Industry   120
   Forest Products   121

Chapter   Page

    Some Regional Agricultural Production   123
        Characteristics
    Production Costs   135
    Rural Family Incomes and Welfare   143
    Rural Employment and Unemployment   145
    Notes   146

6   VENEZUELA'S AGRICULTURAL PROGRESS   148

    Government Institutional Services Available
        to Agriculture and Contributing to
        Progress in Rural Areas   149
        Educational Facilities   149
            Technical Schools of Agriculture   150
            Higher Educational Facilities
                for Agriculture   153
        Technical Agricultural Investigation
            Facilities and Personnel   157
        Agricultural Extension Facilities and
            Personnel   162
        Product Regulation and Control Services
            in Agriculture   166
        Natural Resource Development and Control
            Services in Agriculture   168
            Evaluation of Basic Natural
                Resources   168
            Irrigation Development   170
            Natural Resource Control and
                Conservation Services   172
        Distribution and Market Facilities   174
            Road Facilities   175
            Agricultural Cooperatives   175
            Market Facilities for Agricultural
                Products   177
        Agricultural Credit Facilities   178
        Agrarian Reform Services   189
    Private Services of an Institutional Nature
        Available to Farmers   194
        Private Research and Extension Agencies   194
    Progress in Adoption of Improved Agricul-
        tural Technology   196
        Mechanization in Agriculture   197
        Use of Fertilizer   200
        Use of Pesticides   205

Chapter   Page

       Improved Seed Use   206
       Livestock Breeding Improvements   207
       Livestock Feeding Improvements   210
    Rural Housing Improvements   212
    Summary of Improved Technology and Eco-
       nomic Status by Principal Crop
       and Livestock Activities   215
  Notes   226

7   PROBLEMS AND OBSTACLES   228

  Obstacles Related to Land and Other
       Natural Resource Utilization   229
  Obstacles Related to Labor and Labor Skills   232
  Obstacles Related to Capital Supplies
       and Utilization   234
  Obstacles Related to Organization and
       Management of the Basic Factors
       of Production   239
  Other Impediments to Agricultural
       Development   242
    Marketing and Distribution of Agricul-
       tural Products   243
    General Government Policies and Services
       with Respect to Agricultural Develop-
       ment   245

8   PROJECTIONS TO 1975   248

  Forecasts of Supply and Demand of Important
       Products for 1970 and 1975   248
    Exports   249
    Imports   252
    Other Products   254
  Predictions of Improvements in Institutional
       Services for Agricultural Development   256
    Institutions Involved in Technological
       Improvement Activities   256
    Institutions Providing Credit and Other
       Capital Services   259
    Land Resources and Development   259
  General Forecasts of Agricultural
       Development   260

Chapter   Page

9   ACCELERATING AGRICULTURAL DEVELOPMENT   263

     General Suggestions with Respect to Economic
         Factors of Production   265
     Land and Other Natural Resources   265
             Scientific Description and
                 Evaluation of Natural Resources   266
             Cadastral Survey Work   268
             Strengthening Other Institutional
                 Services Related to Basic
                 Resources   270
     Labor Skills and Their Utilization   273
             General Educational Systems   273
             Agricultural Extension Service   276
             Agrarian Reform Program and
                 Farm Labor Skills   277
     Capital Supplies and Their Utilization   281
     Management of the Factors of Production
         and Distribution of Products   284
             Micro-Economic Studies, Training,
                 and Orientation   284
             Clarification of Objectives in
                 Establishment of Measurable
                 Goals for Agencies Administer-
                 ing Agricultural Development
                 Programs   287
             Establishing a Civil Service Law
                 for Public Employees   288
     Ideas for Increasing Rate of Growth for
         Specific Agricultural Commodities   289
     Priority Action Projects Leading to Higher
         Rates of Agricultural Development
         in Venezuela   298
     Notes   302

APPENDIXES   303

ABOUT THE AUTHOR

LIST OF TABLES

Table   Page

1   Total Income of the Venezuelan Petroleum
     Industry in Relation to the Total
     Fiscal Income of the Venezuelan Govern-
     ment, 1945-65   7

2   Oil Exports and Inflow of Foreign Exchange
     Attributable to the Petroleum Industry
     in Venezuela, 1945-65   7

3   Gross Territorial Product of Venezuela by
     Principal Economic Sectors, 1961-65   12

4   Productivity per Economically Active Person
     and by Economic Sectors in Venezuela,
     1961-65   15

5   Distribution of Venezuela's Gross Terri-
     torial Product Between Production for
     Export and Production for Domestic
     Use, 1960-65   17

6   Distribution of Venezuela's Gross National
     Income According to Contribution of the
     Agricultural and Other Sectors and
     Remuneration of Labor and Capital,
     1961-65   18

7   Fixed Capital in the Agricultural and
     Other Sectors of the Venezuelan
     Economy, 1961-65   20

8   Gross Territorial Product and Fixed Capi-
     tal in the Agricultural and Other
     Sectors of the Venezuelan Economy,
     1961-65   22

xiv

Table   Page

 9   Gross Fixed Investment in the Agricultural
      and Other Sectors of the Venezuelan
      Economy, 1961-65   23

10   Importing Capacity of Venezuela, 1961-65   25

11   Foreign-Exchange Balances and Level of
      International Reserves in Venezuela,
      1961-65   26

12   Venezuelan Exports by Product Groups,
      1961-65   27

13   Venezuelan Imports by Product Groups,
      1961-65   28

14   Total, Urban, and Rural Population of
      Venezuela by Major Age Groups: 1950,
      1961, and 1965   34

15   Distribution of Venezuela's Population
      by Localities, 1961   36

16   Employment in Major Economic Sectors and
      Total Economically Active Persons in
      Venezuela, 1961 and 1964   38

17   Comparison of Total Educational Costs and
      Increases in Gross Territorial Product
      in Venezuela, 1957-65   40

18   Illiteracy Among Persons Fifteen Years of
      Age and Older in Venezuela, 1941-65   41

19   Student Registration and Number of
      Schools and Teachers in Venezuela,
      1964-66   43

20   Extent of Public Service Facilities in
      Venezuela, 1965   46

21   Forecast of Venezuela's Gross Territorial
      Product for 1970 and 1975   48

Table   Page

22   Forecast of Venezuela's Fixed Gross
         Investment for 1970 and 1975   49

23   Forecast of Venezuela's Rural and Urban
         Population for 1970 and 1975   50

24   Forecast of Venezuelan Employment, 1970
         and 1975   51

25   Relationship of Agricultural Product
         Groups to Total Agricultural
         Production in Venezuela, 1961-65   62

26   Comparison of Venezuela's Ten Most
         Remunerative Agricultural Products,
         1961 and 1965   63

27   Venezuelan Population Dependent on
         Agriculture, by Sectors, 1961   64

28   Estimated Venezuelan Population Depen-
         dent on Agriculture, 1961-65   64

29   Venezuelan Government Expenditures
         Allocated to Agriculture, 1962-65   76

30   Estimated Agricultural Expenditures
         and Investments in Venezuela, 1966-68   78

31   Gross Fixed Investment in Venezuelan
         Agriculture, 1961-65   79

32   Value of Permanent Improvements and
         Livestock and Machinery Inventories
         in Venezuelan Agriculture, 1961-65   81

33   Venezuelan Government Grain Storage
         Facilities by Types and Number of
         Locations, 1964   82

34   Storage Capacity in Processing Plants
         for Venezuela's Agricultural
         Products by Regions and States, 1964   84

Table   Page

35   Storage Facilities Related to Population
         Distribution in Venezuela, 1965   86

36   Number and Production of Processing
         Plants Utilizing Agricultural Products,
         by Types of Industries, 1961-65   88

37   Comparison of Land Use on Farms, 1950
         and 1961   98

38   Distribution of Farm Land Area by
         Tenancy Status, 1950 and 1961   100

39   Tenancy Pattern with Respect to Number
         and Size of Farms, 1950 and 1961   101

40   Families Benefited and Areas Involved in
         Venezuela's Land Settlement Activities,
         1959-65   102

41   Number of Farms in Venezuela and Total
         Land Area in Farms, by Size Groups,
         1950 and 1961   104

42   Comparison of Size of Venezuelan Farms,
         1950 and 1961   106

43   Increase in Number of Farms in Venezuela
         Between 1950 and 1961   107

44   Number and Area of Farms in Eight Latin
         American Countries   108

45   Area Harvested and Total Production of
         Important Crops in Venezuela, 1961-65   112

46   Value of Production and Yields of Impor-
         tant Crops in Venezuela, 1961-65   114

47   International Comparison of Yields of
         Four Crops   117

48   Production and Value of Livestock, Fish,
         and Forest Products in Venezuela,
         1961-65   118

Table   Page

49   Land Used for Crops in Venezuela in 1965
         and Percentage Change Between 1961
         and 1965, by Regions   128

50   Average Yields of Important Venezuelan
         Crops in 1965 and Percentage Change
         from 1961 to 1965, by Regions   132

51   Venezuelan Cattle and Hog Inventories
         in 1961 and Percentage Change
         Between 1950 and 1961, by Regions   134

52   Land Area and Population Comparisons:
         Selected Regions and Venezuela as
         a Whole   136

53   Annual Direct Production Costs of Im-
         portant Crops in Venezuela, 1963   138

54   Costs of Machinery and Skilled Labor
         Utilized in Mechanized Farming
         Operations in Venezuela, 1963   140

55   Graduates of Practical and Specialized
         Schools for Agriculture in Venezuela,
         1934-65   152

56   Graduates of Agricultural and Forestry
         Universities in Venezuela, 1940-65   154

57   Funds Spent by Venezuelan Government
         for Subprofessional and Professional
         Education in Agronomy and Veterinary
         Medicine, 1961-65   161

58   Agricultural Research Personnel in Venez-
         uela's Ministry of Agriculture and
         Livestock, 1955 and 1960-64   159

59   Annual Budgets of the Branches of the
         Agricultural Investigation Department
         of Venezuela's Ministry of Agriculture
         and Livestock, 1962-65   160

Table   Page

60   Personnel of the Agricultural Extension
         Service of Venezuela's Ministry of
         Agriculture and Livestock, 1966   163

61   Budgets of the Agricultural Extension
         Service of Venezuela's Ministry of
         Agriculture and Livestock, 1962-66   165

62   5-V Youth Clubs Operating in Venezuela,
         1963-65   167

63   Irrigation Systems and Land Areas Under
         Irrigation in Venezuela, 1965   171

64   Main Roads in Service and Rural Access
         Roads Constructed in Venezuela, 1959-65   176

65   Total Number and Amounts of Loans Approved
         by Venezuela's Agricultural and
         Livestock Bank, 1961-65   180

66   Supervised Credit Program Agricultural
         Loans Made in Venezuela, 1963-65   183

67   Total Funds in the Loan Portfolio of
         Venezuela's Agricultural and Livestock
         Bank, 1961-65   185

68   Source of Loan Funds Utilized by Venez-
         uela's Agricultural and Livestock Bank
         for "Own Account" Loans, 1961-65   187

69   Comparison of Total Administrative Costs
         of Credit Operations of Venezuela's
         Agricultural and Livestock Bank with
         Total Loan Portfolio, Loan Funds Ad-
         vanced, and Amounts Collected, 1961-65   188

70   Expenditures of Venezuela's National
         Agrarian Institute for the Physical
         Resource Base for Land Settlements,
         1959-65   191

71   Value of Agricultural Production of Farms
     in Settlements Established by
     Venezuela's National Agrarian
     Institute, 1961-65   193

72   Number and Types of Tractors in Use on
     Venezuelan Farms, 1961-65   198

73   Land Tilled with Machinery in Venezuela
     by Major Crops, 1965   199

74   Use of Fertilizers in Venezuela, 1961-65   202

75   Prices and Nutrient Content of Fertil-
     izers Sold by the Venezuelan Petro-
     chemical Institute, 1965   203

76   Fertilizer Nutrients Applied per Hectare
     of Total Crop Land in Venezuela,
     1961-65   204

77   Factors Determining Use of Fertilizer on
     Four Important Venezuelan Crops, 1965   204

78   Importation of Pesticides into Venezuela,
     1961-65   206

79   Seed Certified by Venezuela's Ministry
     of Agriculture and Livestock, 1961-65   208

80   Purebred Cattle and Hogs in Venezuela's
     Official Registries, 1962-65   209

81   Production of Feed Concentrates for
     Venezuelan Livestock, 1961-65   211

82   Improvements in Venezuela's Crop Produc-
     tion Methods, Rate of Productivity,
     and Agronomic Practices from
     1961 to 1965   217

83   Effectiveness of Functioning of Certain
     Institutional Services with Regard to
     the Production of Selected Crops in
     Venezuela, 1966   218

Table   Page

84   Influence of Modern Technology on the
         Production of Selected Crops in
         Venezuela, 1966   219

85   Effect of Improved Animal Husbandry
         Practices on Venezuelan Livestock
         Production Between 1961 and 1965   220

86   Effectiveness of Functioning of Certain
         Institutional Services with Regard to
         Selected Livestock Production Activ-
         ities in Venezuela, 1966   221

87   Influence of Modern Technology on the
         Production of Selected Livestock
         Products in Venezuela, 1966   222

88   Supply and Demand, Consumption, and
         Prices of Selected Agricultural Prod-
         ucts in Venezuela, 1965 and 1966   223

89   Economic Feasibility of Production of
         Selected Venezuelan Crops in 1965   225

90   Projection of Supply and Demand and
         Export and Import Possibilities for
         Selected Venezuelan Agricultural
         Products, 1970 and 1975   250

91   Suggested Long-Range Production Possi-
         bilities for Important Venezuelan
         Agricultural Products   290

                            APPENDIX

 1   Land Use on Farms in Selected Regions
         of Venezuela, 1961   305

 2   Estimates of 1965 Fruit Production in
         Venezuela   307

 3   Changes in Amount of Land Harvested and
         in Total Production of Important
         Crops in Venezuela, 1961-65   308

Table   Page

4   Changes in Production of Livestock, Fish,
     and Forest Products in Venezuela,
     1961-65   310

5   Gross Territorial Product of Venezuela
     by Principal Economic Sectors,
     1966-67   312

6   Distribution of Venezuela's Gross National
     Income According to Contribution of
     Agricultural and Other Sectors,
     1966-67   313

7   Fixed Capital in the Agricultural and
     Other Sectors of the Venezuelan
     Economy, 1966-67   314

8   Foreign-Exchange Balances and Level of
     International Reserves in Venezuela,
     1966-67   315

9   Area Harvested, Amount and Value of Total
     Production, and Yields of Important
     Crops in Venezuela, 1966-67   316

10   Production and Value of Livestock, Fish,
     and Forest Products in Venezuela,
     1966-67   318

11   Graduates of Practical and Specialized
     Schools for Agriculture in Venezuela,
     1934-67   319

12   Graduates of Agricultural and Forestry
     Universities in Venezuela, 1940-66   320

LIST OF FIGURES

Figure   Page

1   Venezuela and Its Geographical
           Location in South America   2

2   Comparison of Relative Annual
           Changes in Venezuela's Gross
           Territorial Product and
           Agricultural Production,
           1950-65   14

3   Selected Price Indexes for Venez-
           uela, 1961-65   31

4   Comparison of Indexes of Change in
           Crop Area Harvested, Crop Pro-
           duction, and Crop Yield, 1961-65   116

5   Venezuelan Agricultural Production
           Regions   124

GLOSSARY OF ABBREVIATIONS AND TERMS

Agricultural sector	In Venezuela, this sector includes all crop and livestock production activities, plus forestry and fishing activities, but excludes the manufacturing aspects related to these activities.
AIA	American International Association for Economic and Social Development
BAP	Agricultural and Livestock Bank
BCV	The Central Bank of Venezuela
BID or IDB	Inter-American Development Bank
Bs.	Bolivars, the monetary unit of Venezuela
CBR	Consejo de Bienestar Rural, or Rural Welfare Council (a private agency)
CEPAL or ECLA	Economic Commission for Latin America (a United Nations agency)
CIA	Center of Agricultural Investigation, the Ministry of Agriculture and Livestock
CIDA or ICAD	Inter-American Committee for Agricultural Development (sponsored by FAO, CEPAL, BID, OAS, and IAIAS)
CIP	Fish Research Center of the Ministry of Agriculture and Livestock

CIV	Veterinarian Investigation Center of the Ministry of Agriculture and Livestock
CONZUPLAN	Planning Council for Zulia State
CORDIPLAN	Presidential Office for Coordinating and Planning
CORPOANDES	Development Corporation of the Andes (Mérida, Táchira, and Trujillo)
CVF	Venezuelan Development Corporation
CVG	Venezuelan Guayana Corporation (regional authority in eastern Venezuela)
ECLA	See CEPAL
Economically active population	Total number of persons working or seeking work in economically remunerative activities
FAO	United Nations Food and Agriculture Organization
FEDEAGRO	Federation of Agricultural Producers
FUDECO	Development Fund for West Central States (Falcón, Lara, and Yaracuy)
GTP	Gross territorial product, also known as gross domestic product. In Venezuela, GTP is calculated by the Central Bank of Venezuela on the basis of the total market prices of the products of each sector of the economy, adjusted to 1957 constant bolivar values. In the case of agriculture, the value of the product used in calculating GTP is slightly less than the estimated value of production to producers at estimated prices.

Ha.	Hectare (equal to 2.471 acres)
IAIAS	Inter-American Institute of Agricultural Sciences of the OAS
IAN	National Agrarian Institute
IBRD	International Bank for Reconstruction and Development (World Bank)
ICAD	See CIDA
IDB	See BID
IICA	See IAIAS
IMF	International Monetary Fund
INCE	National Institute for Vocational Education
INTERSAN	International Harvester Machinery Agency
IRFED	French consulting group of CORDIPLAN
IVP	Venezuelan Petrochemical Institute
latifundio	An area with very large farms predominating
MAC	Ministry of Agriculture and Livestock
ME	Ministry of Education
MERSIFRICA	Markets, Silos and Cold Storage Corporation (special government corporation to manage markets and storage facilities in the Federal District)
MINDEFOM	Ministry of Development

minifundio	A cluster of very small farm units
MOP	Ministry of Public Works
MSAS	Ministry of Sanitation and Social Assistance
M.T.	Metric ton
OAS	Organization of American States
OEA	See OAS
UPADI	Pan-American Union of Associations of Engineers
USAID	United States Agency for International Development
Work Force	Total population between ages of 15 and 64

The Agricultural Development of Venezuela

FIGURE 1

Venezuela and its Geographical Location in South America

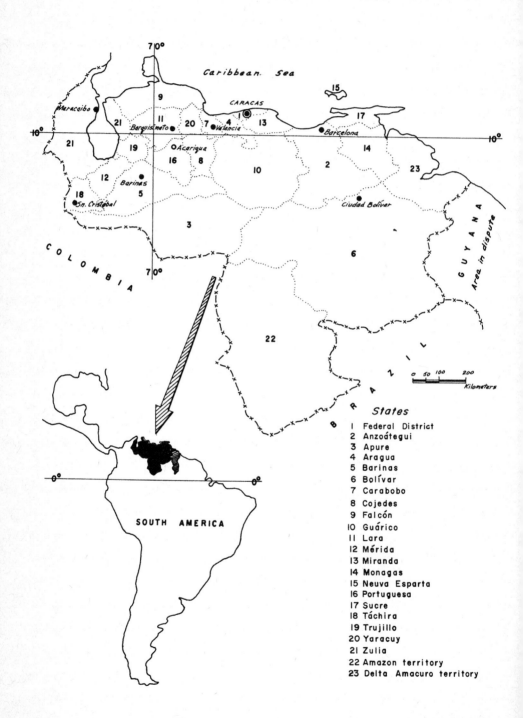

States
1 Federal District
2 Anzoátegui
3 Apure
4 Aragua
5 Barinas
6 Bolívar
7 Carabobo
8 Cojedes
9 Falcón
10 Guárico
11 Lara
12 Mérida
13 Miranda
14 Monagas
15 Neuva Esparta
16 Portuguesa
17 Sucre
18 Táchira
19 Trujillo
20 Yaracuy
21 Zulia
22 Amazon territory
23 Delta Amacuro territory

CHAPTER **1** INTRODUCTION

PURPOSE OF THE STUDY

This analysis of the present situation of agricultural development in Venezuela and its future possibilities was undertaken principally because of the interest of certain private organizations in having a reference base for some future rural development activities. However, because of its scope and the nature of its subject matter, this work is intended also as a guide for public program administrators and planners.

PRINCIPAL OBJECTIVES OF THE STUDY

The objectives of the study are summarized as follows:

1. To determine, for the five-year period 1961-65, the changes that have taken place in Venezuelan agricultural conditions with respect to production, productivity, consumption, human nutrition and welfare levels, and contribution to the nation's economic development--all on a comparative total and per capita basis.

2. To determine what factors are associated with measured changes and the strengths and weaknesses of these factors.

3. To forecast agricultural development to 1975, taking into consideration the most realistic assumptions for future changes in the key economic, social, institutional, and population conditions that are related to agricultural development.

4. To establish, in priority order, means of
improving agricultural development so as to bolster
strengths and minimize identified weaknesses.

SCOPE OF THE INVESTIGATION

The investigation was limited to the collection,
organization, and analysis of statistical data available from various government and private sources,
together with organized interviews with informed
persons in government and private agencies who were
concerned with all phases of rural development. An
important addition to the aforementioned sources of
information was the experience gained during many
years of professional work in rural programs by the
interdisciplinary team that was assembled for the
study. This experience was drawn on heavily for both
the descriptive and the analytic sections of the
study and provided a basis for the ideas and recommendations presented. In this same manner, a basis
for quantitative evaluation was established for most
of the observations and conclusions reached.

2

THE ECONOMIC DEVELOPMENT OF VENEZUELA

Venezuela is located at the northern end of South America on the Caribbean Sea, between approximate latitudes of 1 to 12 degrees north of the equator and longitudes of 60 to 73 degrees west of Greenwich. The total land area covers 912,050 square kilometers. Although the entire area is in the tropical belt, there is a wide range of ecological conditions because of the geological formation and elevations ranging from sea level to over 16,000 feet above sea level in the Andes mountain range, which has one of its northern termination branches in Venezuela. The major political subdivisions of the country include 20 states, 2 federal territories, and a federal district that includes a number of Caribbean islands as dependencies. Venezuela is a federated republic comprised of the aforementioned main political subdivisions, but government powers are very strongly centralized. Physical description of the other principal resources and population patterns of importance to this work are included in the various sections on economic development and agricultural conditions of Venezuela.

RECENT HISTORY OF THE VENEZUELAN ECONOMY

Until the 1930's, when the development of the petroleum industry started to exert an impact, the economy of Venezuela was based almost completely on agriculture. During the colonial period, which began in Venezuela in the sixteenth century, production for internal and export use was based almost entirely on agricultural and livestock products. Cocoa and tobacco were important exports in the seventeenth

century in trade with the Caribbean islands and
Spain. Live cattle and hides were also early exports.
Coffee production began in the eighteenth century
and, during the nineteenth century, became the most
important export. Indigo for dye material also was
an export beginning with the latter part of the
eighteenth century. For the first two decades of
this century, the principal Venezuelan exports were
coffee, cocoa, live cattle, and hides, in that order.[1]

On the traditional, almost self-sufficient, but
low per capita income economic pattern of Venezuela,
the development of the petroleum industry has had
profound effect. This industry provided a large flow
of foreign investment capital and techniques that
began in significant amounts in the 1930's and has
continued. The economic structure of the country,
in many respects, has been drastically changed in a
relatively short period of time.

The petroleum industry has provided an important
stimulus to the nation's economic growth, principally
in providing relatively high-wage occupation of labor,
a generating force for government fiscal income, and
the preponderant source of very significant foreign
exchange that has given Venezuela an extraordinary
capacity for foreign payments.

Although the employment in the petroleum industry is shown by official statistics to be less than
2 per cent of the employable population, in the beginning, the industry employed a much more significant proportion of this sector of the population.
Even today, after much automation and greater competition from other petroleum-producing areas of the
world, the industry is the prime basis for many other
directly and indirectly related service activities,
with significant employment requirements, that would
not be on the scene were it not for the petroleum
industry.

The influence of the oil industry as a generator
of government fiscal income is explicitly shown in
Table 1.

TABLE 1

Total Income of the Venezuelan Petroleum Industry
in Relation to the Total Fiscal Income
of the Venezuelan Government,
1945-65

| Year | Total Fiscal Income (Million Bs.) | Income from the Oil Industry | |
		Amount (Million Bs.)	Per Cent of Total
1945	660	458	69.6
1950	1,917	1,124	58.6
1955	2,992	1,973	65.9
1960	4,968	3,002	61.2
1965	7,264	4,830	66.5

Source: Annual reports of the Central Bank of
Venezuela for 1945-65.

The fact that the petroleum industry provides
the preponderance of both exports and foreign exchange is shown by the percentages in Table 2.

TABLE 2

Oil Exports and Inflow of Foreign Exchange
Attributable to the Petroleum Industry
in Venezuela, 1945-65

Year	Oil Exports as Per Cent of Total Exports of Venezuela	Per Cent of Total Foreign-Exchange Income from the Petroleum Industry
1945	92.6	93.9
1950	96.6	97.7
1955	96.1	96.3
1960	87.7	93.4
1965	92.8	90.7

Source: Annual reports of the Central Bank of
Venezuela for 1945-65.

Before presenting statistically some general economic indicators for recent years in order to demon-
strate the impact generated by the oil industry, some
additional comments are considered desirable to show
how the impulse of the oil industry development has
been superimposed on the traditional Venezuelan agricultural economy.

The process soon resulted in a great increase in
real income, both total and per capita, although this
increase was not distributed to a large proportion of
the total population. This increased purchasing power could not be supplied immediately by the other
sectors of the economy; so, as would be expected,
there was a large increase in imports of consumer
goods to meet the demand. Also, the large fiscal income of the government brought a drastic reorienta-
tion of traditional government services that formerly
had been limited to minor road-building and the erec-
tion of certain other transportation systems. Government services were increased in fields of economic
development, public health and education, and national
public works. In the post-World War II period, the
development of roads, irrigation works, communication
services, education and medical facilities, and other
institutional services has been significant and has
placed Venezuela in a favorable situation with regard
to these facilities in comparison with other Latin
American countries. Also, the increased income,
coupled with the improved facilities for economic development, has led to a significant increase in the
secondary and tertiary sectors of the economy, especially with respect to service activities, which now
occupy over 40 per cent of the economically active
population--higher than several of the economically
advanced countries of the world.

However, in spite of the fact that the remarkable
increase in the product of the Venezuelan economy has
resulted in an increase in per capita income, this
increase has not been sufficient to provide improvement in the general welfare. In real terms, the distribution of the income has been made in such a way
that certain sectors of the population, especially
rural areas, have achieved relatively slight improvement, whereas other sectors have obtained extraordinary

benefits. Agricultural productivity has shown some improvement but is still far behind other sectors of the economy.

In a recent publication of the Central Bank of Venezuela,[2] some brief indicators of the stage of Venezuelan economic development were presented, from which the following are extracted:

Population Statistics and Health and Education Facilities

Annual rate of population growth: 3.5 per cent
Annual death rate per 1,000 persons: 7.2
Annual birth rate per 1,000 persons: 43.4
Annual infant death rate per 1,000 births: 47.9
Life expectancy at birth (1965): 66 years
Number of physicians: 8 for each 10,000 persons
      or 1 for each 1,250 persons
Students in schools: 20 per cent of total popu-
      lation in 1964 (was 10 per cent in 1950)
Number of schools per 10,000 people: 15
Number of school teachers per 10,000 people: 49

Financial Institutions and Investments

Subscribed capital in corporations (at current bolivar values):	1964 - Bs.	1,730	million
	1957 - "	2,034	"
	1940 - "	52	"
Circulating funds in hands of public:	1964 - "	4,417	"
	1940 - "	342	"
Number of business corporations:	1964 - "	2,516	"
	1955 - "	1,081	"

Savings and loan associations established since
      1950: 20
Stock Exchanges established in recent years: 2

Foreign investments in Venezuela during the last 25 years: amount to approximately Bs. 20,000 million

or Bs. 2,265 per capita for the 1964 population of
Venezuela.

Manufacturing and Industry

Electric generating capacity in 1964: 231.4 kilo-
    watt hours per 1,000 persons
Production of cement in 1964: 219.5 metric tons
    per 1,000 persons
Production of pig iron in 1964: 52.3 metric tons
    per 1,000 persons

Miscellaneous

Paved roads per 100 square kilometers of area:
    15.8 kilometers
Number of passenger vehicles, 1963: 34 per each
    1,000 persons
Capacity of cargo ships: 32.2 tons per 1,000
    persons
Number of television receivers: 68 per 1,000
    persons
Number of radio receivers: 165 per 1,000 persons
Number of telephones: 29 per 1,000 persons

The foregoing quantitative measures, which indicate that Venezuela is very favorably placed among
Latin American countries for these indicators of development, were presented to support the thesis that
Venezuela is one of the few Latin American countries
that have reached the "take-off" point in economic
development, according to the W. W. Rostow thesis.[3]
Although there are some inconsistencies and anomalies,
especially with respect to the agricultural sector, it
has been said that the Venezuelan economy has nearly
reached the stage where development could continue on
a self-sustaining basis. However, such development is
still greatly dependent on the petroleum industry and
the national policies and world competitive situation
relationg thereto. Recent indications, especially
during 1966, show that the vigor and impulse of this
industry is tapering off. Whether or not other sectors of the economy have reached the point where they
can grow and improve the national per capita production
and productivity remains to be seen.

STATUS OF ECONOMIC INDICATORS

Changes in the general economic indicators for Venezuela during 1961-65 are shown in the tables below. Projections to 1975 for the more important of the measures will be presented in the penult section of this chapter.

Gross Territorial Product

The gross territorial product (GTP) sometimes called the gross domestic product (which is considered more realistic for representing general economic changes for Venezuela than the factor for gross national product), is shown in Table 3 for the years 1961-65 with fragmentation for the three main sectors and nine subsectors of the economy, calculated in constant bolivar prices at the 1957 level.

The total territorial product registered a steady increase of 25.6 per cent during this five-year period, passing from 26,881 million to 33,766 million bolivars, which is an average annual increase of 6.4 per cent.

All major sectors of the economy show absolute increases in production during the period, but the relative contributions to the GTP show some minor adjustments. The primary sector tended to diminish in its influence on the total, principally because of reduction in the relative contribution of the petroleum industry, although the agricultural sector increased its relative contribution to the GTP from 6.8 per cent to 7.1 per cent. In the secondary sector, the relative contribution to the GTP has tended to increase, principally due to increases in light manufacturing industries. The relative contribution of the tertiary sector to the GTP has tended to diminish. The service industries constitute a relatively high proportion of the GTP (43.9 per cent in 1965). This percentage is higher than for several of the more economically advanced countries. Although the general services subsector of the predominant tertiary group is made up principally of government services financed to a large extent by oil income, there is still a serious question that the primary

TABLE 3

Gross Territorial Product of Venezuela by Principal
Economic Sectors, 1961-65

Sectors	Gross Territorial Product (Million Bs. at 1957 Prices)					Percentage Distribution of GTP				
	1961	1962	1963	1964	1965	1961	1962	1963	1964	1965
Total GTP	26,881	28,586	29,764	32,135	33,766	100.0	100.0	100.0	100.0	100.0
Primary sector	9,742	10,574	10,759	11,434	11,781	36.2	37.0	36.1	35.6	34.9
Agriculture	1,845	1,979	2,084	2,264	2,395	6.8	6.9	7.0	7.1	7.1
Mining	343	316	272	364	402	1.3	1.1	0.9	1.1	1.2
Petroleum	7,554	8,279	8,403	8,806	8,984	28.1	29.0	28.2	27.4	26.6
Secondary sector	4,968	5,384	5,855	6,643	7,151	18.5	18.8	19.7	20.7	21.2
Manufacturing[a]	3,454	3,741	4,002	4,527	4,921	12.8	13.1	13.5	14.1	14.6
Construction	1,097	1,156	1,280	1,472	1,527	4.1	4.0	4.3	4.6	4.5
Water & electricity	417	487	573	644	703	1.6	1.7	1.9	2.0	2.1
Tertiary sector	12,171	12,628	13,150	14,058	14,834	45.3	44.2	44.2	43.7	43.9
Transportation & communication	1,032	1,060	1,113	1,234	1,358	3.9	3.7	3.7	3.9	4.0
Commerce	3,927	4,045	4,160	4,544	4,730	14.6	14.2	14.0	14.1	14.0
Other services	7,212	7,523	7,877	8,280	8,746	26.8	26.3	26.5	25.7	25.9
Total Per Capita Production (Bs.)	3,464	3,558	3,580	3,724	3,770					
Agricultural Sector (Bs.)[b]	749	789	817	873	907					

[a]Includes oil-refining industries. [b]Calculation based on 1961 census summary figure showing the number of persons economically dependent on agriculture (2,458,665) and increased by a 1.3 per cent annual rate, which is the increase in number of persons occupied in agriculture. The resulting population figures were used in relation with total product of the agricultural sector to determine per capita product.

Source: Annual reports of the Central Bank of Venezuela for 1961-65.

and secondary sectors of economic production may not
be sufficiently developed or may not provide a high
enough rate of productivity to support such a high
proportion of service industries in the long range.
This is a particular danger signal in view of the
limited improvement in the total production of the
primary sector during 1961-65.

The large difference in the productivity per
person in the agricultural sector of the economy is
shown at the bottom of Table 3. Although agricultural production value per capita has been increasing, it was still only 907 bolivars in 1965, which
was less than one fourth of the per capita product
of Venezuela for that year (Bs. 3,770). However,
this per capita income, converted to U.S. dollars at
the 4.50 rate, amounts to $838, which places Venezu-
ela at the highest income level for Latin American
countries. More up-to-date information with regard
to gross territorial product and per capita production
will be found in Table 5 of the Statistical Appendix
at the end of this volume.

Figure 2 supplies information on the relative
annual changes in GTP and agricultural production
between 1950 and 1965. All years showed some increase over the previous year throughout the period.
From 1952 to 1959, the rate of increase for agriculture was less than the GTP except for 1958. During
1960-65, production increased at a faster annual rate
than did GTP.

The large difference in productivity per economically active person in four major economic groups
is shown in Table 4. The average product per economically active person in Venezuela was 12,400 bolivars
in 1965. Agricultural workers produced only 2,600
bolivars per person in 1965, whereas in the petroleum
and mining sector, the product per person was 241,000
bolivars. In industries and services, the value of
the product per worker was 12,700 bolivars and 12,400
bolivars, respectively. However, as also shown in
the table, the agricultural worker had a larger rate
of improvement in this period with an increase in
product per capita of 21.4 per cent, whereas all other
sectors had an increase of only 3.7 per cent.

FIGURE 2

Comparison of Relative Annual Changes
in Venezuela's Gross Territorial
Product and Agricultural
Production, 1950-65

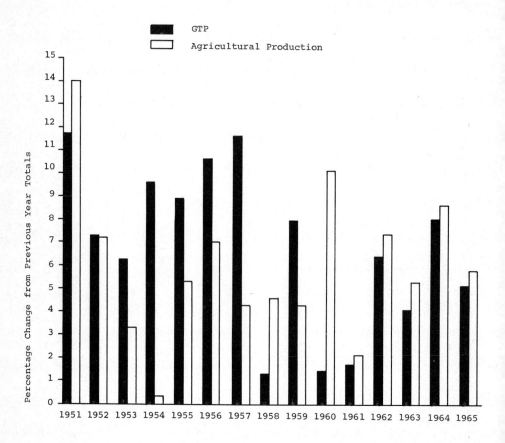

Source: Data in annual reports of the Central Bank of Venezuela for
1950-65.

14

TABLE 4

Productivity per Economically Active Person and
by Economic Sectors in Venezuela, 1961-65
(Thousand Bs. at 1957 Prices)

Sector	Product per Economically Active Person				
	1961	1962	1963	1964	1965
Agriculture	2.2	2.3	2.4	2.5	2.6
Petroleum and mining	170.8	198.5	206.3	224.1	241.0
Industries	11.6	11.6	11.7	12.3	12.7
Services	12.0	12.1	12.2	12.3	12.4
Average product per person	11.5	11.8	11.9	12.3	12.4
Total economy except agriculture	16.9	17.1	16.8	17.4	17.5
Yearly Index in relation to 1961 (per cent)					
Total economy	100.0	102.8	103.5	106.9	108.6
Agriculture	100.0	105.5	109.2	116.7	121.4
All other sectors	100.0	101.5	99.7	102.9	103.7

Source: Annual reports of the Central Bank of Venezuela for 1961-65.

15

Finally, with respect to the GTP, Table 5 presents information to show the distribution of the GTP between production for export and that for internal use in Venezuela. The significantly greater increase of production for internal than for external use indicates the results of the national policy of attempting to diversity Venezuela's production base and substitute local production for imports.

As shown in Table 5, the distribution between production for export and for internal use reached an approximate 30 per cent to 70 per cent comparison, but between 1960 and 1964, annual rates of increase of production for internal use were larger than the rates of production for export in all but two of the five years.

Additional comments on the competitive situation of certain sectors of the Venezuelan economy are presented later on in the section on forecasts for the next decade.

National Income

The national income of Venezuela from 1961-65 at 1957 prices is shown in Table 6. (Additional data for the years 1966-67 will be found in Table 6 of the Statistical Appendix.) The contribution of the agricultural sector is compared with all other sectors, and the national income is broken down into remuneration for labor and capital, as calculated by the Central Bank of Venezuela.

The total national income increased from 18,387.1 million to 23,501.5 million bolivars from 1961 to 1965. This represents an increase of 27.8 per cent for the period, or an average annual increase of 6.9 per cent. Per capita income was 2,694 bolivars at 1957 constant prices in 1965. At 1965 prices, it was 3,552 bolivars.

The portion applied as remuneration for labor diminished on a relative basis from 61.5 per cent to 55.9 per cent, although the absolute amount increased from 12,079 to 16,328 million bolivars from 1961 to

TABLE 5

Distribution of Venezuela's Gross Territorial Product Between Production
for Export and Production for Domestic Use, 1960-65
(Million Bs. at 1957 Prices)

Year	Gross Territorial Product		Production for Export			Production for Internal Use		
	Value (Mil. Bs.)	Per Cent Annual Increase	Value (Mil. Bs.)	Per Cent Total GTP	Per Cent Annual Increase	Value (Mil. Bs.)	Per Cent Total GTP	Per Cent Annual Increase
1960	26,433	-	8,265	31.3	-	18,168	68.7	-
1961	26,881	1.7	8,470	31.3	2.5	18,411	68.5	1.3
1962	28,585	6.3	9,089	31.8	7.3	19,496	68.2	5.9
1963	29,756	4.1	9,179	30.8	1.0	20,586	69.2	5.6
1964	32,135	7.9	9,686	30.1	5.5	22,449	69.9	9.0
1965	33,766	5.1	N.D.			N.D.		

Source: Annual reports of the Central Bank of Venezuela for 1960-65.

TABLE 6

Distribution of Venezuela's Gross National Income According
to Contribution of the Agricultural and Other Sectors
and Remuneration of Labor and Capital, 1961-65
(Million Bs. at 1957 Prices)

Year	Gross National Income	Per Cent of Total		Per Cent of Total as Remuneration for Labor			Per Cent of Total as Remuneration for Capital		
		Agriculture	Other Sectors	All Sectors	Agriculture	Other Sectors	All Sectors	Agriculture	Other Sectors
1961	18,387.1	7.8	92.2	61.5	5.8	55.7	38.5	2.0	36.5
1962	18,453.0	7.9	92.1	60.1	5.8	54.3	39.9	2.1	37.8
1963	19,358.3	8.2	91.8	61.0	5.7	55.3	39.1	2.4	36.7
1964	22,672.4	7.8	92.2	55.1	5.0	50.1	44.9	2.8	42.1
1965	23,501.5	7.7	92.3	55.9	5.0	50.9	44.2	2.8	41.4

(Note: Estimated per capita income in 1965 at 1957 prices is Bs. 2,694; at 1965 prices, it is Bs. 3,352.)

Source: Annual reports of the Central Bank of Venezuela for 1961-65 (figures adjusted to 1957 base period by the General Index of Wholesale Prices from the same source.)

18

1965. The portion applied to capital increased more
rapidly, from 7,559 to 12,910 million bolivars, and
its relative participation in the total increased
from 38.5 per cent to 44.2 per cent in the same period. A similar tendency occurred in the agricultural sector, along with all other sectors. Exact
measurement of the reasons for the increased participation of capital in the national income has not been
made, but it probably represents both an increase in
capital applied for mechanization in the production
processes and higher costs for capital. Agriculture
shows a more disproportionate relationship with regard to the distribution of income between labor and
capital, with labor receiving about two thirds and
capital one third in agriculture, whereas other sectors showed a relationship of about 55 per cent for
labor and 45 per cent for capital. Most of the non-
agricultural development in Venezuela, especially in
the oil and manufacturing industries, has tended to
be a capital-intensive operation because, among other
reasons, capital was available. This meant that employment opportunities did not increase proportionately with the increase in the urban population
(caused partially by rural migration).

Existing Capital and Annual Investment
in the Economy

The existing fixed capital in the Venezuelan
economy from 1961 to 1965, as reported by the Central
Bank, is shown in Table 7. The table also compares
the capital in the agricultural sector with that in
all other sectors on a total and per economically
active person basis.

The table shows an increase in fixed capital
from 56,370 million bolivars in 1961 to 63,512 million
bolivars in 1965. This represents an increase of 12.7
per cent or slightly over 3 per cent annually. An
important indication with respect to the subject of
this study is shown in the "per person" columns for
agriculture and other sectors. The capital existing
in agriculture per economically active person increased slightly, whereas that in other sectors decreased. This occurred in spite of programs of the

TABLE 7

Fixed Capital in the Agricultural and Other Sectors of the
Venezuelan Economy, 1961-65
(1957 Prices)

Year	Fixed Capital in the Agricultural Sector[a]			Fixed Capital in Other Sectors			Total Fixed Capital	
	Total (Mil. Bs.)	Per Economically Active Person (1,000 Bs.)	Per Cent of Total	Total (Mil. Bs.)	Per Economically Active Person (1,000 Bs.)	Per Cent of Total	Total (Mil. Bs.)	Per Economically Active Person (1,000 Bs.)
1961	8,037	9.4	14.3	48,333	32.5	85.7	56,370	24.0
1962	8,516	9.8	14.8	48,911	31.5	85.2	57,427	23.7
1963	8,968	10.5	15.3	49,585	30.0	84.7	58,553	23.4
1964	9,524	10.6	15.6	51,245	29.8	84.4	60,769	23.2
1965	10,072	10.0	15.9	53,440	29.8	84.1	63,512	23.4

[a]Does not include value of land.

Source: Annual reports of the Central Bank of Venezuela for 1961-65.

government sponsoring special incentives in tax exemptions and price and import restriction protection for new industries, along with extensive financial assistance. Apparently, the flow of people to the urban areas has continued to cause developmental imbalances between sectors and is a danger signal indicating more difficulty in meeting future demands for capital investment and jobs.

The capital existing in the agricultural sector per active person (amounting, in 1965, to Bs. 10,000) was less than one fifth of that in other sectors, indicating the low intensity of agricultural production. However, as shown in the table, agriculture had, in 1965, a higher proportion of existing capital in the economy (15.9 per cent) than its contribution to the GTP as shown previously (7.1 per cent). (Additional data for 1966-67 is found in the Statistical Appendix, Table 7.)

Another relationship between GTP and existing fixed capital between 1961 and 1965 is shown in Table 8, wherein the agricultural sector is compared with all other sectors of the economy. As can be seen, the ratio of agricultural output to existing capital was 0.24 during 1964 and 1965, which was considerably less than half the ratio for other sectors (0.59 in 1965). The indication of much lower productivity in agriculture than in other sectors is well substantiated in various forms, especially in the lack of ability of the agricultural sector to attract significant capital from private sources or to compete in the capital markets for available financing.

Table 9 illustrates the gross annual fixed investment in Venezuela's economic development at constant 1957 prices during the 1961-65 period, as divided between the agricultural sector and all other sectors of the economy. As explained below, the figures for 1964 and 1965 were adjusted because of the significant influence of foreign funds in the investment picture in Venezuela, a country that attracts more foreign capital than do most other Latin American countries. The adjustment made probably has had a somewhat excessive effect on the agricultural sector

figures because only small portions of foreign capital were channeled into the agricultural sector. For
purposes of this study, it was not believed necessary
to attempt to make further adjustment in these figures; furthermore, no precise data were available to
permit adjustments by economic sectors.

TABLE 8

Gross Territorial Product and Fixed Capital
in the Agricultural and Other Sectors
of the Venezuelan Economy, 1961-65

Year	Total	Agricultural Sector	Other Sectors
1961	0.48	0.23	0.52
1962	0.50	0.23	0.54
1963	0.51	0.23	0.56
1964	0.53	0.24	0.58
1965	0.53	0.24	0.59

Source: Data from annual reports of the Central Bank
of Venezuela for 1961-65 (GTP divided by
existing fixed capital).

As shown in Table 9, total fixed investments increased from 4,019 million to 4,854 million bolivars
from 1961 to 1965, an increase of 21.0 per cent. This
was somewhat less than the increase in GTP during the
same period (25.6 per cent), a fact that may presage
a future reduction in the rate of growth of the GTP,
which is dependent, to a large degree, on investment
in Venezuela's economic development.

Foreign-Exchange and International
Reserve Balances

As mentioned previously, petroleum exports have
provided Venezuela with an extraordinary capacity to
increase imports and foreign payments.

The strength of the general foreign-exchange situation of Venezuela is well illustrated in Tables 10

TABLE 9

Gross Fixed Investment in the Agricultural and Other
Sectors of the Venezuelan Economy, 1961-65

| Year | Agricultural Sector | | Other Sectors | | Total Fixed Investment (Million Bs.) |
	Amount (Million Bs.)	Per Cent of Total	Amount (Million Bs.)	Per Cent of Total	
1961	674	16.8	3,345	83.2	4,019
1962	767	18.3	3,429	81.7	4,196
1963	765	17.5	3,606	82.5	4,371
1964[a]	696	16.1	3,630	83.9	4,326
1965[a]	718	14.8	4,136	85.2	4,854

[a]Figures adjusted downward by 17.5 per cent for 1964 and 1965 to take into account reduction of the value of the bolivar in international exchange from 3.35 to 4.50 per
U.S. dollar. It was assumed, based on general information of international financial
agencies, that approximately 50 per cent of annual investment in equipment, materials,
and funds came from foreign sources and that the amount of foreign funds actually was
reduced in the last two years, even though the bolivar amounts were higher.

Source: Annual reports of the Central Bank of Venezuela for 1961-65.

23

and 11 and is further substantiated by antecedent
events.   In 1957, the net balance of capital was
$986 million and had been, in positive figures, less
during previous years.   This capital net balance figure changed in 1958 to a negative figure of $-319
million representing a total reduction in only one
year of $1,305 million and continued on the negative
side in substantial amounts until 1963, as shown in
Table 10.   The abrupt change was substantially due
to the decrease in investments that was caused by a
loss of confidence in government policy by many foreign investors.   A consequent devaluation of the
bolivar began in 1960 and was completed in 1964.
However, Venezuela was able to resist the depression
that resulted between 1959 and 1962 and built up its
international reserve balance to levels existing before this critical period, as shown in Table 11.
(More up-to-date information, supplementing Table 11,
will be found in the Statistical Appendix, Table 8.)

Exports and Imports

The value of Venezuelan exports between 1961 and
1965 is shown by general groups of products in Table
12.   Minerals and petroleum predominate the export
picture, with the latter providing about 93 per cent
of the total.   The level of total exports was stable,
with only minor annual fluctuations after bolivar
figures were adjusted to dollars.   Increases in bolivar totals for exports shown in the Central Bank
figures were mainly due to the changed value of the
bolivar and not to the value of exports in the foreign markets.

Food and beverage exports shown in Table 12
have, in previous years, been dominated by coffee
and cocoa product exports, which, before 1962, constituted more than 90 per cent of the food exports.
However, since 1962, other food product exports have
increased in importance.   In 1963, the large rise in
food exports was due to an unprecedented sale of over
45 million bolivars worth of cane sugar that was made
that year and has not occurred in such amounts since.
In 1964 and 1965, sales of plantains and some other
fruit products have increased substantially in markets

TABLE 10

Importing Capacity of Venezuela, 1961-65
(Millions of U.S. Dollars)

Year	Exports	Net Service Balance[a]	Net Capital Balance[b]	Import Capacity[c]	Imports	Balance[d]
1961	2,562	-777	-393	1,392	1,411	-19
1962	2,625	-564	-540	1,521	1,523	- 2
1963	2,552	-673	-352	1,527	1,371	+156
1964	2,580	-867	- 19	1,694	1,598	+ 96
1965	2,564	-893	+ 54	1,725	1,738	-13

[a]Includes all service items.
[b]Includes government and private capital.
[c]Exports plus net service balance plus net capital balance.
[d]Import capacity minus imports.

Source: Annual reports of the Central Bank of Venezuela for 1961-65.

in the United States and in the Caribbean islands.
Also included in food exports were shrimps and some
other fish products that showed considerable fluctuations in annual volume of exports. Consequently,
coffee and cocoa diminished in their relative importance in food exports to about 60 per cent of the
total in 1965. Actually, Venezuela has not been
meeting its quota for coffee exports under the International Coffee Marketing Agreement during recent
years.

TABLE 11

Foreign-Exchange Balances and Level
of International Reserves in
Venezuela, 1961-65
(Millions of U.S. Dollars)

Year	Foreign-Exchange Balance	International Reserves at End of Year
1961	-19.3	585.4
1962	- 2.3	583.1
1963	+156.4	739.6
1964	+ 96.2	835.8
1965	-12.8	823.0

Source: Annual reports of the Central Bank of
         Venezuela for 1961-65.

    Imports into Venezuela by general product groups
during 1961-65 are shown by value in U.S. dollars in
Table 13. The 1965 figures show a substantial increase over the previous four years (which had been
quite stable), due to increases of 15 per cent to
20 per cent in imports of raw materials for manufacture, machinery and accessories, and transport equipment. Consumer goods and materials and equipment for
construction increased, but at rates of only 2 per
cent and 11 per cent respectively. Food and beverage
imports since 1960 have been 30 per cent to 40 per
cent less than they were in 1951-60, as shown in the

TABLE 12

Venezuelan Exports by Product Groups, 1961-65
(Millions of U.S. Dollars)

Product Group	1961	1962	1963	1964	1965	Five-Year Total	
						Amount	Per Cent of Total Exports
Minerals and petroleum	2,391.8	2,483.9	2,384.1	2,437.0	2,392.8	12,089.6	97.7
Food and beverages	36.0	34.4	54.0	28.1	30.6	186.1	1.5
Other products	3.9	3.2	3.0	4.8	3.3	18.2	0.2
Re-exports	20.6	18.9	15.2	10.1	9.3	74.1	0.6
Total	2,452.3	2,543.4	2,456.3	2,480.0	2,436.0	12,368.0	100.0

Source: Calculated from data in bolivars in annual reports of the Central Bank of Venezuela for 1961-65. (Various exchange rates existed during the period of the table, and both time and data on detailed values in dollars for each group of products were not available. Conversion from bolivars to dollars was made on the basis of total value of exports in the two means of exchange, which is not completely accurate for each group but probably does not change the relationship between groups significantly. Rates for conversion used were: 1961, 3.04; 1962, 3.08; 1963, 3.19; 1964, 4.37; 1965, 4.44.)

TABLE 13

Venezuelan Imports by Product Group, 1961-65
(Millions of U.S. Dollars)

Product Group	1961	1962	1963	1964	1965	Five-Year Total	
						Amount	Per Cent of Total Imports
Consumer goods							
Food and bev- erages	382.4	355.4	297.5	314.9	321.7	1,671.9	28.3
Other consumer items	N.D.	N.D.	88.5	93.7	84.7	–	
	N.D.	N.D.	209.0	221.2	237.0	–	
Raw materials for manufacture	326.3	374.4	318.8	372.2	415.7	1,807.4	30.6
Machinery and accessories	217.5	244.1	235.7	274.2	320.4	1,291.9	21.9
Transport equip- ment	152.4	142.2	142.9	161.1	197.4	796.0	13.5
Materials & equip- ment for con- struction	66.4	68.7	71.4	61.6	68.8	336.9	5.7
Total	1,145.0	1,184.8	1,066.3	1,184.0	1,324.0	5,904.1	100.0

Source: Calculated from data in bolivars in annual reports of the Central Bank of Venezuela for 1961-65. (Various exchange rates existed during 1961-65, both for different products and time periods. Detailed data were not readily available for each group on the effect on changing exchange rates, so each group was converted to dollars using the relation between exports in bolivars and dollars. Rates used for conversion were: 1961, 3.08; 1962, 3.25; 1963, 4.13; and 1965, 4.15.)

annual reports of the Central Bank of Venezuela for
that period. From 1956 to 1958, the food imports
amounted to between $125 million and $150 million a
year. One important import that has been almost
completely eliminated since that time because of increased local production is poultry products, including eggs.

Indexes of Product Price Changes

Five indexes of various product price levels are
illustrated in Figure 3, according to data from the
Central Bank of Venezuela. The wholesale price indexes for all products, together with those for agricultural products, are presented in Figure 3A. The
General Wholesale Price Index has steadily increased,
whereas the Agricultural Wholesale Price Index has
fluctuated; however, the general trend has been an
increase over the five-year period of about 9 per
cent. During the decade from 1950 to 1960, both these
indexes were relatively very stable; the steady price
increases have been a phenomena of the last few years.
Of considerable influence on this rise in prices were
the increased bolivar prices for imported goods due
to the devaluation of the bolivar that began in 1960.
(The various rates of exchange were unified in 1964
at Bs. 4.50 per U.S. dollar compared to the old rate
of 3.35 to 1.) For example, in 1965, the index of
wholesale prices of imported goods included in the
General Wholesale Index was 140.7, whereas that of
nationally produced goods was 115.2, which resulted
in the General Wholesale Index of 124.4 with relation
to the 1957 base period. During the five-year period
shown in Figure 3A, the General Wholesale Price Index
increased at an average annual rate of over 4 per
cent, whereas that of agricultural products at the
wholesale level increased at an annual rate of only
slightly over 2 per cent, indicating that the parity
situation of agriculture with other sectors of the
economy was deteriorating.

The indexes at the producers' level shown in
Figure 3B for agricultural products show considerably
less increase than the indexes at the wholesale level,
indicating that producers' share of the consumers'

FIGURE 3

Selected Price Indexes for Venezuela, 1961-65 (1957 = 100)

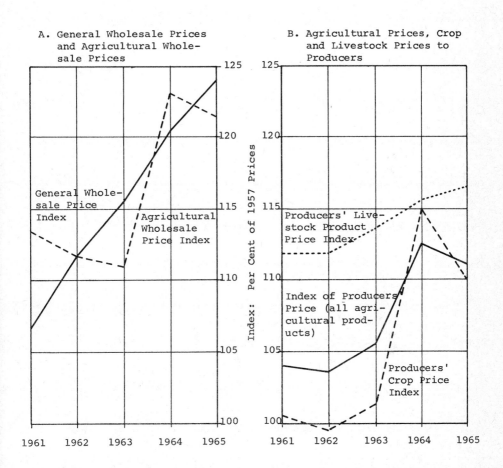

A. General Wholesale Prices and Agricultural Wholesale Prices

B. Agricultural Prices, Crop and Livestock Prices to Producers

Source: Annual reports of the Central Bank of Venezuela for 1961-65.

31

price was diminishing and that an income versus
cost squeeze for agricultural production was probably
developing. Producers' prices for all products included in the agricultural sector (including forest
products and fish products, for which separate indexes are not shown in the figure but which were lower
than livestock and crop product indexes in 1961-65)
showed a five-year increase in the index from 104.2
to 111.0, amounting to a change of 6.8 per cent with
respect to the 1957 base, or an average annual increase of only 1.7 per cent since 1961. This fact
points up the need for more attention to problems of
marketing agricultural products, which will be discussed in later chapters of this study.

Demographic and Employment Situation

Basic data on Venezuela's population are available from census reports for the years of 1936, 1941,
1950, and 1961. Most of the estimations for interim
periods and projections for the future are based on
the last two census periods.

As indicated previously, the total population of
Venezuela increased between 1950 and 1961 at the annually compounded rate of 3.5 per cent. The total
population figures for the last two census periods
(1950 and 1961) with estimations for 1965, together
with distribution among major age groups and urban
and rural localities are presented in Table 14. As
can be seen from these data, the total population
has increased from a total of approximately 5 million
persons in 1950 to 8.7 million between 1950 and 1965.
During the same period, the population shift from
rural areas to urban centers of more than 5,000 inhabitants each was very pronounced, so that as of
1965, almost 63 per cent of the total population was
located in urban areas, compared with 41.5 per cent
in 1950.

With respect to age group distribution, there
was a tendency for the population to become younger
and older at the same time, at the expense of the
middle age group of 15 to 59 years, or the group
most economically active, as shown in the table.

This change was slow but more marked in rural than
in urban areas. There are some serious long-range
implications here with respect to requirements for
the society--especially with respect to school facilities and old-age assistance programs. These will
increase proportionately faster than the general
population and will put a heavier burden of support
on the economically active age group, which, at the
same time, will be decreasing in size relative to the
total population.

In addition to the urban-rural breakdown of the
total population previously shown, the distribution by
location of the population is further illustrated by
figures taken from the 1961 census data (see Table
15).

These figures show that one third of the population was still very dispersed in 1961, with correspondingly high future unit cost requirements for
access roads, schools, and medical and other public
services in population areas of less than 1,000 persons. On the other hand, over one third of the
population was residing in the 16 larger cities of
50,000 inhabitants or more. Although the concentration of population centers will continue, a large
and expensive task still remains to provide essential
development facilities for the widely dispersed rural
population.

Few data are available on population migration
within Venezuela, but as a complement to the foregoing general population description, the following
figures were taken from the IRFED Mission[4] Report of
1965 on general population movements in Venezuela.
This unpublished report showed that total net migration within Venezuela and immigration from other
countries during the period from 1950 to 1961 was
618,817 persons, of whom 281,224 were immigrants from
foreign countries and 337,593 were involved in internal migratory movement. However, the foreign
migration into Venezuela was a characteristic of the
1950's and has had much less significance in the
1960's. The direction of the total net migration
toward states within Venezuela was as follows:

TABLE 14

Total, Urban, and Rural Population of Venezuela by Major
Age Groups: 1950, 1961, and 1965

	Percentage Distribution of Population by Age Groups			Total Population (1,000)	Percentage Distribution Between Urban and Rural[a]
	0-14 Yrs.	15-59 Yrs.	60 Yrs. and Over		
1950					
Total population[b]	42.0	53.5	4.5	5,035	100.0
Urban	39.0	56.5	4.5	2,090	41.5
Rural	45.5	50.0	4.5	2,945	58.5
1961					
Total population[b]	45.7	49.9	4.4	7,524	100.0
Urban	43.8	52.0	4.2	4,319	57.4
Rural	49.8	45.6	4.6	3,205	42.6
1965					
Total population[c]	46.3	48.9	4.8	8,722	100.0
Urban	42.5	52.8	4.7	5,459	62.6
Rural	52.8	42.3	4.9	3,263	37.4

Sources:

[a] Percentage distribution between urban and rural in accordance with the population figures in Long Term Forecasts of the Supply and Demand of Agricultural and Livestock Products in Venezuela (Caracas: Consejo de Bienestar Rural, December, 1965). This study considers the residents of the centers of less than 5,000 inhabitants as rural, whereas the census data enumerates as rural only those residents of centers of less than 1,000 inhabitants. The author of this study believes that the 5,000-and-less breakdown is more representative of the rural population of Venezuela. This constitutes an approximate 10 per cent shift of total population from urban to rural in relation to the census figures for these categories.

[b] Census data of 1950 and 1961, General Statistics Office, Ministry of Development.

[c] Projections for 1965 of the General Statistics Office as of June 30, 1965.

35

TABLE 15

Distribution of Venezuela's Population
by Localities, 1961

Size of Population Centers	Number of Localities	Inhabitants (Per Cent of Total)
Less than 99 persons	16,589	10.3
100 to 999 persons	7,096	22.2
1,000 to 4,999 persons	359	9.8
Total rural	24,044	42.3
5,000 to 24,999 persons	93	13.2
25,000 to 49,000 persons	15	7.6
50,000 and more persons	16	36.9
Total urban	124	57.7
Totals	24,168	100.0

Source: 1961 Population Census.

Direction of Migratory Movements, 1950-61

Federal Entities	Per Cent of Total
Federal District	39.3
Anzoátegui	3.0
Barinas	2.6
Bolívar	4.4
Aragua	7.0
Carabobo	6.0
Guárico	1.6
Miranda	18.9
Portuguesa	3.8
Zulia	13.4
	100.0

Approximately 58 per cent of the above migratory movement was toward Caracas, the capital of Venezuela (Federal District and the state of Miranda); 19 per cent was toward petroleum industry areas (Anzoategui, Zulia, and part of Barinas); 17.4 per cent was toward the areas of new industrial development (principally in the states of Aragua, Bolívar, and Carabobo); and the remaining 6.4 per cent was toward new agricultural development areas (principally in the states of Barinas, Guárico, Portuguesa, and Zulia).

Several organizations have made varying calculations of the number of persons and the proportion of the total population that are economically active and actually employed in Venezuela. One of the activities to be carried out, as indicated in the report of the Presidential Office for Coordination and Planning (CORDIPLAN) in the Plan of the Nation, 1965, is to make additional studies and evaluation of the actual employment and unemployment in connection with planning for the human resources of Venezuela. Data in the Plan regarding the economically active population and actual employment are presented in Table 16.

In both of the years included in Table 16, the economically active population constituted 32 per cent of the total population. These data are based on the census enumeration of 1961, which includes persons 10 years of age or over who were employed in some economic activity.

TABLE 16

Employment in Major Economic Sectors and Total Economically
Active Persons in Venezuela, 1961 and 1964

Economic Sector	Population Employed					
	1961			1964		
	Number Employed (1,000)	Per Cent of Total Employed		Number Employed (1,000)	Per Cent of Total Employed	
Agriculture	778	35.5		793	32.3	
Petroleum and mining	45	2.1		44	1.8	
Industries	425	19.4		531	21.6	
Services	943	43.0		1,088	44.3	
Total employed	2,191	100.0		2,456	100.0	
Total economically active population	2,526			2,765		
Unemployed:						
Number	335			309		
Per cent of economically active	13.3			11.2		

Source: Plan of the Nation, 1965 (Caracas: CORDIPLAN, 1965).

38

There was significant unemployment, as indicated
by the fact that 11.2 per cent of the economically
active population was without work in 1964. Also,
in several sectors, there was considerable underemployment or disguised unemployment. This will be
analyzed more in later chapters on the agricultural
sector of the economy.

Venezuela has made progress in increasing its
educational facilities for regular primary, secondary,
and superior education, as well as its technical
schools and training facilities. Between 1957 and
1965, there was a 320 per cent increase in university
enrollment and a 210 per cent increase in the number
of university professors. Increases in the quantity
of schools, teachers, and students have been very
rapid during 1961-65, and more attention is being
given to improving the quality of the educational
services. The need for improved quality and applied
education is indicated in Table 17, which compares
increased educational expenditures with increases in
GTP, although it is realized that there is considerable lag between increased educational expenses and
increased economic production.

As pointed out in the Plan of the Nation and in
Table 17, the resources applied to education increased by 266 per cent between 1957 and 1965, whereas the increment in the GTP was only 56 per cent,
indicating a need for more practical orientation of
the educational efforts.

The special campaign to reduce illiteracy among
both adults and young people has had spectacular
results according to reports of the Ministry of Education, as shown in Table 18.

The costs of public school education in relation
to total national budgets for recent years have been
the following: 1961, 12 per cent; 1962, 13 per cent;
1963, 18 per cent; 1964, 15 per cent; and 1965, 17
per cent.

Up to 1955, the illiteracy rates in Venezuela
were at about the same level as those of many other

TABLE 17

Comparison of Total Educational Costs and Increases in Gross
Territorial Product in Venezuela, 1957-65

	Total Educational Costs		Gross Territorial Product	
Years	Amount (Million Bs.)	Percentage Variation from 1957	Amount in Current Bolivars (Million Bs.)	Percentage Variation from 1957
1957	434.6[a]	100	23,847	100
1961	1,006.1[a]	232	26,641	112
1962	1,071.9	247	28,506	120
1963	1,415.1	326	30,657	129
1964	1,323.3	305	35,001	147
1965	1,590.3	366	37,001[b]	156

[a]The fiscal year budgets were adjusted to calendar year.

[b]Estimated figure.

Source: Annual reports of the Central Bank of Venezuela for 1957-65.

TABLE 18

Illiteracy Among Persons Fifteen Years of Age
and Older in Venezuela, 1941-65

| Year | Total Population (1,000) | Persons Fifteen Years of Age and Older | | |
		Total Number (1,000)	Number Illiterate (1,000)	Per Cent of Adults Illiterate
1941	3,850	2,277	1,303	57.2
1950	5,035	2,925	1,434	49.0
1961	7,524	4,153	1,391	33.5
1962 (December)	8,008	4,423	1,174	26.5
1963 (July)	8,427	4,609	1,028	22.3
1964 (December)	8,575	4,685	1,017	21.7
1965 (July)	8,722	4,761	947	19.9

Source: Annual reports of the Division of Adult Education, Ministry of Education.

41

Latin American countries, but the literacy campaign
has greatly improved Venezuela's status in this respect, as shown by the following data, taken from a
summary in the 1965 annual report of the Central
Bank of Venezuela, which cited the source as the Food
and Agriculture Organization of the United Nations'
Statistical Yearbook of 1964.

Illiteracy Among Persons Fifteen Years of Age and Older, 1961-63

Country	Per Cent Illiterate
Uruguay	9.7
Costa Rica	15.7
Venezuela	23.6
Peru	39.8
El Salvador	52.0
Ecuador	69.4

Based on the 1961 census data, the illiteracy
rate in Venezuela for rural areas was approximately
double the national rate and about three times the
urban population rate. No data is available as to
the incidence of the literacy campaign in urban and
rural areas but owing to the dispersed nature of
the rural population and to the greater difficulty
rural people must face in order to participate in
adult education programs, it is possible that the
rate of illiteracy in rural areas is higher in relation to the total population or to urban areas
than it was before 1961.

Attendance in Venezuela's public and private
schools, together with the number of schools and
teachers, is shown in Table 19 for the 1964-65 and
1965-66 school years.

According to data in the Plan of the Nation for
1965-68, 23.5 per cent of the population of primary school-age (7-13) still were not attending primary schools as of 1964, indicating that additional
facilities were needed. Student-teacher ratios,
however, are quite reasonable. Problems of high
rates of grade repetition by primary school students

(17 per cent) and annual student dropout (11.3 per cent) were cited by the same source and indicate the need for improved quality in the educational system, which is one of the objectives indicated in the Plan. The great attrition in the number of students progressing to secondary schools and universities is evident in the data in Table 19. Although secondary school enrollment has increased rapidly in recent years, it is only 20 per cent of the primary school enrollment, and university enrollment is only 15 per cent of the secondary level enrollment.

TABLE 19

Student Registration and Number of Schools
and Teachers in Venezuela, 1964-66

	1964-65	1965-66
Total--all levels		
Students	1,736,203	1,823,066
Schools	13,986	14,139
Teachers	60,135	62,958
Preschool and primary level		
Students	1,421,959	1,479,488
Schools	13,088	13,198
Teachers	41,469	43,019
Students per teacher	34	34
Secondary school level		
Students	272,872	297,737
Schools	888	931
Teachers	14,260	15,203
Students per teacher	19	20
University level		
Students	41,372	45,841
Universities	10	10
Professors	4,406	4,736
Students per professor	9	10

Source: 1965 annual report of the Ministry of Education.

Additional comments on educational facilities for the agricultural sector of the economy will be included in later chapters.

Other Service Facilities of Importance to the Economy of Venezuela

The general measures of the status of the development of the Venezuelan economy described previously in this chapter are the principal ones for which data are available. However, inasmuch as one of the purposes of this book is to provide a base or "bench mark" for comparing future changes, it is convenient to present brief data available on the present status of some of the other service facilities that form part of the basis for future development of Venezuela, in addition to those already presented.

Venezuela has built a broad network of main roads that is significant in comparison with most other Latin American countries. Consequently, truck transport and passenger bus service are available between all cities. Also, airline service providing passenger and freight service throughout Venezuela, together with limited railroad service between Caracas and Valencia and between Puerto Cabello and Barquisimeto, are available. Older railroads in the Maracaibo Lake Basin have practically disappeared.

Venezuela was one of the first tropical areas to establish an effective malaria control program, which has been continued for over two decades and has made possible the opening up of large areas of productive land that formerly were practically uninhabitable. According to the Plan of the Nation, in 1965 the elimination of malaria had reached all but 34 municipalities, or 22 per cent of the area formerly affected. Only 6.5 per cent of the total population live in areas in which malaria has not been eradicated.

The internal postal and telegraph communications system is widespread, although the postal service is deficient in speed and reliability for ordinary business transactions, and more expensive systems of special messengers, telegraph, and airpost services are utilized principally for business affairs.

A significant construction industry employing modern machinery and methods has been developed in Venezuela, and although this industry suffers considerable year-to-year fluctuations in volume of business, and costs for the service are relatively high, it is not necessary to look outside Venezuela for construction facilities. The Rural Housing Division of the Ministry of Sanitation and Social Assistance has built 47,600 housing units during 1959-66, with an investment of Bs. 214 million.

Although commercial services for agriculture are too deficient in quantity and quality to fill the real need of rural areas (which will be discussed in later chapters), these services in cities, for most types of supplies, are quite highly developed.

National programs aimed at providing cities and towns with electrification and an improved domestic water supply have obtained substantial results.

Radio and television transmission services are widespread throughout Venezuela and the number of receivers is substantial. Cities are well supplied with newspaper services.

The figures in Table 20 provide a basis for comparison with future conditions for several of the aforementioned service factors in the economy of Venezuela.

PROJECTIONS FOR 1970 AND 1975 FOR GENERAL ECONOMIC INDICATORS

Government policies play a critical role in the nature of the future development of the economy of Venezuela, and the confidence of the private investors and businessmen in the government are of prime importance to the orderly development of the production and distribution of Venezuela's wealth. These points will be treated extensively in connection with the agricultural sector in later chapters.

In this section, the projections, for the principal economic measures of development will be presented

TABLE 20

Extent of Public Service Facilities in Venezuela, 1965

Item	Amount
Paved roads	
Total kilometers (1-1-65)	14,429.0
Construction	
Total value (Million Bs.)	3,802.0
Public "	1,629.0
Private "	2,173.0
Transportation	
Total automobiles registered (1-1-65)	298,819.0
Total passenger buses registered (1-1-65)	5,910.0
Total trucks registered (1-1-65)	107,354.0
Trucks of ½- to 2½-ton capacity	60,662.0
Trucks of 3-ton and more capacity	46,692.0
Average cost per ton kilometer for freight	Bs. 0.156.0
Airline service	
Number of airplanes in Venezuela (excluding military)	700.0
Passenger-kilometers, national flights (1,000)	276,299.0
Air cargo ton-kilometers, national and international flights (1,000)	109,904.0

Railroad service
Passenger-kilometers (1,000) — 43,661.0
Ton-kilometers " — 31,960.0

Maritime freight service
Number of ships in the merchant fleet (100 tons and more) — 103.0

Public health
Total budgeted amount for public health service agencies (Ministry of Sanitation, Military Health, Water Works, Social Security Health Programs, Public Health of Federal District, and regional agencies) (Million Bs.) — 1,201.0
Birth rate per 1,000 persons (1964) — 43.7
Death rate per 1,000 persons (1964) — 7.4
Number of medical doctors (1964) — 6,584.0
Number of nurses (1964) — 3,506.0

Estimated final value of industrial production (Million Bs.) — 12,802.6

Gross income in communications industries (Million Bs.)

Telephone services — 157.7
Telegraph services — 25.4
Cable services — 10.1
Postal services — 24.3

Gross income of advertising agencies (Million Bs.) — 133.7

Source: Motor vehicle registration statistics taken from the 1965 Anuario Estadistico of the General Office of Statistics, Ministry of Development. All other items taken from the annual report of the Central Bank of Venezuela for 1965.

47

mainly in statistical form. In the subsequent and
final sections of this chapter, the strong and weak
points of economic development will be briefly commented on and observations will be made on the international competitive and comparative advantage that
is foreseen for major sectors of the Venezuelan
economy.

Forecasts for Gross Territorial Product

The forecasts for the future gross territorial
product as of 1970 and 1975 that are presented in
Table 21 are based on the study by the Consejo de
Bienestar Rural entitled Long Term Forecasts of the
Supply and Demand of Agricultural and Livestock
Products in Venezuela and adjusted in 1966 by Robert
A. Butler of the Centro Latino-Americano de Venezuela
to take into account more recent historical data and
changes that have occurred since the original esti-
mates and forecasts were made.

TABLE 21

Forecast of Venezuela's Gross Territorial
Product for 1970 and 1975
(Million Bs. at 1957 Prices)

	1970		1975	
Sector	Amount	Per Cent of Total	Amount	Per Cent of Total
Agriculture	2,799	5.9	3,813	5.7
Mining & petroleum	14,373	30.2	18,667	28.0
Manufacturing	6,621	13.9	9,000	13.5
Construction	2,500	5.3	3,712	5.6
Electricity & water	412	0.8	600	0.7
Transport & communications	2,159	4.5	3,298	4.9
Commerce	5,887	12.4	9,197	13.8
Services	12,826	27.0	18,531	27.8
Total GTP	47,577	100.0	66,618	100.0

The principal future changes in the relationship between the various economic sectors and their contributions to the GTP of Venezuela, as indicated in Table 20, are reductions in the portion provided by agriculture, electricity and water, and services. Increased portions contributed by the other sectors offset these reductions. Per capita GTP in 1975 is projected at Bs. 4,959, which is Bs. 1,189 (31.5 per cent) more than in 1965.

Forecasts for Fixed Gross Investment

The forecasts for the investments in Venezuela for 1970 and 1975 are taken from the same source as that for GTP in the foregoing section and are presented in Table 22.

TABLE 22

Forecast of Venezuela's Fixed Gross Investment
for 1970 and 1975
(Million Bs. at 1957 Prices)

Sector	1970		1975	
	Amount	Per Cent of Total	Amount	Per Cent of Total
Agriculture	1,212	15.4	1,651	14.6
All other sectors	6,671	84.6	9,663	85.4
Total Investment	7,883	100.0	11,314	100.0
(Per capita investment (Bs.)	758		910	

These forecasts indicate that annual investment in economic development will more than double by 1975 and are based on the projected increases in government investment in productive facilities according to current national plans and the continued high rates of foreign investment and reinvestment of local

private entrepreneurs. There are some anomalies in
the investment picture. If the government continues
a high rate of investment in some fields usually
handled as private enterprises, private investment
could be reduced because of government competition
and because of increased dependence on government
investment.

Forecasts for Population Growth

Many population forecasts are based on recent
figures, which indicate an annual increase of approximately 3.5 per cent. However, in the Consejo de
Bienestar Rural study that was previously cited and
from which the data in Table 23 are taken, the assumption is that a gradual reduction of this rate
of increase between 1970 and 1975 will be at the
rate of 3.03 per cent per year. This estimate takes
into account the projected increase in longevity and
the general tendency for birth rates to go down as
incomes increase, together with the fact that the
big breakthrough in reducing deaths has already occurred and only nominal improvements in this respect
can be expected in the future.

TABLE 23

Forecast of Venezuela's Rural and Urban
Population for 1970 and 1975

Locality	1970		1975	
	Number (1,000)	Per Cent of Total	Number (1,000)	Per Cent of Total
Rural[a]	3,384	33.2	3,473	29.4
Urban[a]	6,817	66.8	8,339	70.6
Total	10,201	100.0	11,812	100.0

[a]Inhabitants in population centers of 5,000 and more
persons are classified as urban and those in centers
of less than 5,000 are classified as rural.

Forecasts for Employment or Occupation

Projections of employment and the number of
people who will be occupied in the various production
and service activities in Venezuela in 1970 and 1975
are presented in Table 24. These projections are made
on the assumption that the annual geometric rate of
increase in productivity per worker observed between
1950 and 1960 will continue. The rate of increase in
productivity per person for all employed persons in
that period was 3.85 per cent per year. Agriculture
had a higher-than-average rate at 4.97 per cent, and
all other sectors of the economy had a 3.56 per cent
rate. These increased productivity rates were continued along with calculations of increased economic
activity and population in the estimates of future
employment presented in Table 24.

TABLE 24

Forecast of Venezuelan Employment
1970 and 1975

	1970		1975	
Sector	Number (1,000)	Per Cent of Total	Number (1,000)	Per Cent of Total
Agriculture	729	25	777	22
All other sectors	2,233	75	2,975	78
Total employed	2,962	100	3,752	100
Economically active population	3,227		4,003	
Unemployed	365		261	
Per cent unemployed	8.9		6.7	

As a summary of the product and income projections, the following figures of several levels of

product and income on a per capita basis as of 1975
are presented:

	Amount Per Capita, 1975
Gross territorial product	Bs. 6,041
National income	4,531
Personal income	3,624
Disposable income	3,564
In the agricultural sector	731
In all other sectors	4,744

OBSERVATIONS ON MAJOR OBSTACLES AND PROBLEMS
IN FUTURE GENERAL ECONOMIC DEVELOPMENT
OF VENEZUELA

The foregoing sections have presented a general
picture of the economic development of Venezuela and
some projections into the future of growth that are
presently foreseen. Several strong points are indicated in these data, but at the same time, there
appear to be some serious problems and obstacles that
will have a strong influence on the nature of future
development. No clear-cut path for resolving several
of these problems is evident at this time, given the
existing rate of consumption of basic resources and
level of human capacities, together with the indicated
policies and practices now in use. Without doubt,
considerable investigation and ingenuity must be applied in the future to confront these problems and to
reach solutions that will permit orderly and satisfactory future development. This final section of
the chapter will be concerned with brief observations
on those problems considered most important, because
the agricultural sector, which is the main focus of
this work, will be treated more in detail in later
sections of this volume, and some of the obstacles
confronting agricultural development are the same as
those confronting the general economy.

One of the basic problems, from an economic standpoint, is that the efficiency in production methods

and in the organization and management of the basic
factors of production (manpower, capital, and land
area) is lower than is needed for increased productivity and sound future development. This applies
to all sectors of the economy, with the possible exception of the petroleum industry--and even this
activity, as previously pointed out, has encountered
a diminishing competitive advantage compared with
other producing areas of the world; its role as the
predominant impulse in Venezuelan economic development has begun to taper off.

Oil production, which has yielded such significant economic returns for Venezuela in comparison
with other Latin American countries and has formed
the basis for the spectacular economic growth during
the last three decades, continues to be the strongest
point in the Venezuelan economy. The recent plans
of the country are generally based on continuance of
this income for at least two decades. These plans,
however, do place considerable emphasis on diversification of the productive pattern of the economy
through the development of manufacturing industries
and agriculture, and significant steps have already
been taken in this direction, especially with respect
to substituting domestic production for imported
goods. In practice, these efforts have not achieved
satisfactory results from the productivity standpoint
for various and complex reasons. Some of these
reasons are:

1. Lack of adequate consideration of the real
economic framework for these diversified production
activities, which, in most instances, are established
under a protective policy with respect to foreign and
local competition that includes price supports, special exoneration of import duties on raw materials,
and, in certain cases, exoneration of other taxes and
restriction of competitive imports through licensing
regulations. The temporary protection of new industries in developing countries is a recognized economic need in order that such new enterprises can
have a limited time to become competitive, both on
internal and external markets. However, it is clear
that careful enough selection has not been made, and

many of the industries selected by industrialists
for establishment in Venezuela are far outside the
realm of being able to compete in the world market,
either now or in the future. Consequently, protection will have to continue indefinitely for them to
exist. This cuts into the real income of the general
public and is a luxury that cannot be justified on
an economic basis. The several years of high income
from the oil industry have provided capital that has
permitted development of some enterprises that were
unsound from the national welfare standpoint but that
were established because capital was available and
because protective price and cost facilities, together
with a strong public support for nationalism, supported their establishment. Some of these industries,
and especially government activities and programs of
a production nature that were established under these
conditions, are already proving a very heavy drain
on the national treasury and the purchasing power of
the general public.

2. The educational and experience levels for all
types of personnel needed for increased productivity,
from ordinary laborer to top management, have been
drastically low. Great strides have been made in recent years in improving education, including technical and vocational training, but the process is slow.
In the meantime, because of the influence of the
highly productive and automated oil industry, general
wage rates have been raised considerably higher than
those in all neighboring countries of Venezuela and
most other Latin American countries, even though the
workers available for other industries are not equally productive with the higher wages. For example,
common labor wage rates in Venezuela are four or five
times as high as those in Colombia and the northern
part of Brazil. This is a great burden for new industries to bear, as are the relatively liberal labor
laws, which were based on the high productivity of
the oil industry but which cover most other industries, regardless of the capacity of the available
force.

3. The relatively high wages, together with
availability of capital, have tended to cause the new

industries and service activities that are developing
to be capital-intensive activities that create very
few employment possibilities for people maturing and
entering the labor market. This availability of capital for expensive machinery and automation in diver-
sifying industries could be expected to compensate
for higher wage costs and make a final product price
that was competitive with foreign competition. However, in practice, because of excessively idealistic
approaches in original planning that have often led
to construction of excess capacity for the market
condition, together with the shortage of adequately
trained management and supervising personnel, the result has not always been increased production. A
solution to the problem of high unemployment versus
new capital-intensive industries will require a great
deal of ingenuity.

The foregoing comments on the problem of low productivity are especially cogent with respect to the
immediate economic future of Venezuela. As mentioned
previously, the vigor of the oil industry has been
tapering off. Venezuela still ranks third (following
the U.S.A. and Russia) in total crude oil production,
but it has been losing some of its former comparative
advantages over other oil-producing areas, especially
those of the Middle East. Its former logistic advantage with respect to the principal petroleum markets
in the Northern Hemisphere has been largely nullified
by the rapid development of super-tanker fleets by
other countries that can now deliver oil from the
Middle East to any point in the world at costs equal
to or less than such costs of delivery from Venezuela.
Lowering of prices in the international oil market
due to discounting practices adopted in attempts to
hold market outlets has created a considerable squeeze
on profits together with higher taxation of the oil
output and increased labor and machinery costs.

An eloquent fact with regard to the competitive
situation of the Venezuelan oil industry was illustrated in the Central Bank of Venezuela's 1965 Annual
Report, which quoted these figures:

Average Daily Yields of Producing Oil Wells

Country	Barrels Per Day, 1964
Iran	12,708
Iraq	10,760
Saudi Arabia	6,810
Kuwait	4,485
Libya	2,429
Venezuela	313
United States	13

In addition to yields from 12 to 40 times more than Venezuela per well, the depths that must be reached to obtain these yields in the Middle East are much less, and the costs for developing each well are correspondingly lower. Also, the restriction of further oil concessions in 1959 and the resulting political climate greatly reduced investment in exploration and development activities in this industry. This national policy continued up to 1966, and although the economy has recuperated from the depressed conditions of 1961 and 1962, the oil situation is still a critical question because of the adverse effect it is having on the general economy.

It is clear that as the impulse provided by the oil industry diminishes, other diversified activities will be called up more to stand on their own economic feet. Further, the recent entry of Venezuela into the Latin American Free Trade Association will, no doubt, force a more careful consideration of the economic effects of national policies and practices with respect to all production and consumption.

Other problems that are foreseen for future economic development are related to the problem of low productivity and are serious problems from both economic and sociological standpoints. They must be confronted soon so that concrete corrective efforts may be initiated. For example, there are high rates of unemployment and underemployment (especially in rural areas), and a large proportion (estimated at 35 per cent or more) of the total population does not contribute significantly to the Venezuelan economy,

either as producers or as consumers of the products
of the various economic sectors. A critical need
exists for the creation of more job or employment
opportunities, but at the same time, the fulfillment
of this need may require consideration of external
markets, and the requisite high levels of efficiency
and productivity will be slow to develop. In the
manufacturing field, fulfillment of productivity
goals will usually mean the previously mentioned
capital-intensive type operations, which may not provide the employment opportunities needed. For example, it is estimated that during 1965, new jobs were
created by manufacturing industries for 22,000 persons, whereas only 90,000 persons entered the labor
market during the year. Once production for foreign
markets enters the picture, important decisions must
be made regarding internal price and cost conditions
to avoid complete demoralization of the industries
concerned, which are accustomed to higher prices and
costs than the world competition will permit. Adequate reduction of the cost structure would be difficult in a short-run period, so the decision would
need to be with regard to whether or not to limit
production to national needs, which may be justified
under a protective policy, or to subsidize export.
As mentioned in the beginning, no clear-cut path is
evident, and a great deal of investigation and application of hard economic thought are necessary to
reach suitable and sound solutions.

In the following sections of this study, dealing
with the agricultural sector, some ideas will be
presented for that part of the economy on how to attack the aforementioned and other problems facing
economic development.

NOTES

1. Principal reference for the traditional economic pattern is a publication prepared for the Ministry of Agriculture and Livestock, El Rendimiento
de los Factores de Producción en la Agricultura
Venezolana, Part I (Caracas: Estudios Económicos
y Financieros, S.A., 1958).

2. La Economía Venezolana en los Ultimos 25 Años (Caracas: Central Bank of Venezuela, 1966).

3. W. W. Rostow, The Stages of Economic Growth (Boston: Cambridge University Press, 1961).

4. French technical group sponsored by CORDIPLAN for several economic studies in Venezuela.

CHAPTER **3** AGRICULTURE'S ROLE
IN THE ECONOMY

Throughout the previous chapter on the general
economy of Venezuela and in most of the statistical
tables presented therein, the agricultural sector
has been separated so that comparisons could be made
with other sectors of the economy. Consequently,
the participation of the agricultural sector in the
total economy of the country has already been indicated for the following general measures of economic
conditions:

Economic Measures	Agricultural Sector (1965)
Gross territorial product (Table 3)	7.1 per cent of total
Product per econom- ically active person (Table 4)	Bs. 2,600 (compared with Bs. 12,400 for all sectors)
Existing fixed cap- ital in the economy (Table 7)	15 per cent of total
Relation between gross territorial prod- uct and fixed capital (Table 8)	0.24 (compared with 0.53 for all sectors)
Gross fixed invest- ment during the year (Table 9)	14.8 per cent of total
Rural population (Table 15)	37.4 per cent of total
Population employed (Table 16)	32.3 per cent of total

These general economic measures show at first
glance that possibly agriculture is receiving more

from the Venezuelan economy than it is producing, as
indicated by the figures of 15.9 per cent of the
total existing fixed capital and 14.8 per cent of the
annual, gross fixed investment, compared with the
contribution of only 7.1 per cent of the GTP of Venezuela. However, when the relatively large proportion of the economically active population that is
engaged in agriculture (32.3 per cent is taken into
consideration, the possible favorable situation of
agriculture in sharing Venezuela's resources is somewhat reversed. Also, when considered in the light
of the capital needed to bring per capita income in
rural areas up to reasonably decent levels that are
more in line with other sectors of the economy and
to improve living conditions and opportunities for
rural families, it must be concluded that agriculture, although a primary productive sector of the
economy, is not receiving sufficient attention. This
will be touched upon in subsequent chapters of this
volume in the considerations of the present status
and future needs of the agricultural sector. Agriculture must catch up with and improve its productivity in harmony with other sectors of the economy
in order to provide its economically feasible portion
of the food and fiber needs of the population of
Venezuela and of other areas of the world that have
an unfavorable balance between food-producing resources and population.

Inasmuch as the principal factors for determining the role of agriculture in the economy of the
country have been presented in the foregoing chapter,
the discussion in this chapter will be limited to
presenting some additional details on the relation
of the agricultural sector to the whole economy, principally with regard to production for use both within
Venezuela and for export.

CONTRIBUTION TO THE GROSS TERRITORIAL PRODUCT

As shown in Table 3, the contribution of the
agricultural sector to the GTP of Venezuela ranged
from 1,845 million to 2,395 million bolivars at constant 1957 prices from 1961 to 1965, which constituted

6.8 per cent to 7.1 per cent of the total during this
five-year period. The principal groups of agricultural products that make up the total agricultural
product are indicated in Table 25 as percentages of
the total value of agricultural production for the
five-year period.

There are no particularly significant trends to
be noted in the relative importance in the groups of
products between 1961 and 1965, as shown in Table 25.
There are some adjustments, however, in the importance of specific products, which will be described
in Chapter 5. As a preview of some of these product
shifts, the ten most remunerative products in 1965
are listed in Table 26, together with the per cent
that the value of each was of the total value of agricultural production. A comparative rating as of 1961
is also shown for these products.

The increase in diversification in farm products
is indicated in the foregoing figures, inasmuch as
the ten most remunerative products in 1965 constituted
58.4 per cent of the total, whereas in 1961, they
constituted almost 65 per cent of the total.

PORTION OF THE TOTAL POPULATION DEPENDENT
ON AGRICULTURE

Available population data do not provide exact
figures for the total number of persons dependent on
the agricultural sector, although the 1961 census did
provide information on the dependency distribution
among the three main divisions of economic activity
(primary, secondary, and tertiary). The percentages
of the population, by locality, that were dependent
on these three main sectors, according to the 1961
population census, are shown in Table 27.

Applying these percentages to the total 1961 population, the figure of 2,694,448 persons is arrived
at as the number dependent on the primary sector of
the economy. By deducting the number of persons depending on the petroleum and mining sectors of the
economy and projecting the figure to 1965 by increasing

TABLE 25

Relationship of Agricultural Product Groups to Total
Agricultural Production in Venezuela, 1961-65
(1957 Prices)

Product Groups	Per Cent of Total Value of Agricultural Production				
	1961	1962	1963	1964	1965
Cereals	7.0	8.6	8.9	10.1	10.2
Legumes	2.0	1.6	1.6	1.6	1.5
Roots and tubers	9.4	11.6	9.9	10.1	8.2
Fiber and oil crops	4.0	3.5	5.0	5.4	5.9
Fruits and vegetables	7.9	7.3	8.3	6.6	7.0
Coffee, cocoa, and others	26.6	24.6	23.6	23.7	23.5
Total crop groups	56.9	57.2	57.3	57.5	56.3
Milk and derivatives	11.6	11.6	12.9	12.8	13.6
Eggs	3.0	3.3	3.2	3.3	3.3
Livestock	22.1	21.4	20.4	19.9	20.1
Total livestock and livestock products	36.7	36.3	36.5	36.0	37.0
Total fish	2.6	2.8	2.6	2.5	2.6
Total forest products	3.8	3.7	3.6	4.0	4.1
Total agricultural products	100.0	100.0	100.0	100.0	100.0

Source: Ministry of Agriculture and Livestock, for 1961-65; and the annual reports
of the Central Bank of Venezuela for 1961-65.

TABLE 26

Comparison of Venezuela's Ten Most Remunerative Agricultural
Products, 1961 and 1965 (at Farm Prices)

| Product | Per Cent of Total Value of Agri-cultural Production | | Rating in 1961[a] |
	1965	1961	
Milk and derivatives	13.6	11.6	3
Cattle	11.1	14.1	1
Coffee	7.0	13.7	2
Sugar cane	5.8	5.7	4
Corn	4.4	5.1	5
Poultry	4.1	4.7	6
Rice	3.9	2.1	12
Plantains	3.1	1.4	16
Eggs	2.7	3.0	11
Bananas	2.7	3.5	7
Total	58.4	64.9	

[a]Mandioc (yucca), tobacco, and hogs were in the top ten of 1961 and were displaced
by rice, plantains, and eggs in the 1965 listing.

Source: Calculated from data in the annual reports of the Central Bank of Venezuela
for 1961 and 1965.

it by the same annual rate as agricultural employment has increased (1.3 per cent), the estimate for
the number of people dependent on agriculture in
1965 can be obtained (see Table 28).

TABLE 27

Venezuelan Population Dependent on Agriculture,
by Sectors, 1961 (Per Cent)

Locality	Pri- mary	Second- ary	Ter- tiary	Not Declared	Total
Rural areas	78.7	4.8	11.5	5.0	100.0
Intermediate areas	45.6	12.6	34.5	7.3	100.0
Urban areas	12.7	24.2	52.8	10.3	100.0

Source: 1961 census.

TABLE 28

Estimated Venezuelan Population Dependent
on Agriculture, 1961-65[a]

	Persons Dependent on Agriculture	
Year	Number	Per Cent of Total Population
1961	2,458,665	32.3
1962	2,508,636	31.9
1963	2,550,069	31.3
1964	2,593,508	30.8
1965	2,639,711	30.3

[a]Calculated from total population data provided by
the Census Division of the General Office of Statistics. Adjusted by reducing the total number dependent on the primary sector of the economy by a
number obtained by multiplying the number of persons
employed in the petroleum and mining industries (as
reported by the Central Bank of Venezuela each year)
by the average number of members per family (5.1).

The figures in Table 28 show that almost one third of the total population was still dependent on agriculture for its income during 1961-65. As shown previously (Table 6), the agricultural sector received only 7.7 per cent (1,810 million bolivars) of the national income in 1965, which yielded a per capita income in this sector of Bs. 686 ($152 U.S.) at constant 1957 prices. This was compared with a per capita income of Bs. 2,694 for all the population, so the farm population clearly was lagging far behind the other sectors of the economy in reaching a decent living level. It is estimated by home economists in Venezuela that rural families should have at least three times this indicated per capita income in order to live decently under present conditions.

SOURCE AND CONSUMPTION OF AGRICULTURAL PRODUCTS IN VENEZUELA

The total cost of all products and services consumed in Venezuela in 1965 amounted to 21,562 million bolivars, which was approximately two thirds of the gross territorial product.[1] The value of food consumed amounted to 6,808 million bolivars or Bs. 781 per capita, which constituted 32 per cent of the total consumption cost of goods and services.

The predominant proportion of agricultural products consumed are produced domestically. Direct comparison of absolute figures on production cannot be made with the above figures because such figures represent costs to consumers, whereas the production data are available only at the producers' price level. However, the following percentage comparison can be made, based on production data and export and import information for 1965.[2]

Total value of agricultural production	100
Total value of agricultural products exported (per cent of total production)	5
Total value of agricultural products imported (per cent of total production)	20
Total value of agricultural products consumed (per cent of total production)	115

In relation to the total consumption of agricultural products, the portion that was imported in 1965 was 17.5 per cent, whereas as shown above, the value of the imported items amounted to 20 per cent of the total national production. As mentioned previously, during 1951-60, the imports of food products were much higher than in 1966, reaching 30 per cent to 40 per cent of total consumption.

The average diet per person in Venezuela provides a total of from 2,300 to 2,500 calories per day,[3] which is considered barely adequate. Although there is a great deal of variation by areas and income levels, nutritional deficiencies are still considered a major cause of illness in Venezuela. The quantities of animal protein and fresh fruits and vegetables consumed are much below desirable dietary standards. However, in spite of nutritional problems and low incomes of significant portions, it is not anticipated that Venezuela will be faced with the severe food crisis that is facing some heavily populated areas of the world. This is due to the fact that very substantial margins exist in the natural resource base for food production and some progress is being made in increasing the rate of productivity. During the slow process required for increased productivity and general agricultural development, Venezuela is endowed with an extraordinary capacity to import food as the demand requires. In a longer range period, some critical food supply problems may develop if ways and means of developing Venezuela's agricultural potential are permitted to lag too much behind population needs and when the high-value petroleum exports become exhausted.

POLITICAL INFLUENCE OF THE AGRICULTURAL SECTOR IN DETERMINING DEVELOPMENT POLICIES

Bicameral legislative structures were designed during the early history of several countries to provide for a mixture of legislative representation based on both population density and geographical factors. Thus it was possible for rural areas to have representation in Congress in numbers greater than the proportional population distribution would

have permitted. This has been an important factor in
some countries, especially in the United States, for
it enabled rural areas to defend their interests and
resulted in a more uniform development throughout
Venezuela.

Although Venezuela has had a bicameral national
legislature for most of its democratic history, the
strongly centralized nature of its government in recent decades and the application of the representation in Congress, based on party affiliations without
residence requirements in the state or region from
which the members of Congress, both Senate and Deputy
branches, are elected, has deprived rural areas of
government consideration of their developmental problems. This fact, together with the traditional tenancy structure, based on land ownership centered in
the hands of few people who did not live in rural
areas, has meant that rural people have not had the
same opportunities for advancement in income and in
cultural fields as the residents of cities and towns.

This does not mean that the agricultural sector
has not had a voice in national affairs. Especially
during 1940-65, some institutional structures have
been developed, designed to give the agricultural
sector a reasonable representation in national affairs. The Ministry of Agriculture and Livestock was
established in 1936 to look after farmers' interests.
Also, several autonomous institutions, such as the
Agricultural and Livestock Bank, established in 1928,
and the National Agrarian Institute, established in
1950 through a reorganization of previously established agencies, have been involved exclusively in
agricultural activities for many years. However, all
of these agencies have been somewhat limited in meeting problems as they occurred and in providing effective leadership for the agricultural sector because
of limited funds assigned to them, lack of continuity
in administrative and technical personnel, and the
extremely limited number of professional people concerned with agriculture.

During 1956-65, organizations representing rural
interests have been formed at a rapid pace, and federated farmers' organizations, together with several

important producers' associations organized on commodity lines, are giving agriculture a more vocifer-
ous and powerful participation in national affairs.
Although some of these groups represent special interests and have achieved special considerations for
certain segments of the agricultural sector to the
detriment of the general public, agriculture now
has an institutional structure that can form a foundation for its voice to be heard in national policies.
There is, of course, considerable subdevelopment in
these institutional structures with respect to technical and administrative competence and dedication,
and these will only be improved by education and
training in all aspects so that the public can understand and demand the type of competence required.

With respect to the influence that farmers not
organized into political action groups may have had
or have in the determination of development policies
in agriculture, there are three general categories
to consider:

1.   The traditional large rural landholders
operating under the paternalistic hacienda system

2.   The modern commercial farmer group, recently
formed, on the whole (often in connection with special commodity development programs) members of which
have been the principal innovators in applying modern
technology and farm management to agricultural production

3.   The largest group, made up of the subsistence
farmers (campesinos or conqueros), who operate very
small parcels of land, mostly on a "shifting cultiva-
tion" basis and utilizing only hand tools

The first group, the large property owners, were
traditionally fairly powerful with respect to national
affairs. However, most of these property owners did
not live on their farm properties a major portion of
the time and were more oriented to the affairs of the
cities than to the development of their rural properties. In fact, most were very conservative in economic activities and were firm believers of the status

quo with respect to investments in rural facilities
and other development. Many had and still have significant business activities apart from their land
holdings and more frequently would side with the
urban sector than with the rural sector when it came
to assignment of development funds, both government
and private. Most observers conclude that this group
had a more negative than positive effect on rural development policies.

The second group of newly established commercial
farmers are generally quite aggressive businessmen who
go after what is needed to make their farming operations a success. Although many of them lived on
their rural properties during the development stages,
which generally were marked by liberal doses of government assistance through liberal credit, technical
assistance, and guaranteed markets, apparently significant proportions of these farmers considered their
farming activities as only transitory experiences.
Consequently, beyond the aggressive action needed to
successfully operate their individual properties,
their interests have not extended to taking a strong
stand in national affairs as far as general rural development is concerned. In fact, there has been a
strong tendency for these operators, once they have
gained a certain degree of success and affluence, to
take the path of the traditional hacendado, or large
property owner, by becoming involved in nonfarm business completely and getting into urban-oriented business. Consequently, this group is not constituting
a strong influence in national policies for rural
development beyond aggressive action to get additional aid or to maintain special commodity assistance
and protection enjoyed in their particular farm business.

The third group, made up of the small subsistence
farmers, is marked by low educational levels and is
generally without significant leadership from among
their own group to constitute a significant voice in
rural development activities. The farmers' syndicates
that have been developed in recent years have many
farmers from this group as members. However, most
sociological studies of these organizations show

conclusively that leadership comes from outside the
campesino group and that they are generally very
silent members. They belong to the syndicate mostly
because they think it is necessary in order to participate in the agrarian reform program or to obtain
credit.

In summary, except for the farm agencies established by the Venezuelan Government and the centrally
organized farm organizations that provide leadership
from the top down, the farm operators per se have not
had much of a voice in rural development policies.

NOTES

1. Annual Report of the Central Bank of Venezuela for 1965, pp. 139 and 144.

2. Annual Report of the Central Bank of Venezuela for 1965, pp. 325 and 327.

3. Report of Fermín Velez Boza (Caracas:
National Nutrition Institute, May, 1965).

CHAPTER **4** PUBLIC ATTITUDE
TOWARD AGRICULTURE

It has already been indicated in previous portions of this volume that agricultural development
has lagged behind most other sectors of the economy
as far as total production and productivity is concerned, which, in itself, is an indication of public
attitude and support for the rural sector. At the
same time, the increases during 1960-65 in total
production of agriculture at rates higher than the
increases in total GTP, as shown in Figure 1, indicate both a changing attitude and the application
of more resources and effort to improve agricultural
conditions and bring about a better balance in the
distribution of the wealth of the country. In this
chapter the available indications of support and attention to agriculture will be discussed.

A comprehensive agricultural development policy
is not clearly stated in official reports of a general nature or in the annual reports of agencies
concerned principally with agricultural development,
welfare, and control. However, the general policy
of the Venezuelan government is to encourage the
substitution of domestic for imported products, including food and fiber and industrial products. This
policy has been implemented by special import licensing and contingency arrangements for such products
as dried milk, sesame, and some pork products. The
policy has also been implemented through customs duty
protection or exoneration of duties, in the case of
some raw materials that are later manufactured into
products used locally, such as animal feed. The
Agrarian Reform Law also states some general policies
for the agrarian reform program, encompassing not only
land distribution to those who work the land but also

social and economic improvement goals for the small
and medium farmer group in Venezuela. The laws and
decrees implementing these policies are described
in the following section of this study.

REVIEW OF RECENT LAWS AND DECREES
CONCERNING AGRICULTURE

One of the most significant legislative actions
concerning agriculture and rural areas in Venezuela
that has been approved by the Congress has been the
Agrarian Reform Law, which went into effect in March
of 1960. This is a comprehensive and far-reaching
law and has served as a model for many of the laws
passed in fifteen other Latin American countries
since that time to provide an orderly manner for re-
distributing land resources to, and providing certain
social and economic improvement goals for, the people
who work the land. Although Venezuela has had a pattern of concentration of land holdings in few hands,
it also has had areas with excessive subdivision of
land ownership. Venezuela did not, however, have an
acute problem of large land holdings from which the
owners lived exclusively on the income and rents from
rural holdings without any economic and social concern
as to the status of the rural areas. The implementation of the law has had faults from an economic view-
point because of lack of attention to technical
factors of a micro-economic nature, especially with
respect to size of farms and requirements for efficient
and productive farm units, the lack of clearly established goals for the land distribution activities,
general problems of institutional development, and
the legal delays in land-title activities that char-
acterize most agrarian-reform programs. These factors,
together with the low educational level of the rural
population, have kept accomplishments far below the
levels expected from the law. However, an active
program has been carried out and more than 100,000
families have already received parcels of land, or at
least use rights, since the law was passed. Additional
evaluation of this program will be made in the following two chapters.

Most of the legal decrees and resolutions concerning agriculture that appear in the official government register (Gaceta Oficial) originated in the Ministry of Agriculture and Livestock and the Ministry of Development and deal with action taken in connection with control activities for imports, exports, prices and sanitation requirements for agricultural products. Many of these resolutions deal with the policies on contingency requirements for use of nationally produced goods, which importers must comply with before import permits are issued. These requirements had been applied to powdered milk, pork, beans, and some other products, as indicated in the summary of legal decrees and resolutions included in the annual reports of the Ministry of Agriculture and Livestock.

Some specific decrees and resolutions that have been made during 1961-65 and that are of general interest and importance to agriculture are listed below:

1. Decree of January, 1961, to establish the National Fund for Agricultural and Livestock Research as an autonomous organization to sponsor and coordinate work in this field.

2. Decrees to establish national funds for coffee and cocoa and to help create the various funds for cotton, fruit culture, and sesame. Also, special committees for developing corn production methods and for conducting research on tobacco-growing.

3. Resolution (RNR No. 147) of June 6, 1960, establishing a national Commission for Renewable Natural Resources.

4. Resolution of April, 1961, establishing a system of national producers' councils on commodity lines. The 1965 Annual Report of the Ministry of Agriculture and Livestock indicated that eleven of these advisory councils were functioning, representing the commodities of cotton, rice, poultry, coffee, beef, pork, milk, oil seed crops, potatoes, sisal,

and tobacco. These councils are coordinated in the Ministry of Agriculture and Livestock.

5. Decree approved by Congress in July, 1964, for the participation of Venezuela in the International Coffee Agreement. Venezuela had participated in this agreement since 1962, with an export quota of 465,000 sacks (60 kilograms each), which it has not filled in any year since entering this agreement.

In addition to the above decrees concerned principally with agricultural products, a Venezuelan Commission for Industrial Standards was established under the direction of the Ministry of Development. This commission has issued standards for classifying pork and some other products for industrial use on a provisional basis. However, product classification standards still have not gained much headway with respect to agricultural products.

In March of 1966, a Forestry, Soils, and Water Law was passed regulating the control of these resources and establishing national parks, monuments, and forest reserves.

Also during 1966, proposed laws were presented to the Venezuelan Congress for reorganizing the Agricultural Bank by separating its commercial farm credit operations into a special Agricultural Development Bank. Another law proposed the establishment of a special marketing corporation to assume the commodity price support, storage, and other marketing functions formerly provided by the Agricultural Bank along with other market development and control activities for agricultural products. No action had been taken in Congress on these proposed laws as of the time this book was written, and there was considerable public reaction against the proposed marketing law because it was claimed that it would give the Venezuelan Government too much power and responsibility in the distribution of agricultural products and that this would be detrimental to the efficiency and free flow of supply and demand in marketing.

The influence of some of these legally created organizations and their effects on agricultural development will be dealt with in later chapters.

PUBLIC INVESTMENT IN SUPPORT OF AGRICULTURE

It is difficult to obtain a complete picture of the total amount of public funds that are budgeted for and spent in agriculture because these funds are dispersed among various ministries and agencies. In Table 29, an attempt is made to summarize the total budget situation between 1962 and 1965 with respect to agriculture. The table indicates that agriculture has been receiving between 10 per cent and 11 per cent of total government expenditures, distributed among activities of the Ministry of Agriculture and Livestock, the Agrarian Institute, the Agricultural and Livestock Bank, and funds appropriated for agricultural purposes to the Ministries of Public Works, Sanitation, and Social Assistance and Development. During the period indicated in the table, funds for construction and maintenance of irrigation projects amounted to approximately one fourth of the total public expenditures for agriculture. From 1962 to 1965, the agricultural sector public expenditures increased from 657.4 million to 818.0 million bolivars at an average annual rate of 8.1 per cent, whereas total government expenditures increased at the average annual rate of 3.6 per cent. Thus, during this period, agriculture apparently was receiving proportionately more increases than were other sectors of the economy. In fact, the increase in government expenditures for agriculture was approximately 1 per cent more than relative increases in the agricultural product as shown in Table 3. The relatively small proportion of the budget provided for research and extension activities points up one of the main problems for improved technology and productivity in Venezuelan agriculture.

The projections for government expenditures in the agricultural sector, as included in the Plan of the Nation for 1965-68, show substantially increasing

TABLE 29

Venezuelan Government Expenditures Allocated to Agriculture, 1962-65
(Million Bs.)

Year	Budgets of Ministry of Agriculture and Livestock and Dependencies								Total for Agricultural Sector		Total Government Costs
	Research & Extension	Special Credit Programs[a]	Other Ministry Costs[b]	Agrarian Institute	Agricultural & Livestock Bank	Irrigation Projects[c]	Rural Water Systems & Housing[d]	Milk Industry Development & Subsidies[e]	Amount	Per Cent of Total Government Costs	
1962	24.0	56.0	123.2	139.3	63.0	153.6	28.0	70.3	657.4	10.0	6,553.4
1963	28.6	59.1	135.8	107.8	50.0	171.4	57.1	63.8	673.6	10.2	6,633.3
1964	34.2	54.1	143.4	150.8	130.0	202.2	31.8	65.7	812.2	11.3	7,205.8
1965	31.9	75.0	171.5	150.8	150.0	156.8	29.6	52.4	818.0	11.3	7,260.2
Total, 1962 to 1965	118.7	244.2	573.9	548.7	393.0	684.0	146.5	252.2	2,961.2	10.7	27,652.7
Agricultural Sector, Per Cent of Total	4.0	8.2	19.4	18.5	13.3	23.1	4.9	8.5	100.0		

a Includes Livestock Development Plan and Coffee and Cocoa Development Plan, administered jointly by Ministry of Agriculture and Livestock and the Agricultural and Livestock Bank. Practically all of the amounts shown were for loan funds.

b All other costs in the Ministry of Agriculture and Livestock budgets except those listed in the four other columns.

^cConstruction and maintenance costs for irrigation work of the Ministry of Public Works. Includes costs of the Division of Hydraulic Works of the Ministry, which varied from 7 to 7.8 million bolivars per year.

^dPrograms of the Ministry of Sanitation and Social Assistance.

^eMilk subsidy program administered by the Venezuela Development Corporation. According to Decree No. 1006, dated March 20, 1963, the amount of this subsidy was fixed at Bs. 40 million annually.

Source: National Budget Program, 1966, published by CORDIPLAN.

Note: Prior to 1962, national budgets were made on a fiscal year basis, from July 1 to June 30. Consequently, comparable data for 1961 and previous years were not available.

77

amounts for practically all activities and programs
shown in Table 29.   Projections of agricultural sector investments and expenditures of government funds,
as well as private funds, are shown in Table 30.

TABLE 30

Estimated Agricultural Expenditures and
Investments in Venezuela, 1966-68
(Million Bs.)

| | Government Appropriations | | | Private | |
Year	Current Costs	Capital Invest- ments	Total	Capital Investment	Total
1966	321.3	913.9	1,235.2	729.0	1,964.2
1967	321.6	1,023.8	1,345.4	764.0	2,109.4
1968	324.7	1,104.1	1,428.8	802.0	2,230.8

Although there was a considerable jump in total
government funds allocated to agriculture between the
data to 1965 shown in Table 29 and those shown for
1966 in the Plan of the Nation projections, this follows the history of previous projections of the Plan
of the Nation, which have placed the goals from 25
per cent to 30 per cent more than historical data
support.   In other words, the national planning operation deals with goals toward which government action is leading and not necessarily with forecasts of
what is probably going to happen.   The figure on private investment is not explained in the Plan but is
believed to be high.

An alternative set of figures, which are probably
on the conservative side for recent investment in
agriculture, are those furnished by the Central Bank
of Venezuela, as shown in Table 31.

These data are alleged to show the total investment in agriculture, both public and private.   However, as previously indicated in Table 9, which shows

annual investment figures for all of agriculture,
the total amounts varied from 674 million to 767 million bolivars per year with the total for the five-
year period of 3,924 million bolivars as shown in
Table 31.

TABLE 31

Gross Fixed Investment in Venezuelan
Agriculture, 1961-65
(Million Bs. at 1957 Prices)

Item	Amount	Per Cent of Total
Construction and improvements		
Deforestation	181	4.6
Irrigation works	507	12.9
Planting permanent pastures	252	6.4
Fencing	122	3.1
Housing	580	14.8
Other constructions	332	8.5
Total	1,974	50.3
Livestock investments	978	24.9
Machinery and equipment	694	17.7
Vehicles	278	7.1
Grand total	3,924	100.0

Source: Annual reports of the Central Bank of
Venezuela for 1961-65. (Figures for 1964
and 1965 were not adjusted for changed bolivar values in foreign exchange because very
little foreign capital is invested in agriculture.)

As additional detail regarding the fixed capital
existing in agriculture and as a fragmentation of
total figures shown in Table 7 taken from the Central

Bank of Venezuela Annual Reports, which exclude land
values, the data in Table 32 are presented for the
years 1961 to 1965.

As indicated previously, the investment estimates
of the Central Bank of Venezuela are very conservative, especially for livestock inventory. However,
they are reliable in showing changes between years.
In the case of capital existing in agriculture, there
appears to be little significant change taking place
in the relative importance of the various types of
capital improvements, livestock inventories, and machinery items, although all lines show steady absolute
increases.

The government of Venezuela has involved itself
in several direct service activities and some manufacturing activities that affect agriculture. For
example, the petrochemical complex at Moron, state of
Carabobo, is a government-developed manufacturing
operation for manufacture of fertilizers and other
chemical products. The use of fertilizers in agriculture will be analyzed in later chapters. In connection
with special campaigns for producing more of certain
specific products (such as rice and corn) under artificial price situations and high costs, the Venezuelan
Government has assumed the responsibility of providing
most of the storage capacity, together with some of
the drying and milling services required. Price-
support programs, especially for rice and corn, have
resulted in the government's having to purchase the
major portions of these crops each year, a procedure
that has required large investments in commodities
and storage facilities. The price regulatory function
has not been operated so that the main direct services
could remain in the hands of private businesses.
Finally, some of the sugar-processing centrals have
been developed by the government and are operated by
the Development Corporation of Venezuela.

In Table 33 are presented data on the storage
facilities, principally for rice and corn, that were
built by the government and are now in the hands of a
government-sponsored company, Almacenes de Depositos
Agropecuarios, C.A. (ADAGRO), a subsidiary of the

TABLE 32

Value of Permanent Improvements and Livestock and Machinery Inventories
in Venezuelan Agriculture, 1961-65
(Million Bs. at 1957 Prices)

Item	1961		1962		1963		1964		1965	
	Amount	Per Cent of Total	Amount	Per Cent of Total	Amount	Per Cent of Total	Amount	Per Cent of Total	Amount	Per Cent of Total
Construction & improvements										
Deforestation	837	10.4	871	10.2	907	10.1	945	9.9	984	9.8
Irrigation works	587	7.3	705	8.3	786	8.8	906	9.5	971	9.6
Planting permanent pastures	991	12.4	1,017	11.9	1,043	11.6	1,070	11.2	1,097	10.9
Fencing	268	3.3	268	3.2	268	3.0	275	2.9	285	2.8
Housing	955	11.9	1,022	12.0	1,094	12.2	1,172	12.3	1,256	12.5
Other construc- tions	378	4.7	406	4.8	436	4.9	467	4.9	500	5.0
Total	4,016	50.0	4,289	50.4	4,534	50.6	4,835	50.8	5,094	50.6
Livestock inventories	3,265	40.6	3,457	40.6	3,653	40.7	3,853	40.5	4,056	40.3
Machinery & equipment	451	5.6	459	5.4	466	5.2	508	5.3	570	5.6
Vehicles	305	3.8	311	3.6	315	3.5	328	3.4	352	3.5
Grand Total	8,037	100.0	8,516	100.0	8,968	100.0	9,542	100.0	10,072	100.0
Per cent of annual increase	—		6.0		5.3		6.2		5.8	

Source: Annual reports of the Central Bank of Venezuela for 1961-65. (Data on land values was not available.)

81

Agricultural Bank of Venezuela. In later tables,
the government participation in other service businesses will be indicated.

TABLE 33

Venezuelan Government Grain Storage Facilities
by Types and Number of Locations, 1964

Type of Storage Facility	Number of Locations	Capacity (Metric Tons)
Silos (with elevators)	20	87,087
Warehouses	22	104,433
Tanks (Australian-type)	7	11,700
Total	49	203,220

Source: 1965 report of Almacenes de Depósitos
         Agropecuarios.

The 203,220 metric tons of storage capacity indicated in Table 33 corresponds to 28 per cent of
Venezuela's total production of rice and corn in 1965.

In addition to the storage facilities shown in
Table 33, the Venezuelan Government has plans under
way for increasing storage capacity by 150,000 tons
in the near future. Furthermore, the government has
established, over the years, cold storage facilities
of considerable size in six locations, but four of
these are now inactive and only the cold storage
plants in the "Coche" Market in Caracas and in Maracay
are operating under government control. There were,
however, twelve privately owned cold storage plants
with capacities of 300 cubic meters or more in operation in Venezuela in 1965.

PRIVATE INVESTMENT IN DEVELOPMENT AND
SERVICES FOR AGRICULTURE

Data on the participation of the private sector
in agricultural development and service functions in

Venezuela are scarce, so only indicators of some of
these activities can be presented here. The data in
Table 34 describe private storage facilities related
to processing industries for important grain and other
products, included imported wheat.

The total storage capacity for the five crops indicated in Table 34, 386,060 metric tons, was provided
by private industries and constitute 90 per cent more
capacity than the government facilities. However,
government plans for an increase in capacity by
150,000 metric tons will make the government facilities almost equal to private facilities, and the government will control the predominant proportion of
storage for corn and rice. The purchase of corn and
rice by the government in connection with minimum
price-support programs has far exceeded the storage
facilities available, and temporary storage devices
have been used. The losses of products due to spoil-
age and damage have been high throughout the storage
system, although the major portion of the facilities
constructed are relatively new and of modern design.

The excessive concentration of economic facilities
and activities around the capital of Venezuela is indicated by the location of the storage facilities for
important crops as shown in Table 34. Sixty-five per
cent of the private storage facilities are concentrated
in the three states and the Federal District around
the capital city of Caracas. This area has approximately one third of Venezuela's population, but it is
clear that double transportation is involved in the
distribution process because products are brought into the central part of Venezuela for storage and are
later shipped back again to interior areas. The location of government facilities ameliorates this situation somewhat, and additional storage facilities
will be built closer to the producing areas than at
present. However, the principal processing plants are
located in the Central region, which also explains the
concentration of storage facilities there.

A regional breakdown of storage facilities, both
government and private, with comparisons with the
population distribution, are shown in Table 35.

TABLE 34

Storage Capacity in Processing Plants for Venezuela's Agricultural Products by Regions and States, 1964 (Metric Tons)

Region	Storage Capacity by Crops					Storage Capacity by Type of Facility		
	Corn	Rice	Sesame	Cotton	Wheat	Silos	Warehouses	Total
Andes								
Mérida	108	0	0	0	0	0	108	108
Táchira	154	8,200	0	0	0	0	8,354	8,354
Trujillo	328	0	0	0	0	0	328	328
Total	590	8,200	0	0	0	0	8,790	8,790
Western								
Zulia	8,034	2,000	0	0	10,000	14,100	5,934	20,034
West Central								
Falcón	135	0	0	0	0	0	135	135
Lara	4,784	0	0	0	2,000	0	6,784	6,784
Yaracuy	15,795	0	0	0	0	14,400	1,395	15,795
Total	20,714	0	0	0	2,000	14,400	8,314	22,714
Central								
Federal District	1,748	0	5,000	0	39,930	32,930	13,748	46,678
Aragua	28,980	17,700	2,000	1,000	70	18,000	31,750	49,750
Carabobo	50,834	28,900	17,800	0	26,200	54,000	69,734	123,734
Miranda	4,132	100	25,000	0	320	0	29,552	29,552
Total	85,694	46,700	49,800	1,000	66,520	104,930	144,784	249,714

Western Plains							
Barinas	68	10,500	0	0	0	0	10,568	10,568
Cojedes	94	7,000	0	0	0	0	7,094	7,094
Portuguesa	369	35,000	0	2,200	0	0	37,569	37,569
Total	531	52,500	0	2,200	0	0	55,231	55,231
Eastern & Southern Plains							
Anzoátegui	2,122	500	0	0	0	0	2,622	2,622
Apure	90	500	0	0	0	0	590	590
Guárico	2,531	13,000	0	1,000	0	0	16,531	16,531
Monagas	241	900	0	0	0	0	1,141	1,141
Total	4,984	14,900	0	1,000	0	0	20,884	20,884
Eastern							
Bolívar	136	450	0	0	0	0	586	586
Nueva Esparta	209	0	0	0	0	0	209	209
Sucre	331	400	0	0	5,000	4,000	1,731	5,731
Territory of Delta Amacuro	367	1,800	0	0	0	0	2,167	2,167
Territory of Amazonas	0	0	0	0	0	0	0	0
Total	1,043	2,650	0	0	5,000	4,000	4,693	8,693
Grand Total	121,590	126,950	49,800	4,200	83,520	137,430	248,630	386,060

Source: "Información Básica para la Programación del Desarrollo-Venezuela." Special Report of Colegio de Ingenieros for Pan American Union of Associations of Engineers.(UPADI) (October, 1966).

TABLE 35

Storage Facilities Related to Population
Distribution in Venezuela, 1965

| Region | Per Cent of Total Population | Per Cent of Total Storage Capacity | | Total |
		Private Facilities	Government Facilities	
Andean	13	2	10	5
Western	12	5	4	5
West Central	15	6	9	7
Central	32	65	24	50
Western Plains	5	15	51	27
Eastern & Southern Plains	13	5	0[a]	4
Eastern	10	2	2	2
Total	100	100	100	100

[a]A 40,000 metric ton storage facility in the state
of Guárico under construction by the government
will increase facilities in this region, which has
an important rice-producing area near Calabozo.

Sources: 1965 report of Almacenes de Depósitos
Agropecuarios; "Información Basica para la
Programación del Desarrollo-Venezuela,"
special report of Colegio de Ingenieros
for Pan-American Union of Associations of
Engineers (October, 1966).

The Western Plains region, made up of Barinas,
Cojedes, and Portuguesa, is a large producer of grains
that were developed through a special rice production
program of the government, which explains the large
capacity of government storage facilities in this area.

The storage facilities of the government have been
costly and still constitute a serious drain on public

funds because of government inefficiency. Most an-
alysts of this problem agree that such direct functions would be better managed as private enterprises.
The frequent shifts of administrative personnel and
reorganization of these services that have occurred
indicate the problems faced by government organizations to gear themselves to the requirements of direct service operations to producers and business.

Data available on processing plants utilizing
agricultural products are presented in Table 36. The
data in this table do not cover all aspects of the
processing industries for agricultural products. For
example, data were not included for the tanning industry, the processing of cocoa beans, the bakery
industries, and sisal processing. However, an important fact is revealed in the table with respect
to the problem that agricultural production must be
adapted and organized to supply the needs of the
processing industries. With very few exceptions, the
industrial use of domestic agricultural products has
not increased at the same rate as total agricultural
production, whereas industries based principally on
imported agricultural products increased at rates
much higher. This is illustrated by the following
figures, calculated on the basis of the data in Table
36.

Average Annual Rate of Increase
in Production, 1961-65 (Per Cent)

Industries based on imported products (mainly wheat)	15.9
Industries based on domestic products (excluding sugar and tobacco)	3.9

Sugar production has increased at about 12 per
cent per year but is excluded from the above comparison because substantial sugar surpluses have not
been marketed in recent years and a substantial part
of the production was in government centrals. Tobacco

TABLE 36

Number and Production of Processing Plants Utilizing Agricultural
Products, by Types of Industries, 1961-65
(Production in Metric Tons Unless Indicated Otherwise)

Product	1961 No. of Plants	1961 Production	1962 No. of Plants	1962 Production	1963 No. of Plants	1963 Production	1964 No. of Plants	1964 Production	1965 No. of Plants	1965 Production
Sausage & cured meats	24	10,764	28	13,927	31	14,419	31	16,970	33	18,908
Milk & milk products										
Pasteurizing plants	16	161,057	17	163,457	16	178,895	15	190,165	15	163,837
Other milk products	138	31,095	150	35,326	154	43,086	162	51,197	150	60,274
Fruit preserves & juices	45	39,015	44	33,978	46	33,244	47	30,700	46	33,615
Spices, mayonnaise & mustard	20	2,202	19	2,491	17	2,541	18	3,474	19	3,811
Tomato products (purée & catchup)	11	2,091	13	2,809	12	3,637	13	3,642	14	4,458
Rice mills (milled rice)a,c	97	56,470	100	50,309	102	55,304	115	61,957	118	77,485
Coffee factories	106	17,050	101	17,369	96	17,551	95	18,547	100	18,576
Sugar centrals (refined sugar)c	13	215,388	14	245,221	14	275,569	13	289,909	13	340,377
Sugar cake mills (papelón)	1,303	44,690	1,166	42,296	985	44,226	904	43,495	900	46,259
Flour mills (wheat)	14	212,864	14	236,426	14	257,204	14	302,802	14	N.D.
Margarine & cooking oils	37	64,809	40	67,933	41	69,144	43	73,921	45	78,271
Starch	7	2,385	7	3,739	8	3,593	8	2,739	13	4,740
Pastas (spaghetti, etc.)	72	43,433	72	43,470	73	47,513	73	54,826	83	57,696
Animal feed mills	14	267,328	14	297,546	20	322,764	22	415,548	22	446,354
Cigarettes (million units)	4	7,386	4	7,844	4	8,256	4	8,662	4	9,549
Cigars (million units)	27	88	26	91	23	93	21	92	19	93

Cotton gins[a]		14	15	15	13
(fiber)	8,481	11,358	10,034	12,316	14,217
cotton seed)	13,578	18,888	17,563	21,236	24,636
Corn-hulling plants (pilones)[b]	505 176,346	521 187,223	568 183,126	725 207,359	685 175,388

[a]Data from Agricultural Statistics Annual, 1965.

[b]Data from Agricultural Statistics Annual, 1965; includes hulled corn (72.2 per cent), flour (1.4 per cent), and bran (26.4 per cent).

[c]Part of these rice mills are government-owned. Also, five of the sugar centrals are government-owned and produce approximately 40 per cent of Venezuela's total production of sugar.

Source: Dirección General de Estadística, Ministry of Development special surveys.

is excluded because available data are not in units
of measure comparable with other products. Cigarette
production increased at a 7 per cent rate per year.
Among the industries based on domestic products,
those manufacturing tomato products showed the most
significant increase, amounting to about 30 per cent
per year. Sausage and cured meat production, along
with milk products (excluding pasteurized milk) increased at approximately 20 per cent per year. The
Fourth Conference on Agricultural Raw Materials for
Industries, held in Caracas in November, 1966, pointed up the critical problem of industries obtaining
adequate supplies on a uniform and continuous basis,
classified for efficient use, and at prices that permit establishment of a sound processing industry.
Generally speaking, the advantages for the industry
based on imported raw material compared with the existing pattern of domestic production and distribution have been greater than such industries utilizing
domestic products. Financing arrangements have been
easier for imported than for domestic products because funds are tied up for shorter periods in the
case of imported products. Seasonal factors for domestic products generally required more storage capacity than processing plants have been able to justify
because of the lack of intermediate assembly, classification, and packing services.

The transportation services in Venezuela are generally adequate as far as number of trucks and cargo
capacity are concerned, although precise data are not
available to separate services available for agriculture in this respect. There is a lack of specialized
transportation services needed for low-cost and waste-
free transportation of some products, especially
fruits and vegetables, and there is little organized
effort to provide efficient channeling of the transport facilities in accordance with needs. However,
there is surplus trucking capacity (even without the
serious overloading of individual units, which is
common) to move products wherever roads will permit.
A large proportion of the trucks are individually
owned, and the trucker often provides the services of
wholesale buyer and seller, as well as the transportation to the consuming markets. In 1964, the total

number of trucks registered in the transport department of the Ministry of Development, according to
general size categories, were the following:

Truck Size	Number of Trucks
½ ton to 2½ tons	60,662
3 to 5 tons	26,480
6 to 10 tons	14,599
10 tons and more (including those with trailers)	5,613
Total	107,354

Total vehicle registrations have increased at an
average annual rage of 3.4 per cent during 1961-65.
During the previous five-year period (1956-60), the
average rage of increase was about 12 per cent per
year. , The lower rate of increase in recent years
has been due to controls in imports to force development of local assembly plants for automotive vehicles
and the corresponding large increase in cost of vehicles to support the luxury of domestic production
of these machines.

The average cost per ton-kilometer of freight in
Venezuela was Bs. 0.156, as previously indicated. The
improvement of truck roads and the increase in truck
size have permitted transport costs to be reduced
substantially during 1956-65. However, during the
last three of those years, with the exception of long-
haul runs such as those between Caracas and San Cris-
tóbal and Ciudad Bolívar, the ton-kilometer cost of
freight started to rise, especially for short- and
medium-haul distances, due to higher equipment costs
and operating costs. For example, ton-kilometer
freight rates from Caracas to Puerto Cabello and
Valencia, which accounts for a significant volume,
increased 3 and 2 céntimos of the bolivar, respectively, between 1964 and 1965.

The larger cities of Venezuela, such as Caracas,
Maracaibo, Barquisimeto, and Valencia, and a few regions such as the state of Portuguesa, the southern
part of Zulia and the western part of Guárico, where

commercially oriented and modern agricultural technology have become well established, have fairly
adequate private businesses providing supply outlets,
repair and maintenance services for farm machinery,
fertilizers, insecticides, and other requirements
for modern farm practices. Included in these services
are airplane and helicopter facilities for applying
agricultural chemicals. However, in the majority of
the agricultural areas where industrial crops are
not produced, farmers do not have such services available on an efficient and reliable basis. The present
underdevelopment of the farms in these areas, of
course, does not provide sufficient demand for high-
cost input factors of modern farming to attract private businesses to establish necessary service
installations. During the interim period, when such
farm units are progressing to commercially oriented
production, the lack of such services is a serious
handicap. However, there is considerable competition,
especially in the farm machinery field, and it has
been demonstrated that private interests will extend
services as the demand justifies, although with some
lag. In the case of veterinary services and supplies,
there is a serious problem in the livestock-producing
areas of Venezuela. There are very few technicians
in relation to the demand, and practically all the
services available in this respect are tied to government programs. There has been an obvious lag and
hesitancy on the part of professionals involved in
this field to enter into a real competitive situation
in providing these services, and development of the
livestock industry is suffering because of this lack
of essential service for modern technology. There
has probably also been a hesitancy on the part of
livestock producers to assume the costs of such services because the services now available, although
inadequate, are usually provided to producers who can
obtain them at very low cost.

No data are available as to the amounts of private
investment in providing farm production supplies and
services. Substantial investments have been made in
the commercially oriented production areas but are
almost totally lacking in the predominantly subsistence-
type farming areas.

As will be discussed in more detail in the following two chapters, credit services from private
sources to agriculture, adapted to the needs of, and
providing a reasonable basis for, agricultural development are practically nonexistent. Considerable
credit is, of course, extended to farmers by local
stores, principally for consumer items, but the terms
are usually very onerous to the farmers and practically remove any possibility for such farmers to ac-
cumulate any capital by their own efforts. No studies
have quantified the amount of such credit extended.
Most of the agricultural credit designed to meet
reasonable credit needs of farmers is provided by
government programs with a limited participation of
private credit institutions.

AGRICULTURAL EDUCATION FACILITIES AND SUPPORT
FOR AGRICULTURE

Venezuela made a determined drive during 1958-65
to develop at least primary educational facilities
for all areas of the country and achieved notable
success in this respect; large sums have been invested in building schools and training teachers. Rural
areas, of course, are difficult to cover adequately
with needed educational facilities and, in general,
are lagging behind urban areas; a long-range and continuous program will be required to bring all rural
areas within the scope of essential educational services. Improvements in Venezuela's general educational facilities were described in Chapter 2. The
technical and vocational educational facilities
oriented to agriculture will be described in Chapter 6.

Large-scale investments and efforts are still required to solve the educational problems, both general and technical, in Venezuela's rural areas, but
government plans and public attitudes are favorable
to making a continued effort in this respect. One
specific problem with respect to the educational
system, as such, that needs more attention and
facilities is that concerning the present extreme
difficulties encountered by rural youths in advancing
through the educational system available to them so

that they can qualify for higher education and take
on professional responsibility for solving rural
problems. A low proportion of the professional-level
technicians now available in agriculture have real
farm backgrounds. This is due to the fact that complete primary- and secondary-level education has not
been available to rural people in order to qualify
them to enter universities. Further, the practical
agricultural and home demonstration schools, which
have had notable development in Venezuela and which
are available to the few rural youths who complete
primary education, are still dead ends as far as
qualifying for higher education opportunities is
concerned. This situation is principally due to institutional weaknesses that could be resolved with
only minor adjustment in curriculums and educational
administrative attitudes. In addition, there are no
university-level home economics courses available in
Venezuela because the development of this important
science has been restricted. Properly trained home
economists could provide a strong impulse for improving rural living conditions, as well as a more
scientific basis for necessary research and development in the food processing and textile industries,
which are struggling to find a sound basis for operations in Venezuela.

CAPITAL TRANSFERS IN AND OUT OF AGRICULTURE AND CAPITAL FORMATION IN THIS SECTOR

Data are not available to permit an adequate
quantification of the total flow of capital between
economic sectors in Venezuela, so only some comments
and observations can be presented in this respect.

As previously mentioned, the general indicators
of investment and production have shown that capital
is generally not being withdrawn from agriculture to
finance development in other sectors of the economy.
This is due to the fact that Venezuela has had the
substantial oil resources to provide the principal
capital source for both development and consumer
goods, although all segments of the population or geographical areas have not benefited directly from this

resource. Many other Latin American countries are
having to depend on their agricultural resources to
provide the capital for development in other sectors
of the economy, and this has constituted a serious
restriction--not only on further development of the
agricultural sector but also on amounts of capital
needed in other sectors to develop the economic activities and occupational opportunities required in
modern societies. Venezuela does have serious problems in achieving balanced development of its various
economic sectors and in providing employment for its
people. However, the demand on agriculture as a
source of capital for this development is much less
acute than in most other lesser-developed countries.
Administrative and technical skills needed to adequately plan, develop, and operate the complex aspects
of production and distribution facilities are much
more critical and scarce than capital supplies in
Venezuela.

Credit made available to agriculture principally
through government programs has been substantial and
will be quantified and described later on. This service could have been an important aid in capital formation, but the record is not good in this respect,
and a serious problem exists in the rural sector to
overcome the misuse of credit funds made available for
agricultural production efforts. The low collection
rates have required substantial additions to the government credit agencies each year, and not very much
headway has been made in improving administrative
techniques to correct the deficiencies of credit programs. Consequently, the credit services made available to agriculture have not contributed substantially
to capital formation in this sector. It is true that
credit has been limited mainly to annual production
financing and that very little has been made available
for basic improvements in the resource base of the
producing units. Clearly, basic adjustment in the
organization and development of the productive factors
on farms is essential to improve productivity, and
this usually requires credit for long- and medium-term
investments, which has not been available in sufficient
quantities.

As indicated in previous chapters, the low productivity in the agricultural sector has given this
sector very little capacity for savings and capital
formation for further improvements and, at the same
time, has limited agriculture's ability to attract
investments from private sources. Consequently, it
is clear that the rate of capital formation in agriculture is low. The channeling of additional resources into this sector will continue to be a major
responsibility of the public sector until the educational processes needed to improve productivity and
resource management among rural people can be effective. Such investments will be required to ensure
that the food and fiber production mechanism remains
a dynamic force in the Venezuelan economy and to develop a more significant base for the secondary and
tertiary sectors of the economy, which depend on this
foundation.

CHAPTER 5 DYNAMICS OF THE
AGRICULTURE

This chapter will describe the characteristics
of the production structure of the agricultural sector in Venezuela. Details will be presented on types
of agricultural producing units and commodities and
an analysis will be made of changes occurring in 1966.

LAND USE ON FARMS

The data from the Agricultural Censuses of 1950
and 1961 on land use on farms is summarized in Table
37, and certain percentage comparisons have been calculated from this data.

The total land in farms shown in Table 37, amounting to 26,215,000 hectares, constitutes 28.7 per cent
of the total land area of Venezuela. This is 4.4 per
cent more than in 1950. The low proportion of the
total land area included in farms, together with the
low proportion of the land in farms that is dedicated
to permanent and annual crop use (6.4 per cent in
1961), indicates the low level of development and intensity of land use in Venezuela. Although ecological
conditions restrict the farm land that can be utilized
for crops, it is clear that a considerable margin of
unused land suitable for crops and the possibility of
more intensive use than now practiced exist in Venezuela, both within farm boundaries and in public lands
as yet unclaimed for farm use. Resource surveys have
not been completed in sufficient portions of Venezuela to permit precise quantification of this margin
of unused arable land; however, it is estimated that
without major reclamation or conditioning work, at
least 15 per cent more of the total land area of

TABLE 37

Comparison of Land Use on Farms, 1950 and 1961

Land Use	Number of Hectares (1,000)		Per Cent of Total		Per Cent Change
	1961	1950	1961	1950	
Permanent crops	653	593	2.5	2.7	10.1
Annual and semipermanent crops	1,025	709	3.9	3.2	44.6
Idle crop land	2,447	1,334	9.3	6.0	83.4
Cultivated pastures	2,748	1,640	10.5	7.4	67.6
Natural pastures	13,958	11,862	53.2	53.6	17.7
Forest land	4,476	4,435	17.1	20.1	0.9
Other land	908	1,554	3.5	7.0	-41.6
Total Land in Farms	26,215	22,127	100.0	100.0	18.5
Total number of farms	315,215	248,734	-	-	26.7
Average hectares per farm	83	90	-	-	-7.8

Source: 1950 and 1961 agricultural censuses.

98

Venezuela could be brought into productive use. In
addition, as demand requires, significant portions
of the pasture lands could be converted to more intensive crop use, especially the riverside lands in
the Western Plains region.

The intercensal rates of annual increase in the
more intensive land uses were: permanent crops, 0.9
per cent; annual and semipermanent crops, 3.4 per
cent; and cultivated pastures, 4.8 per cent. These
approximate rates of increase have continued during
1961-65, with a probable higher rate for permanent
crops because of increased fruit growing, which will
be described later on. The rates of increase in land
in crops are generally lower than the increase in'
production, so it is clear that technological improvements are resulting in some increased productivity
per land unit.

Additional data on land use by selected regions
of Venezuela are presented in the appendix.

LAND TENANCY

The census data on distribution of land areas in
farms, by the tenancy status of the farm operators,
are presented in Table 38.

Unfortunately, similar data by number of farms
has not yet been published for the 1961 census, but
a breakdown of total number of farms by tenancy
categories from the 1950 census data is available.
Also, preliminary data from the 1961 census were obtained that had not been rectified and still contained
some errors. Based on this, the percentage comparisons shown in Table 39 can be made.

As shown in Table 39, the relative position of
owners, both with respect to number of farms and the
amount of land controlled, did not change significantly between the census periods. The relative
number of squatters compared with the other forms of
tenancy increased about 6 per cent, whereas land areas
controlled by this group increased only negligibly.

TABLE 38

Distribution of Farm Land Area by Tenancy Status,
1950 and 1961

Tenancy Status of Farm Operators	Total Has. in Farms (1,000)		Per Cent of Total		Per Cent Change
	1961	1950	1961	1950	
Owners	22,065	18,399	84.2	83.2	19.9
Cash renters	582	741	2.2	3.3	-21.4
Sharecroppers	154	486	0.6	2.2	-68.4
Squatters	3,414	2,501	13.0	11.3	36.5
Total	26,215	22,127	100.0	100.0	18.5

<u>Source</u>: 1950 and 1961 agricultural censuses.

It is expected that the agrarian reform program
should have materially reduced the number of squatters since 1960, but a complete analysis of the effect of this program on the tenancy structure has not
been completed and available records do not indicate
a clear-cut change.[1] The high rate of turnover in
the recipients of land parcels, and the lack of a
clear-cut method of eliminating duplication in both
numbers of families and land areas, together with a
significant abandonment of parcels in land settlements, make it difficult to get a complete picture
from published statistics in this respect. Also,
spot studies that have been completed indicate a
strong tendency for settlers to continue to operate
land as squatters outside the settlement areas in
addition to the parcel in the agrarian reform settlements. Consequently, it is not certain that the
number of squatters has been significantly reduced
since the 1961 census.

TABLE 39

Tenancy Pattern with Respect to Number and
Size of Farms, 1950 and 1961

Tenancy Status of Farm Operators	Per Cent of Total Farms		Per Cent of Total Land in Farms	
	1961	1950	1961	1950
Owners	41.5	41.6	84.2	83.2
Cash renters	9.4	15.2	2.2	3.3
Other forms of tenancy (squatters, etc.)	49.1	43.2	13.6	13.5

Source: 1950 and 1961 agricultural census data.

The number of settlements, the number of families
benefited, and the area of land involved in the parcels of land acquired and redistributed by the National Agrarian Institute are shown in Table 40. (Additional comments on the agrarian reform program are
included in Chapter 6.)

TABLE 40

Families Benefited and Areas Involved in Venezuela's
Land Settlement Activities, 1959-65

Year	Number of Settlements	Number of Families Benefited	Land Involved in Settlement Activities (1,000 Has.)		
			Public Lands	Private Lands	Total
1959	53	5,875	275.5	185.3	460.8
1960	308	25,221	263.3	485.6	748.9
1961	141	11,074	62.2	93.9	156.1
1962	135	14,603	36.2	131.1	163.3
1963	60	9,656	121.1	16.0	137.1
1964	-	11,527	96.2	106.7	202.9
1965	-	40,782	437.3	347.0	784.3
Total	697	118,737	1,291.8	1,365.6	2,653.4

Source: Agricultural Statistics, 1965 Annual, Ministry of Agriculture and Livestock.

Referring back to Table 38, the absolute increase
in the number of farm owners and the land controlled
by owners was probably due principally to bringing
new land into production. This is also true of the
squatter category, which increased more. The only
basic adjustment in the tenancy pattern between the
two census periods was the reduction of the land operated by renters, both cash and share. This amounted
to a reduction of 491,000 hectares in these categories, which amounts to only 2.8 per cent of the
total land in farms in 1961. The existence of a decree preceding the Agrarian Reform Law provided
strong protection for squatters, as soon as they were
established on either public or private land, by requiring land owners to reimburse the squatters for
any improvements made before the squatters could be
removed. With unguarded land areas available in
many parts of Venezuela, the small farmers were in-
clined, as a result of this protection, to occupy
land rather than to pay rent. Rent could be collected only in the relatively intensively developed areas.

SIZE OF FARMS

Census data are the only source of information
available on a national basis with respect to farm
sizes in Venezuela. Data from the 1950 and 1961 censuses are presented in Table 41 for the number of
farms and land area by size groups. These show a
quite typical pattern for Latin American countries,
with a combination of latifundio and minifundio in
land area in individual farms. However, the combination is not as extreme as in some other Latin
American countries. Generally speaking, a large number of farms (65 per cent or more of the total) are
too small for economical, efficient production and
provide the families thereon with low incomes. At
the same time, these smaller units control a small
proportion (usually less than 3 per cent) of the
total farm land. At the other extreme, a low proportion of the total farm operators (less than 1.5
per cent) control 70 per cent or more of the land
area in farms.

TABLE 41

Number of Farms in Venezuela and Total Land Area
in Farms, by Size Groups, 1950 and 1961

| Hectares | Number of Farms (1,000) | | | | Total Land Area in Farms (1,000 Has.) | | | |
| | 1961 | | 1950 | | 1961 | | 1950 | |
	Number	Per Cent of Total	Number	Per Cent of Total	Amount	Per Cent of Total	Amount	Per Cent of Total
Less than 1.0	17.3	5.5	14.3	6.1	9	0.1	7	0.1
1.0 to 4.9	137.9	43.8	111.7	47.6	344	1.3	260	1.2
5.0 to 9.9	57.8	18.4	42.0	17.9	390	1.5	276	1.2
10.0 to 19.9	41.4	13.1	27.5	11.7	504	1.9	363	1.6
20.0 to 49.9	28.6	9.1	18.9	8.1	815	3.1	548	2.5
50.0 to 99.9	11.6	3.7	7.1	3.0	722	2.8	464	2.1
100.0 to 199.9	7.3	2.3	4.3	1.8	946	3.6	541	2.4
200.0 to 499.9	6.2	1.9	3.5	1.5	1,775	6.8	1,044	4.7
500.0 to 999.9	2.8	0.9	1.9	0.8	1,846	7.1	1,221	5.5
1,000.0 to 2,499.0	2.3	0.7	1.7	0.7	3,456	13.3	2,468	11.2
2,500.0 and more	1.9	0.6	1.8	0.8	15,198	58.5	14,935	67.5
Total	315.1	100.0	237.7	100.0	26,005	100.0	22,127	100.0

Source: 1950 and 1961 agricultural censuses.

In general, with the present technology employed
in Venezuela, farms of less than ten hectares are
inadequate to provide a decent living for farm families. There has been some improvement in developing
relatively more farms in the medium sizes and reducing the relative importance of the very small and
very large farms in the period between 1950 and 1961,
but this has been slow, as shown in Table 42.

As shown in these figures, the number of smaller
farms of less than ten hectares has decreased from
71.6 per cent in 1950 to 67.7 per cent in 1961,
whereas the area in farms of this size showed a relative increase. At the same time, the large farms
(1,000 hectares and more) decreased relatively, with
respect to both number and land area. Means of accelerating these trends of adjustments in farm size
are needed because such adjustments are necessary to
improve agricultural efficiency and productivity.
Also, the absolute changes in number of farms by
size groups between the census periods indicate that
the problem of small, inadequate farms (minifundios)
is continuing because these farms constitute the
largest number of additional farm units developed
between 1950 and 1961. This is illustrated by the
figures in Table 43, which were calculated from the
data in Table 41.

The percentage figures confirm the trend, indicated previously, that the farm units in the medium
range are increasing faster than those in the extremely small and large groups. When considered with
respect to the actual number of farms involved, it is
clear that the desirable adjustments are occurring at
a rate too slow to permit the rapid improvement of
the productivity of the major proportion of the farms
in Venezuela. Providing units of sufficient size
to justify necessary investments in improved production techniques and to provide reasonable remuneration for farm families is an essential part of this
improvement process.

Existing information on the operation of the
agrarian reform program indicates that it has contributed very little to increasing the amount of land

TABLE 42

Comparison of Size of Venezuelan Farms,
1950 and 1961

Hectares	Per Cent of Total Number of Farms		Per Cent of Total Land Area in Farms	
	1961	1950	1961	1950
Less than 10.0	67.7	71.6	2.9	2.5
10.0 to 49.9	22.2	19.8	5.0	4.1
50.0 to 199.9	6.0	4.8	6.4	4.5
200.0 to 499.9	1.9	1.5	6.8	4.7
500.0 to 999.9	0.9	0.8	7.1	5.5
1,000.0 and more	1.3	1.5	71.8	78.7

Source: 1950 and 1961 agricultural census data.

106

available to the family-type farmers of Venezuela. Surveys of economic conditions of settlements, made in connection with agricultural credit activities,[2] have shown a very high incidence of farm units of less than ten hectares and have indicated that one of the most critical problems of these settlements is an inadequate land base for each family, which mitigates against significant improvement in incomes and living standards of the farm families involved.

TABLE 43

Increase in Number of Farms in Venezuela
Between 1950 and 1961

Hectares	Number	Per Cent Increase from 1950
Less than 10.0	45,000	27
10.0 to 199.9	31,100	54
200.0 to 499.9	2,700	77
500.0 to 999.9	900	47
1,000.0 and more	700	20

Source: Data in Table 41.

In Table 44 are presented data comparing the size of farm distribution in eight Latin American countries. This information indicates that Venezuela is in a medium category with respect to the severity of the extremes of minifundios and latifundios in comparison with the seven other countries. Ecuador, Guatemala, and Peru have larger proportions of the farm units classified as minifundios (subfamily) than Venezuela. Chile and Peru have a larger proportion of the farm land in latifundios units (multifamily, large) than does Venezuela. The fact that a larger proportion of the farm units are grouped in the two middle-sized groups indicates more progressive agricultural development situations. As a side note, less than 1 per cent of the cultivated land area in the United States is included in the category of "multifamily, large" farm units, which is a great contrast to the conditions for Latin America as shown in Table 44.

TABLE 44

Number and Area of Farms in Eight Latin American Countries

| Country and Item | Percentage of Total Farms in Each Country by Size Class | | | | |
	Subfamily[a]	Family[b]	Multifamily Medium[c]	Multifamily Large[d]	Total
Argentina					
Farms	43.2	48.7	7.3	0.8	100
Area in Farms	3.4	44.7	15.0	36.9	100
Brazil					
Farms	22.5	39.1	33.7	4.7	100
Area in Farms	0.5	6.0	34.0	59.5	100
Chile					
Farms	36.9	40.0	16.2	6.9	100
Area in Farms	0.2	7.1	11.4	81.3	100
Colombia					
Farms	64.0	30.2	4.5	1.3	100
Area in Farms	4.9	22.3	23.3	49.5	100
Ecuador					
Farms	89.9	8.0	1.7	0.4	100
Area in Farms	16.6	19.0	19.3	45.1	100

	a	b	c	d	
Guatemala					
Farms	88.4	9.5	2.0	0.1	100
Area in Farms	14.3	13.4	31.5	40.8	100
Peru					
Farms	88.0	8.5	2.4	1.1	100
Area in Farms	7.4	4.5	5.7	82.4	100
Venezuela					
Farms	67.7	22.2	7.9	2.2	100
Area in Farms	2.9	5.0	13.2	78.9	100

[a]Farms employing fewer than 2 persons.

[b]Farms employing 2 to 3.9 persons.

[c]Farms employing from 4 to 12 persons.

[d]Farms employing more than 12 persons.

Source: Data for all countries except Venezuela taken from article by Solon L. Barraclough and Arthur L. Domike in Land Economics, XLII, 4 (November, 1966), on tenancy studies made by the Inter-American Committee for Agricultural Development. Venezuelan data added by approximation from agricultural census data for 1961.

AGRICULTURAL PRODUCTION AND PRODUCTIVITY

The crop areas, production, value of production,
and yields per hectare for the most important crops
in Venezuela are summarized for the years 1961 to
1965 in Tables 45 and 46. (Additional data for the
years 1966-67 will be found in Table 9 in the Statistical Appendix.)

Crop Production Data

As shown in these tables, corn and coffee predominated in the use of crop land, with 461,800 and
340,000 hectares respectively in 1965, which constituted 29.4 per cent and 21.2 per cent, for a total of
over half the crop land. The relationship of corn
areas to the total crop land continued at about the
same percentage throughout the five-year period with
the exception of 1962, when it constituted over 33
per cent of the total crop land area. This was due
to a special corn-producing campaign of that year
sponsored by the Ministry of Agriculture and Livestock and the Agricultural Bank of Venezuela, which
resulted in surplus production for the usual market
demands of that year and thus was not repeated. Coffee areas remained constant, so with the increase in
total crop areas each year, the relative position of
coffee in land use on farms decreased from 24.2 per
cent of the 1961 crop land area to the aforementioned
21.2 per cent in 1965. Rice, plantains, sesame,
cocoa, black beans, sugar cane, bananas, and cotton
followed in order of magnitude of crop land use at
percentages descending from 6.7 per cent to about
3 per cent of the total. Among the other crops, none
utilized more than 2 per cent of the total crop land
areas.

Between 1961 and 1965, rice, the individual root
crops indicated (except mandioc), sesame, plantains,
bananas, and sugar cane showed increases in crop
land areas of from 25 per cent to 80 per cent.

Total crop land area increased from 1,307,900 to
1,573,200 hectares between 1961 and 1965, or a total
of 20.2 per cent or an annual compound rate of 4.8
per cent.

As shown in Figure 4, the index of all crop production showed an increase of 33 per cent between
1961 and 1965, which amounts to an annual compound
increase of 7.4 per cent. The same figure shows that
the increase of crop yields per hectare was 15 per
cent during the same period, for an average annual
increase of 4.3 per cent. The interrelationship
among these rates of increase indicates that increases
in crop land areas were more significant in bringing
about the total increases in production than were
improved yields. The aforementioned rates of annual
increase show that the greater area of land in crops
contributed approximately 55 per cent and greater
productivity about 45 per cent toward the growth in
total crop production that occurred between 1961 and
1965.

Table 46 shows that the crops with the most significant increases in yields were rice, sesame,
cotton, coconuts, sisal fiber, some tubers, and
plantains. The yield of black beans, peas, and coffee
decreased. In most other crops, no significant change
in productivity is indicated.

International comparisons of yields of four crops
of major importance in Venezuela are shown in Table 47,
based on data taken from the United Nations Food and
Agricultural Organization Agricultural Yearbook of 1964.

These comparisons show that the yields for coffee
in Venezuela were very much below those of Venezuela's
chief competitors. Cotton productivity was greater
than in Brazil but less than in other countries indicated. For corn and rice, the yields in Venezuela
were similar to other Latin American countries but
were considerably below North American and European
yields, as represented by the United States and Spain,
respectively.

Livestock and Livestock Production

In Table 48 are presented data on the production
and value of production of livestock and principal
products derived therefrom, together with data on
fish and forestry products. As shown previously in

TABLE 45

Area Harvested and Total Production of Important Crops in Venezuela, 1961-65

Crop	Area Harvested (1,000 Has.)					Production (1,000 Metric Tons)				
	1961	1962	1963	1964	1965	1961	1962	1963	1964	1965
Cereals										
Rice (paddy)	58.4	69.0	73.7	90.7	105.1	80.7	103.1	131.1	165.8	199.9
Corn	388.7	483.3	426.7	443.0	461.8	419.5	540.5	430.2	475.0	521.0
Wheat	2.3	1.2	2.1	2.2	2.3	1.2	0.6	1.1	1.2	1.3
Legumes										
Black beans	64.6	47.4	54.8	64.1	65.2	31.0	23.0	24.1	25.1	26.1
Other beans	24.9	21.0	26.0	27.8	28.9	13.0	12.4	14.1	15.1	16.2
Peas & pigeon peas	7.1	11.0	13.7	13.6	14.1	3.6	6.0	6.6	6.1	6.9
Roots & tubers										
Yams	5.1	9.2	8.0	8.4	8.5	41.9	68.8	62.6	70.6	71.5
Taro root	6.6	8.6	9.8	10.0	10.5	51.7	71.3	84.9	90.5	96.6
Mandioc	25.7a	25.7	25.1	24.7	24.5	344.2a	322.8	342.4	311.7	301.4
Potatoes	9.3	16.0	14.7	14.9	16.2	74.1	121.2	110.9	123.5	135.9
Other roots & tubers	4.9	8.1	9.6	9.6	9.9	32.3	55.3	63.7	59.6	64.7
Fibers & oil seed crops										
Sesame	53.9	56.7	61.4	68.3	87.1	24.9	28.1	30.9	46.6	54.1
Cotton (unginned)	50.3	37.4	47.5	43.7	45.9	36.4	24.2	34.4	41.3	44.6
Coconut (copra)	25.8	25.0b	25.0b	24.1	25.4	10.8	11.8	15.4	17.0	15.3
Peanuts	1.1	1.9	1.4	1.9	1.9	1.2	1.8	1.5	1.7	1.8
Sisal fiber	10.5	10.5	10.1	11.1	11.0	8.4	8.5	11.6	10.8	13.3
Fruits & vegetables										
Bananas	46.7	39.7	68.1	55.8	58.3	341.4	297.1	493.0	408.9	418.1
Other fruits	6.5	6.8	7.3	7.5	7.8	83.2	86.6	93.0	96.2	106.9
Onions	1.7	1.4	1.5	1.9	1.9	23.3	19.4	21.8	33.5	34.9
Tomatoes	4.3	3.5	3.9	4.8	4.7	65.9	52.6	53.8	71.9	72.1
Other vegetables	1.7	1.7	1.8	1.8	1.9	41.8	43.1	44.2	45.8	47.2

Coffee, cocoa & others										
Cocoa	72.0	70.0	70.0	70.0	70.0	13.1	14.8	15.9	19.9	20.4
Coffee	316.6	340.0	340.0	340.0	340.0	53.7	48.9	53.5	49.3	54.1
Sugar cane	51.6	55.1	61.0	63.2	63.6	3,242.1	3,172.9	3,827.3c	3,189.0	3,520.0
Plantains	60.1	85.7	79.4	92.6	100.0	223.7	373.0	410.8	484.8	547.1
Tobacco	7.5	6.0	6.6	6.2	6.5	10.4	8.8	8.4	8.4	9.0
Total	1,307.9	1,436.6	1,490.4	1,502.0	1,573.2					

aAdjusted lower than source figure.

bEstimated.

cPapelon production converted to sugar cane and added to production figure for cane used for refined sugar.

Source: Agricultural Statistics Annual, Ministry of Agriculture and Livestock, for years 1961-65.

113

TABLE 46

Value of Production and Yields of Important Crops in Venezuela, 1961–65

Crop	Value of Production at 1957 Prices (Bs. 1,000)					Yield per Hectare (Kgs.)				
	1961	1962	1963	1964	1965	1961	1962	1963	1964	1965
Cereals										
Rice (paddy)	37,172	47,543	60,426	76,412	92,154	1,380	1,495	1,779	1,827	1,902
Corn	88,548	114,049	90,738	100,225	109,931	1,079	1,118	1,008	1,072	1,128
Wheat	552	280	451	540	589	540	525	523	554	581
Legumes										
Black beans	23,003	17,095	17,820	18,589	19,388	479	486	438	391	401
Other beans	9,548	9,121	10,386	11,095	11,874	523	555	544	543	560
Peas & pigeon peas	2,038	3,558	4,174	3,641	4,116	507	545	482	445	490
Roots & tubers										
Yams	20,948	32,740	28,375	33,603	34,027	8,156	7,512	7,798	8,441	8,393
Taro root (ocumo)	26,961	35,347	40,013	44,903	47,912	7,774	8,292	8,630	9,050	9,198
Mandioc (yucca)	57,607	72,019	66,858	69,508	67,217	5,561	12,542	13,665	12,620	12,290
Potatoes	46,599	50,910	31,079	51,885	57,073	7,935	7,584	7,549	8,295	8,403
Other roots & tubers[a]	12,068	26,076	28,635	28,429	31,020	6,592	6,827	6,635	6,300	6,500
Fibers & oil seed crops										
Sesame	23,260	26,267	28,882	43,525	50,607	461	495	502	681	621
Cotton (unginned)	32,508	24,736	39,952	42,148	45,492	723	647	725	945	971
Coconut (copra)	9,309	10,210	13,304	14,715	13,221	419	472	616	705	600
Peanuts	1,025	1,689	1,491	1,547	1,685	1,067	938	890	890	926
Sisal fiber	4,029	4,225	6,035	5,376	6,662	802	804	1,152	968	1,210

114

Fruits & vegetables									
Bananas	60,743	60,332	86,344	82,998	84,874	7,310	7,484	7,241	7,326	7,169
Other fruits	19,006	18,965	19,535	21,068	23,411	12,800	12,735	12,740	12,770	13,620
Onions	11,697	10,464	12,666	18,064	18,846	13,617	13,734	14,379	17,671	17,761
Tomatoes	25,672	20,031	20,040	27,390	27,469	15,216	15,209	13,809	15,021	15,229
Other vegetables	20,008	26,332	34,472	27,984	28,839	24,588	25,353	24,555	25,000	25,000
Coffee, cocoa & others									
Cocoa	42,950	40,645	36,726	54,795	56,125	182	211	227	284	291
Coffee	237,949	207,270	216,599	209,059	229,499	170	144	157	145	159
Sugar cane[b]	99,700	109,333	122,956	125,246	134,483	62,831	57,584	62,743	58,101	62,805
Plantains	24,845	55,901	81,932	71,261	80,428	3,722	4,352	5,174	5,287	5,475
Tobacco	56,479	46,913	50,679	46,771	50,656	1,375	1,385	1,342	1,344	1,391
Total	993,129	1,082,042	1,150,574	1,230,767	1,327,498					

[a]Includes celery root, sweet potatoes, and lotus root (mapuey).

[b]Includes both sugar and sugar cakes.

Source: 1965 Agricultural Statistics Annual, Ministry of Agriculture and Livestock (MAC); Central
Bank of Venezuela (BCU), Informes Económicos.

FIGURE 4

Comparison of Indexes of Change in Crop Area
Harvested, Crop Production, and Crop
Yield, 1961-65

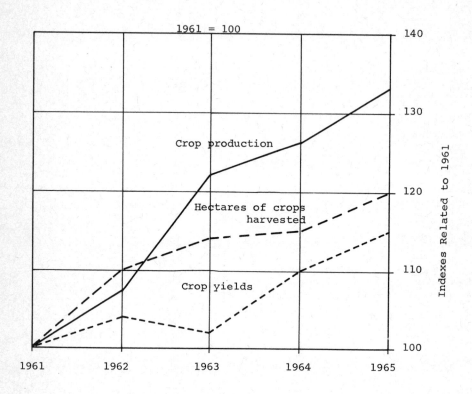

Source: Crop production index from the annual reports of the
Central Bank of Venezuela; crop areas and yield indexes
calculated from data in Tables 45 and 46. Total harvested
hectares were utilized for the crop area index calculations. The yield index was calculated on the basis of the
ten annual and semipermanent crops that occupy 90 per cent
of the harvested area of all annual and semipermanent crops.
(Crops included in the yield index, which is weighted by
the hectares harvested of each crop, were: corn, black
beans, plantains, rice, sesame, sugar cane, cotton, bananas,
potatoes, and yams.)

Table 25, the distribution of the total value of agricultural products in Venezuela among principal segments during 1961-65 was in the following approximate proportions: crops, 57 per cent; livestock and products, 36 per cent; fish, 3 per cent; forest products, 4 per cent.

TABLE 47

International Comparison of Yields of Four Crops
(Yields per Hectare)

Country	Corn (100 Kgs.)	Rice (100 Kgs.)	Cotton (100 Kgs.- Fiber)	Coffee (Kgs.)
Venezuela (1961)	10.7	18.3	2.8	170[a]
Brazil (1964)	10.7	17.7	1.8	367
Colombia (1964)	10.7	21.6	4.5	400-500
Mexico (1964)	9.5	21.8	5.8	415
Spain (1964)	24.0	62.3	3.6	-
United States (1964)	42.4	44.4	5.8	-

[a] 1961 census figure.

Source: 1964 FAO Agricultural Yearbook.

Beef and milk products predominated the livestock production picture, with each constituting approximately one third of the total value of livestock and its products. Poultry and eggs together constitute 25 per cent of the total value of livestock products, but poultry products have registered the most notable increases in production during 1961-65. This has been largely due to the efforts of a few large-scale enterprises operating at a high rate of efficiency, which is necessary to overcome the disadvantage of relatively high feed prices in Venezuela.

TABLE 48

Production and Value of Livestock, Fish, and Forest
Products in Venezuela, 1961–65

Product	Production					Value of Production at 1957 Prices (1,000 Bs.)				
	1961	1962	1963	1964	1965	1961	1962	1963	1964	1965
Livestock & products						638,429	680,730	711,696	816,185	879,941
Milk (million liters)	444.6	481.4	521.5	585.5	646.1	201,425	218,152	236,229	265,251	292,671
Cattle (1,000 head)	863.8	878.1	927.5	1,004.3	1,070.8	244,449	248,582	262,594	284,221	303,041
Hogs (1,000 head)	694.3	678.7	697.8	744.5	779.5	54,149	52,960	54,429	58,074	60,811
Goats (1,000 head)	375.8	376.4	377.2	378.1	378.8	3,758	3,765	3,772	3,780	3,788
Sheep (1,000 head)	46.3	46.0	45.8	45.5	45.2	463	460	458	455	452
Poultry (million head)	25.8	30.0	29.7	38.1	38.3	81,239	95,220	93,591	119,892	120,771
Eggs (million units)	273.2	317.7	313.4	436.1	507.8	52,946	61,591	60,623	84,512	98,407
Fish										
Fish (1,000 M.T. fresh equiv.)	83.6	94.9	97.4	110.4	119.2	45,536	51,696	53,125	60,175	64,948
Forest Products						66,468	68,423	72,879	91,960	88,876
Lumber (1,000 M³)	268.2	287.5	320.2	407.6	410.2	64,029	65,184	69,933	89,148	86,074
Fine	74.4	58.2	44.8	65.1	55.0	16,567	21,548	27,539	24,079	20,350
Hard	37.9	43.9	64.9	70.3	65.2	24,130	16,325	14,113	26,146	24,254
Soft	155.9	185.4	210.5	272.2	290.0	30,108	26,506	22,296	38,923	41,470

Latex (M.T.)	229.0	170.0	111.0	201.0	171.0	550	408	266	482	410
Charcoal (M.T.)	8,646.0	12,797.0	12,484.0	9,882.0	10,200.0	1,665	2,463	2,405	1,903	1,964
Firewood (M.T.)	1,957.0	5,150.0	5,495.0	7,253.0	4,400.0	98	257	275	363	225
Chicle (M.T.)	126.0	111.0	—	64.0	203.0	126	111	—	64	203

Source: Informes Economicos, Central Bank of Venezuela, 1963; and 1965 Agricultural Statistics Annual, Ministry of Agriculture and Livestock.

119

Pork products constitute 7 per cent of the total
value of livestock products. Goats and sheep were
of relatively minor importance, with the value of
production amounting to less than 1 per cent of the
total livestock products and with total production
maintaining the same level during the five-year
period shown in Table 48.

An analysis of crop and livestock production and
productivity on a regional basis will be presented
later in this chapter after the following brief discussion of the fish and forestry production picture
of Venezuela that is shown in Table 48. (Additional
information for the years 1966-67 is found in Table
10 of the Statistical Appendix.)

Fishing Industry

Venezuela has 2,800 kilometers of sea coast and
an estimated continental shelf of shallow depths of
9,000 square kilometers consisting of warm sea water,
so it has a significant basic resource for production
of ocean fish, plus a network of large rivers abound-
ing with catfish and other river fish. The data
available on the fishing industry apply principally
to ocean fishing, although local fishing industries
on the Orinoco and Apure rivers make commercial use
of catfish (bagre) and some other varieties, generally in dried form.

Approximately 44 per cent of the total fish extracted from the Caribbean Sea, which has exceeded
100,000 tons per year on a fresh equivalent basis in
recent years (as shown in Table 48), is made up of
sardines and anchovies, of which about 30,000 tons
are processed in canning factories. Various types
of larger fin fish (red snapper, bill fish, and tuna
species) constitute about 47 per cent of the total
tonnage: shrimps and lobsters amount to 5 per cent
and the various types of mollusks amount to 4 per
cent of the total. In 1964, there were 35,500 fish-
ermen in the industry producing an average of 3,405
kilograms per person, which had a gross value of approximately Bs. 2,000, so in Venezuela the average
fisherman has an income less than that of the average

farmer. It was estimated that in 1964, the value of
the fishing boats and gear was Bs. 56 million and
that during the year, Bs. 30 million was invested in
the industry. There have been recent improvements
in tuna and shrimp fishing methods, but the industry
is characterized by small-scale operations--under-
capitalized and of low productivity.

Oceanography institutes were established in 1966
at Cumaná and on the Island of Margarita, and the
Ministry of Agriculture and Livestock has established
a Center for Fishing Industry Investigations to carry
on basic research for the fishing industry, but improvement in technology in this activity is a slow,
long-range process. However, the potential for greater production is considered to be very promising.
Venezuela has a joint project with the Food and Agriculture Organization of the United Nations to develop
fishing research facilities.

Forest Products

In addition to the information in Table 48 on the
forest products, the following summary of the characteristics of the forest industries is presented, based
on information obtained from forestry technicians in
the Department of Natural Resources of the Ministry
of Agriculture and Livestock:

1. Forested areas cover approximately 40 per
cent of the total area of Venezuela. However, inventories and descriptions of the forest resources
have been made only in very limited areas.

2. The Western Plains region, comprising the
states of Cojedes, Portuguesa, and Barinas, has only
7.2 per cent of the forested areas of Venezuela but
63 per cent of the total officially registered commercial production came from this region in 1964.

3. In recent years, the average exploitation of
standing trees has amounted to 5,180,000 cubic meters,
of which 15 per cent is utilized in manufacturing
industries making such wood products as furniture.
Only 0.3 per cent of the economically active population

of Venezuela is occupied in the forest extraction
activities that are included in the agricultural
sector. Approximately 10 per cent of the total economically employed persons of Venezuela are occupied
in the wood manufacturing industries that are included in the secondary sector of the economy.

4. There are 128 saw mills, of which only 40
have a capacity considered to be a minimum for economic feasibility. In 1964, these saw mills processed 407,553 cubic meters of saw logs, producing
203,776 cubic meters of sawed lumber. A high loss
and wastage rate is thus indicated, demonstrating
the low level of technology utilized. There are also seven plywood factories in operation, which produced 12,000 cubic meters of these products in 1964.
There is one pulp mill in operation preparing material for paper manufacture, and this produces 65,000
tons of pulp per year. The plant was established in
1957.

5. It is estimated that only 1.2 per cent of
the total forest areas of Venezuela are being made
to produce economically; current methods of exploitation are generally very selective and destructive.
A very limited number of species are utilized because of lack of integrated forest exploitation
enterprises and lack of technological information
about the numerous species existing in the tropical
forests of Venezuela.

6. Forest protection services have been in operation for many years under the direction of the
Ministry of Agriculture and Livestock, but it is
estimated that fire control services are effective
for only about 10 per cent of the forested areas of
Venezuela.

7. A new Forestry, Soils, and Water Law was
passed in 1966 but it still leaves responsibility
for forest conservation dispersed among too many
federal and state agencies to permit effective administration of forestry development programs. This,
together with the limited number of foresters available, points up a serious problem in the administrative
and technical fields with respect to forest resources.

8. There are large forest reserves covering a
total of 5,304,440 hectares, eight national parks
covering 1,437,283 hectares, and three national monuments in natural resource areas now established in
Venezuela. However, the same problem of limited administrative and technical capacities, characteristic
of these public areas, has limited their use by the
public, and these areas have lacked adequate control
facilities to protect them as a true natural resource
for future generations.

9. A soil conservation service has been in operation in Venezuela for more than twenty-five years,
but it is active in only the Andean states, the state
of Sucre, and the island of Margarita, because of
limited administrative and technical support.

In general, the picture for the forests of Venezuela, from both the economic and cultural standpoints,
is one of underutilization; but at the same time, the
exploitation carried out is on a highly destructive
and irrational basis. It is clear that a great deal
of additional attention and effort needs to be applied
to this important resource.

SOME REGIONAL AGRICULTURAL PRODUCTION
CHARACTERISTICS

For a regional fragmentation of the data on production and productivity, seven regions were selected, based on state line boundaries for convenience
in separating available statistical data. However,
in general, the separations made follow general natural divisions because of geographical and ecological
differences, together with population patterns. The
regions selected and shown in Figure 5 are described
below.

1. Andean. Comprising the three Andean states
of Mérida, Táchira, and Trujillo, this region is
generally characterized by rough topography and a
wide range of climatic conditions because elevations
vary from just above sea level to over 5,000 meters
above sea level. The area was settled early in
Venezuelan history because of the health problems in

FIGURE 5

Venezuelan
Agricultural Production Regions

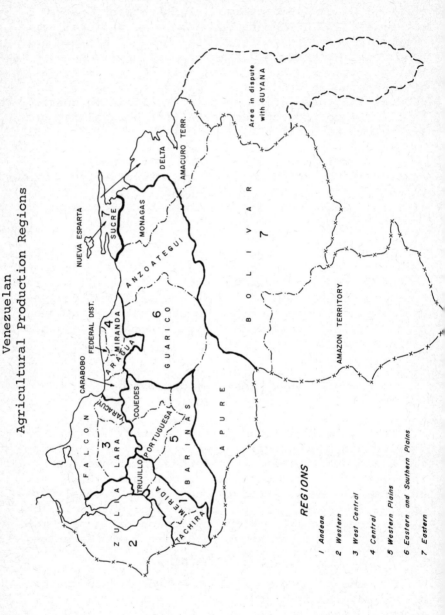

REGIONS

1 Andean
2 Western
3 West Central
4 Central
5 Western Plains
6 Eastern and Southern Plains
7 Eastern

lowland areas. The area has a relatively higher
proportion of rural population than do other sections
of Venezuela. The Andean region has had considerable
out-migration since 1950, but still has the greatest
problem in Venezuela with respect to excessive farm
land subdivision (minifundio) with correspondingly
low family incomes. Coffee production predominates.

2. Western (the state of Zulia). This region
is made up of the large Maracaibo Lake basin. Its
topography is relatively level, but there is a wide
range in rainfall. The northeastern side of the lake
is almost arid and the southwest side is very wet.
Some parts of the southern and western sides of the
lake have experienced considerable agricultural development, especially with regard to plantains and
beef and milk production. The southern lake area
now has a large flood control and drainage project
under way that is expected to reclaim 500,000 hectares of highly productive land. This area had been
largely passed over in the past because of tropical
disease problems, which are now under control.

3. West Central. Comprised of the states of
Falcón, Lara, and Yaracuy, this is a relatively
large region with a very arid climate and relatively
rough topography in the areas where rainfall is adequate to support nonzerophytic vegetation. There
are, however, important agricultural areas in several
river valleys and the region has a considerable margin for greater production, especially in the Yaracuy
valley.

4. Central. Comprised of the Federal District
and the states of Aragua, Carabobo, and Miranda,
this is the heaviest populated region of Venezuela,
and land areas utilized for agricultural production
here are the most intensively used. However, arable
land areas constitute a small proportion of the total
area because all these states are in the coastal
mountain range, which is characterized by very rough
topography. The Lake Valencia basin and the few
river valleys leading into it and the El Tuy River
valley flowing to the Caribbean Sea are the agricul-
turally productive areas of most importance, as are
some higher mountain valleys in the state of Carabobo.

5. Western Plains. Comprised of the states of Barinas, Cojedes, and Portuguesa on the southeast side of the Andean Mountains and extending well out into the Orinoco River basin, this is an area of relatively level topography, except on the western side in the Andean foothills. Considerable strides have recently been made in the control of tropical disease and in the extension of all-weather roads along the foothill area. The Western Plains area, especially the savanna regions, generally has very poor soils. However, large areas of land along the numerous rivers coming out of the Andes have highly productive soils in the more recent alluvial deposits. Rainfall is high in the mountain areas and high tropical forests predominate there, although many areas have already been deforested. Rainfall diminishes rapidly as the plains extend eastward toward the Orinoco River and merge into a dry-tropical ecological condition marked by a four- or five-month wet season and a seven- or eight-month dry season where extensive livestock production areas predominate.

6. Eastern and Southern Plains. Comprised of the states of Anzoátegui, Apure, Guárico, and Monagas, which constitute the major portion of the plains area north and west of the Orinoco River, this region is principally an extensive livestock-producing area, although the large Guárico River irrigation project within the region has recently become one of the most important rice-producing sections of Venezuela. Although topography is generally level, the principal ecological limitations of the region include relatively poor soils and long dry seasons.

7. Eastern. Comprised of the states of Bolívar, Nueva Esparta, and Sucre and the territories of Delta Amacuro and Amazonas, this region is made up of the large area south and east of the Orinoco River plus the north coast state of Sucre and the island state of Nueva Esparta. Because of the extremely old geographical formations with limited fertility, which are now exposed to the surface in a large part of the area, together with the need for expensive drainage, flood control, and irrigation systems, this region has limited agricultural development possibilities

compared with other areas of Venezuela. Also, the
states of Sucre and Margarita Island have serious
limitations on agricultural production because of
adverse topography and surface water shortages.

The production and productivity situation for
important crops in these seven regions in 1965, together with indications of changes since 1961, is
summarized in Tables 49 and 50.

As shown in these tables, the Western Plains
region had the largest portion (21.5 per cent) of
the total crop land of Venezuela in 1965 and had the
largest increase (54 per cent) in crop land area between 1961 and 1965 of any region. This region has
more corn and rice areas than any other region and
has practically all of the sesame areas of Venezuela.
It is second among the regions in cotton land. All
these crops showed very substantial increases in
harvested areas during the period 1961-65, and with
the exception of corn, which showed a decrease in
yield, the other three important crops showed significant yield increases of from 30 per cent to 50
per cent. This region produces the most tobacco of
all seven regions, but tobacco yield decreased slightly during this period.

The most important crops in land area in the
Central region, which had the second highest increase
in crop land (45 per cent), are corn, food legumes,
cocoa, sugar cane, cotton, potatoes, and tobacco, all
of which, with the exception of cocoa, had significant increases in crop areas--especially corn. Corn
and beans showed decreasing yields, whereas other
crops mentioned showed important increases in yields,
with sugar cane and cotton most outstanding.

The Western region showed a total increase in
crop areas of 31.3 per cent, made up mostly of large
increases in plantain and banana areas. Plantains
showed increasing yields, whereas banana yields decreased during the five-year period. This region
had large areas of improved pasture and is more
noted as a cattle-producing than a crop-producing
area.

TABLE 49

Land Used for Crops in Venezuela in 1965 and Percentage Change
Between 1961 and 1965, by Regions
(1,000 Has.)

Crop	Andean	Western	West Central	Central	Western Plains	Eastern & Southern Plains	Eastern
Corn	38.0	38.1	76.2	73.0	121.2	80.2	35.1
Per cent change	-38.7	-23.8	10.4	176.5	60.7	18.6	-10.5
Coffee[a]	154.4	--	61.3	33.0	22.3	42.3	26.8
Per cent change	0.0	--	0.0	0.0	0.0	0.0	0.0
Legumes	21.3	3.9	15.8	20.8	12.4	25.8	8.3
Per cent change	23.8	-11.4	-7.1	32.5	34.8	29.0	-36.6
Plantains	13.1	59.3	11.2	6.7	5.3	2.1	2.3
Per cent change	6.5	84.7	93.1	179.2	23.3	61.5	27.8
Rice	5.1	2.0	1.3	4.6	58.9	28.0	5.3
Per cent change	112.5	185.7	85.7	411.1	77.9	71.8	17.8
Cocoa[a]	1.0	0.2	0.3	31.5	0.1	0.7	36.7
Per cent change	0.0	0.0	0.0	0.0	0.0	0.0	0.0
Sesame	--	--	0.5	--	86.4	0.6	--
Per cent change	--	--	-37.5	--	64.9	0	--

Roots & tubers	13.4	5.6	8.3	13.0	6.4	14.9	8.3
Per cent change	61.4	-18.8	36.1	71.1	48.8	25.2	27.7
Sugar cane[b]	5.4	3.2	27.6	13.1	–	–	4.8
Per cent change	68.8	-13.5	-44.5	21.3	–	–	41.2
Bananas	15.6	27.9	3.5	2.8	2.8	3.0	2.8
Per cent change	– 7.1	220.7	-59.3	-20.0	-41.7	76.5	7.7
Cotton[c]	–	–	0.5	7.0	15.4	18.8	4.2
Per cent change	–	–	-16.7	18.6	111.0	– 9.6	50.0
Tobacco	0.2	–	0.3	1.7	2.0	1.6	0.8
Per cent change	100.0	–	-50.0	-15.0	-35.5	23.1	60.0
All other crops[d]	2.6	3.3	22.7	8.1	0.1	1.9	7.6
Per cent change	– 3.7	26.9	4.6	– 3.6	0.0	11.8	-11.6
Total crops	270.1	144.5	229.6	216.3	333.3	219.9	143.0
Per cent change	– 3.7	31.3	8.5	45.1	54.0	18.1	– 2.4
Per cent of total crop land	17.4	9.3	14.8	13.9	21.5	13.9	9.2

[a]National figures for coffee and cocoa crop area show practically no variation during the five years. Data are not available for each year by states, but it is assumed that no variation occurred in the regions in order to agree with national figures.

(Continued)

(Table 49 Continued)

b The crop areas for sugar cane include only those areas whose production is processed into refined sugar. The one sugar central in the Western region (Central Venezuela, in Zulia) that operated during the period covered above was closed in 1966.

c Changes in cotton crop area calculated from 1962 because fragmented data was not available for 1961.

d Some fruit and vegetable crop areas included in national totals are not included here because of the lack of data on a state-wide basis.

Source: Agricultural Statistics Annual, Ministry of Agriculture and Livestock. Regions comprised of federal entities as follows. Andean: Mérida, Táchira, and Trujillo; Western: Zulia; West Central: Falcón, Lara, and Yaracuy; Central: Aragua, Carabobo, Federal District, and Miranda; Western Plains: Barinas, Cojedes, and Portuguesa; Eastern and Southern Plains: Anzoátegui, Apure, Guárico, and Monagas; Eastern: Bolívar, Delta Amacuro territory, Nueva Esparta, Sucre, and Amazonas territory. Totals for land in crops by regions do not equal total crop land shown previously because of omission of sugar cane and other crop areas for which data was not available by states.

The Eastern and Southern Plains region showed an increase of 18.1 per cent in total crop areas since 1961. This region is an extensive livestock-producing area. It had important increases in rice areas in the Guárico irrigation project and is second among the regions in rice production, and rice yields showed significant increase. It registers the largest area in roots and tubers, mainly mandioc, yams, and taro root, because potato areas are limited in this region. It also has the largest area in cotton, which showed increasing yields of over 50 per cent. This crop is usually produced on the fertile riverside lands in the region, which are limited in size.

The West Central region registered an increase of 8.5 per cent in land in crops from 1961 to 1965. This was mainly in corn, plantains, and sugar cane. Over half the sugar cane area of Venezuela is in this region (along the riverside areas, which can be irrigated), and a small increase in yields was registered during the period. Corn, as in most other areas, showed decreased yields.

The Eastern region had the most cocoa area but without significant change in area or yields. Total crop land reduced in area by 2.4 per cent between 1961 and 1965. Plantains registered decreased yields only in this region.

The crop land of the Andean region reduced by 3.7 per cent during 1961-65, mainly because of a large decrease in corn areas. The Andean region has a wide variety of crops but predominates only in coffee areas, which had little change in amount or yield. Its legumes, roots and tubers, and fruits constituted an important segment in the production of Venezuela. Bean yields declined from 1961-65, as in all areas.

Cattle and hog inventories on farms and ranches, as indicated in the agricultural censuses of 1950 and 1961, are shown for seven regions in Table 51. The total increase of cattle inventories did not keep pace with the population growth during the period. However,

TABLE 50

Average Yields of Important Venezuelan Crops in 1965 and Percentage Change
from 1961 to 1965, by Regions (Kilograms per Hectare)

Crop	Andean	Western	West Central	Central	Western Plains	Eastern & Southern Plains	Eastern
Corn	837	997	1,118	1,085	1,291	1,104	1,194
Per cent change	4.9	- 3.6	- 4.9	- 8.3	- 4.4	- 0.2	-38.4
Coffee[a]	161	--	158	108	154	161	168
Per cent change	3.9	--	10.5	10.2	10.8	10.3	10.5
Legumes	420	530	425	440	449	420	515
Per cent change	-10.6	- 9.1	- 7.0	-17.9	-15.1	-19.8	-22.6
Plantains	5,006	6,117	4,593	3,273	5,350	4,671	3,223
Per cent change	13.3	39.9	15.5	74.1	41.8	35.8	-24.2
Rice	1,308	2,969	1,477	1,122	1,756	2,472	1,470
Per cent change	-13.8	125.3	-40.6	- 7.5	51.1	43.6	- 1.9
Sesame[b]	--	--	--	--	623	--	--
Per cent change	--	--	--	--	32.3	--	--
Potatoes	8,431	--	8,811	7,964	--	4,500	--
Per cent change	1.9	--	7.2	5.7	--	-36.7	--

Sugar	4,600	5,100	6,200	7,500	–	–	4,900
Per cent change	-17.9	18.6	5.1	36.4	–	–	0.0
Bananas	6,477	7,940	6,496	6,462	6,777	6,081	6,676
Per cent change	11.3	- 2.7	-33.2	-10.7	8.9	-16.2	-17.9
Cotton	1,500	–	854	1,188	1,109	755	1,079
Per cent change	50.0	–	19.6	30.7	30.5	51.9	45.2
Tobacco	882	–	1,000	1,699	1,313	1,755	519
Per cent change	17.6	–	5.0	18.6	- 5.4	3.2	-11.7

[a]Coffee yield change shown is between 1964 and 1965.

[b]Sesame has negligible importance in all regions except the Western Plains.

[c]Cotton yield change shown is from 1962 to 1965 except for Andean region, which is from 1963 to 1965.

Source: Agricultural Statistics Annual, Ministry of Agriculture and Livestock.

133

TABLE 51

Venezuelan Cattle and Hog Inventories in 1961 and Percentage
Change Between 1950 and 1961, by Regions

Region	Cattle		Hogs	
	Inventory, 1961 (1,000 Head)	Per Cent Change Since 1950	Inventory, 1961 (1,000 Head)	Per Cent Change Since 1950
Andean	594.38	47.8	186.82	27.2
Western	908.81	80.9	196.60	3.4
West Central	515.59	22.4	245.45	12.4
Central	247.75	12.6	165.71	30.3
Western Plains	913.20	9.6	336.28	18.4
Eastern & Southern Plains	2,788.8	- 1.8	457.70	13.0
Eastern	472.81	14.2	192.27	9.6
Total	6,440.71	11.7	1,780.84	22.5

Source: Agricultural censuses, 1950 and 1961.

134

there were some important shifts in the importance
of cattle-producing regions. The Western and Andean
regions showed the greatest increases in cattle inventories, and the West Central region showed an increase greater than the national average increase,
which was 11.7 per cent, whereas the traditional
cattle-producing areas of the plains regions and the
eastern part of Venezuela have been losing ground.
The Central and Andean regions showed the largest increases in hog inventories; all other regions showed
increases at rates below the national average of 22.5
per cent.

As additional descriptive material on these regions, Table 52 presents data that will assist in
comparing each region to Venezuela as a whole. Although the two plains regions account for a relatively high percentage of the total farm land, the major
portion of this land is made up of natural savanna-
type pastures, and crop land constitutes only 2 per
cent of the total land area of these two regions.

PRODUCTION COSTS

There is a serious lack of micro-economic studies
of individual farm operations in Venezuela, so only
general estimates of production costs are available,
together with data on costs of a few specific items
that have indicated changes during 1961-65. Further,
the available estimates of costs of production apply
to the commercial-type farms only and are not intended to represent average costs for all the areas utilized for each crop. The Ministry of Agriculture and
Livestock made a preliminary estimate of costs of
production in 1956, and this was revised in 1961 and
1962 for most of the crops covered. The Ministry of
Public Works (Department of Irrigation) has made more
recent estimates of costs of production in connection
with its feasibility studies for irrigation projects.

In Table 53 are presented available data on costs
of production for twenty important crops in Venezuela.
Table 54 provides data on unit factors utilized in
calculating figures for Table 53. As mentioned

TABLE 52

Land Area and Population Comparisons: Selected
Regions and Venezuela as a Whole

Region	Per Cent of the Total Land Area of Venezuela (1965)	Land Area in Farms (1961)		Per Cent of Total Population of Venezuela (1965)	Rural Population (1965)	
		Per Cent of Total Area of the Region	Per Cent of Total Land in Farms in Venezuela		Per Cent of Total Population of the Region	Per Cent of Total Rural Population of Venezuela
Andean	3.3	64.4	7.3	13	57	23
Western	6.9	29.5	7.1	12	16	7
West Central	5.7	42.2	8.3	15	43	17
Central	2.4	75.8	6.3	32	10	11
Western Plains	7.1	62.2	15.5	5	56	10
Eastern & Southern Plains	23.4	52.6	42.9	13	44	18
Eastern	51.2	7.1	12.6	10	44	14
Total	100.0	29.0	100.0	100	37	100

Source: 1961 Agricultural Census; and 1965 Vital Statistics Annual, General Statistical
Office, Ministry of Development.

previously, these cost estimates are based on
commercial-type farming operations, from which better-
than-average yields are obtained, and apply only to
direct costs. Such indirect costs as interest, depreciation on buildings, and capital returns are not
included. For this reason, a calculation of net
profits possible for most crops, based on average
yields, shown in Table 46, and the inputs shown in
Table 53, cannot be made because the average cost
per kilogram of many important crops, including corn
and beans, is considerably more than current prices
to farmers. The same problem exists with respect to
costs of production for livestock and livestock products in obtaining reliable data on costs of production
that have a sound relation to product prices. Much
of the writing in this respect has been aimed at justifying special subsidies and assistance programs for
these activities and is believed to be biased to a
large degree.

A recently published report by the Consejo de
Bienestar Rural[3] on the extensive cattle ranches in
the state of Apure summarized the following results
of annual operations based on the total number of
head of cattle on thirty ranches:

Gross income per head	Bs. 39.10
Gross income per hectare in the ranches	13.10
Direct operating costs per head	23.50
Direct operating costs per hectare	8.00
Net income per head	15.50
Net income per hectare	5.30

The low returns for beef operations are typical
of the all plains area. Costs of production and returns are considerably higher in the beef-producing
areas in Zulia and in the central areas of Venezuela.

Milk production costs vary greatly by region.
Estimates of costs in the Zulia state, which is the
major producing area, vary from 45 to 60 céntimos
per liter of milk; in the Central regions (states of

TABLE 53

Annual Direct Production Costs of Important Crops in Venezuela, 1963
(Bolivars per Hectare)

Crop	Materials and Specialized Services				Other Materials & Special Services[e]	Labor Costs		Total Direct Costs per Ha.
	Machinery Used[a]	Seed	Fertil-izers	Pesticides & Herbicides[b]		Skilled Labor[a]	Common Labor	
Corn	149	36	70	144	27	33	40	499
Black beans	92	44	35	28	9	24	202	434
Rice (irrigated)	305	125	210	134	464	60	136	1,434
Rice (upland)	152	125	105	56	105	32	50	625
Sesame	105	8	53	36	21	186	100	509
Potatoes (irrigated)	141	725	210	156	356	49	600	2,237
Sugar cane (planting year--irrigated)	282	240	280	140	755	65	475	2,237
Sugar cane (ratoon crop--irrigated)	116	50	280	140	695	23	435	1,739
Bananas (irrigated)[c]	0	0	120	42	172	0	470	804
Cotton	271	25	105	218	52	56	150	877
Tobacco (Virginia-type--irrigated)	105	9	525	260	303	33	2,411	3,735

Onions (irrigated)	88	150	210	320	290	23	2,890	3,971
Peanuts	117	125	70	19	56	33	220	640
Yams[d]	66	300	0	0	60	27	590	1,660
Tomatoes (irrigated)	96	53	193	120	555	27	960	2,004
Mandioc (yucca)[f]	108	50	105	30	150	29	340	812
Coconut[c,f]	39	0	158	60	30	9	1,130	1,394
Citrus (irrigated)[c,g]	39	0	105	50	1,160	9	1,850	3,713
Pineapple (2-year costs, irrigated)	118	2,000	280	30	380	32	1,400	4,240

[a] Calculated on basis of supplemental data in Table 54.

[b] Two days' labor per hectare estimated for hand application is included in "labor" column. For corn, rice, sesame, and cotton, application by airplane costs included in "special services" column.

[c] Costs based on crop in production, excluding costs of establishing the permanent crops.

[d] Ministry of Agriculture and Livestock figures for labor in yams adjusted from Bs.8 to Bs.10 for common labor and Bs.16 to Bs.24 for skilled labor.

[e] Costs of stakes and their placement included in column, "other materials."

[f] Irrigation costs removed from Ministry of Public Works figures.

[g] Harvesting costs for labor based on eighth-year production estimate of 156,000 fruits per hectare.

Source: Ministry of Agriculture and Livestock, Estimaciones de Costos de Producción--1963 for yams; Ministry of Public Works, Treinta Cultivos--Datos sobre sus Costos de Producción, 1963, for other crops.

TABLE 54

Costs of Machinery and Skilled Labor Utilized in Mechanized Farming Operations in Venezuela, 1963

Mechanized Farming Operation	Hectares Covered per Day	Tractor Operator Salary Cost per Hectare (Bs.)	Machinery Cost per Hectare (Bs.)	Total Cost per Hectare (Bs.)
Plowing	3.0	8.0	37.0	45.0
Disc harrowing	8.0	3.0	13.0	16.0
Furrowing (30- to 40-horse-power tractor)	4.0	6.0	12.0	18.0
Furrowing (50 H.P.)	6.0	4.0	14.0	18.0
Planting (30 to 40 H.P.)	6.0	4.0	9.0	13.0
Planting (50 H.P.)	8.0	3.0	10.0	13.0
Planting, sesame and rice (30 to 40 H.P.)	8.0	3.0	9.0	12.0
Planting, sesame and rice (50 H.P.)	9.0	2.7	9.3	12.0
Cultivating--2 rows (30 to 40 H.P.)	6.0	4.0	8.0	12.0
Cultivating--2 rows (50 H.P.)	8.0	3.0	10.0	13.0
Cultivating--4 rows (50 H.P.)	12.0	2.0	8.0	10.0

Dusting (30 to 40 H.P.)	10.0	6.6	9.0
Dusting (50 H.P.)	12.0	8.0	10.0
Spraying (30 to 40 H.P.)	6.0	10.0	14.0
Spraying (50 H.P.)	8.0	11.0	14.0
Rice combine harvester	4.0	49.0	55.0
Cotton picker	3.0	62.0	70.0
Corn harvester	2.2	99.0	110.0
Spike tooth harrowing	12.0	10.0	12.0
Cane stubble shredding	3.0	37.0	45.0
Sugar cane loading	2.7	61.0	70.0

Source: Ministry of Public Works, Treinta Cultivos--Datos sobre sus Costos de Produccion, 1963.

Carabobo and Aragua), costs are estimated at 60 to 75 céntimos per liter.

Costs of agricultural production have been moving upward quite rapidly during 1961-65, especially for the inputs required by modern agriculture. Machinery costs have risen approximately 50 per cent between 1961 and 1965, according to estimates provided by one of the major machinery dealers of Venezuela.[4] According to this source, approximately 35 per cent of the increase was due to devaluations of the bolivar; the remainder was due to an approximate 4 per cent annual increase in foreign prices of machinery, as well as increased freight rates, insurance, and other costs. This is reflected on a more extreme scale by changes in the custom costs of machinery services, as indicated by the amounts allowed in the loans made by the Agricultural Bank of Venezuela in 1961 and 1965:[5]

Costs of Tractor Services per Hectare

	1961	1965
Plowing	Bs. 15	Bs. 25-30
Disc harrowing	10	15-20

About 35 per cent of the increase in custom service costs was due to increased machinery costs (previously mentioned); the remainder (about 60 per cent) was due to increased salaries of tractor operators and other operating costs.

Analysis of data on costs of imported fertilizers and fertilizer elements in the annual customs statistics shows that costs of these items in foreign currency increased by approximately 10 per cent between 1961 and 1965, but the reduction in the value of the bolivar added another 35 per cent, so the total increase was about 45 per cent. However, the nationally owned petrochemical industry, which since 1964 has imported and produced the major portion of fertilizers sold in Venezuela, claims that the average price of about Bs. 950 per ton for nutrient elements used in fertilizers is considerably below production costs.

In any event, the local price of fertilizer elements at main distribution points maintained throughout Venezuela is only 10 per cent to 15 per cent higher than in the United States ($.187 per kilogram in the U.S., compared with about $.206 in Venezuela).[6]

Costs of hired labor have also increased significantly between 1961 and 1965. Complete analyses are not available on this point, but tasks done on a piecework basis, such as picking coffee beans and cotton, have risen from 50 per cent to 65 per cent during the period. This is illustrated by the following data on costs of hand-picked cotton in Venezuela:[7]

Costs of Cotton Picking per Kilogram

	1961	1966
First picking	Bs. 0.15	Bs. 0.25
Second picking	0.20	0.30-0.35

The index of farmers' prices for all agricultural products shown in Figure 3 showed an increase in prices of only 7 per cent between 1961 and 1965, so it is clear that a definite cost-price squeeze for agricultural production has been occurring in recent years, when compared to increases in costs amounting to 30 per cent to 65 per cent, although data are very incomplete in this respect.

RURAL FAMILY INCOMES AND WELFARE

As indicated in Chapters 2 and 3, income per capita and per person employed in agriculture increased over 20 per cent between 1961 and 1965, which was a considerably higher rate of increase than occurred in all other sectors. However, even with these increases, the per capita income in agriculture had reached, in 1965, only Bs. 686 ($152 U.S.), which would indicate family incomes on the average are less than Bs. 3,500 per year. Home economists[8] estimate that a farm family of five should have Bs. 9,000 or more disposable income per year in order to have a decent level of living. Consequently, the rural areas

still have a long way to go to raise family incomes
to desirable levels.

Welfare services in most Latin American countries
are not available on a continuous and organized basis,
with the exception of certain Social Security systems
that principally provide medical assistance to some
segments of the population. Venezuela has had a
Social Security system for many years, and a decree
in 1966 has extended the service to a wider range of
income groups. The goal is to have nationwide coverage for this service, principally of a medical nature
but with the recently added old-age pension provision.
However, while coverage is provided in major city
areas and is being slowly extended to smaller cities,
rural areas and farm families continue to be outside
the sphere of such public services. Also, private
medical care is limited in rural areas because rural
families do not have incomes to support these services
or to attract the necessary professional people.

Of a total of 2,500 school lunch centers maintained in Venezuela by the school lunch program and
the National Nutrition Institute in 1966, 1,473 were
in rural areas.[9]

As indicated previously, the school system, especially at primary levels, has been expanded rapidly
since 1961, and many rural areas that did not have a
school before that date now have one. However, because of the dispersed nature of the rural population,
making schools available to all rural children is an
expensive process and, consequently, it has low priority. Lack of adequate rural access roads limits
the possibilities of efficient transportation services
needed to bring rural youths to larger and more adequate consolidated schools.

Rural domestic water systems have been increased
substantially. In 1959, there were 149 rural centers
with community water systems for 726,000 persons. In
1965, there were 700 such rural population centers,
with water systems serving 1.6 million persons. A
total expenditure of Bs. 133 million was made during
the five-year period. It is estimated that these

rural water systems serve 44 per cent of the people
living in population centers of fewer than 5,000
persons.[10]

Although improvements in rural family incomes and
living conditions can be seen and measured, there is
still a large bloc of farm families, estimated at
more than 30 per cent of the total, that is not participating in the improved conditions due to its
isolation from this trend because of geographical
location and limited educational opportunities. The
incorporation of this significant segment of the
rural population into Venezuela's improvement programs is one of the most difficult problems yet to
be confronted.

RURAL EMPLOYMENT AND UNEMPLOYMENT

National estimates of employment by economic
sectors were presented in Table 16 and showed that
in 1964, 793,000 persons were employed in the agricultural sector, which constituted 32.3 per cent of
the total persons employed in Venezuela. The same
table showed that there was an 11.2 per cent rate of
unemployment in all sectors in 1964. This rate probably applies to other sectors of the economy more
than to agriculture, because in agriculture there is
not a clear-cut distinction as to whether or not a
person is seeking work. However, there is an obvious
underemployment in the agricultural sector, because
even the most optimistic estimates of the manpower
required to carry out the production activities
amount to less than half the manpower available on a
yearly basis, even with the present low rate of productivity of these workers.

This point is illustrated by the following data
taken from the Plan of the Nation, 1965, which utilized data provided by the Agricultural Statistics
Annual of the Ministry of Agriculture and Livestock
and the annual reports of the Central Bank of Venezuela.

Year	Average Number of Days of Work per Person Occupied in Agriculture
1961	134
1962	143
1963	148
1964	155
1965	159
Goal for 1968	184

A comparison of the figures on number of days worked with the total work days per year (which could, for agriculture, be conservatively placed at 300 days) indicates that only about 50 per cent of the time of the active work force is being utilized, and the goal to increase the days worked to 184 by 1968 raises this estimate to 61 per cent.

A large margin exists for intensification of agricultural operations without overtaxing available manpower, providing that marketing and distribution problems can be solved.

The strong and weak points observed in agricultural development in Venezuela will be presented in the next two chapters, which focus on factors contributing to and detracting from agricultural progress.

NOTES

1. An evaluation of the Venezuelan agrarian reform program is in progress under the sponsorship of the Inter-American Committee for Agricultural Development and the Venezuelan Centro de Estudios del Desarrollo.

2. Series of technical studies made between 1963 and 1965 by representatives of the Agricultural Bank of Venezuela, the Agrarian Institute, and Consejo de Bienestar Rural in sixteen states and the Federal District. Reports prepared by Consejo de Bienestar Rural, Caracas.

3. Hugo Estrada, La Ganadería en el Estado Apure
(Caracas: Consejo de Bienestar Rural, October, 1966).

4. Henry Fernández, Maquinaria Mendoza, Caracas.

5. Data provided by Alejandro Cos, Agricultural
and Livestock Bank, December, 1966.

6. U.S. price taken from U.S. Department of
Agriculture, Changes in Agriculture in 26 Developing
Nations, 1948 to 1963, Foreign Agricultural Economic
Report No. 27 (Washington, D.C.: U.S. Government
Printing Office, 1965).

7. Data provided by Gaston Vivas B., Cotton
Grower's Association of Venezuela.

8. Data provided by Irma de González, home
economist, Consejo de Bienestar Rural, Caracas, 1966.

9. Idem.

10. Plan of the Nation, 1965 (Caracas: CORDIPLAN,
1965).

CHAPTER **6** VENEZUELA'S
AGRICULTURAL
PROGRESS

Although agriculture has lagged behind some other
sectors in the economy in Venezuela, recent attention
to rural problems has started to yield some measurable
results, some of which have been pointed out in previous chapters. Progress in agriculture is dependent
upon the intelligent use of the natural resources of
land and water and the application of continuously
changing and improving technology in the use and management of all the production factors. This involves
continuous capital investment in the necessary inputs
and adjustments in the resource base at the individual
farm level. Progress also requires a continuous educational process, so that the individual farm operator
can intelligently utilize technological improvements
in increasing the efficiency with which the factors
of production are combined to obtain increasingly
higher productivity. One of the most important problems, which has the least definite answers now available for existing and future problems, is the question
of equitable marketing of the agricultural products
so that they may be available to the consumer in the
place, time, form, and price that he can use.
Finally, public demand for more adequate dietary
standards could shape the pattern for future development of agricultural production.

This chapter will deal with the public and private
institutional services and policies contributing to
the improvement of agricultural production and management of natural resources, together with measures
of the application of improved technology in the individual farms.

GOVERNMENT INSTITUTIONAL SERVICES AVAILABLE TO
AGRICULTURE AND CONTRIBUTING TO PROGRESS
IN RURAL AREAS

With the increasing awareness of the public and
government agencies to the necessity of broadening
the productive base of the economy and of providing
for more diversification in the primary sector of the
production activities in Venezuela, an institutional
structure has been developed to assist in improving
the productive capacity of the agricultural sector.
Efforts in this respect have been plagued with many
problems, which will be described specifically in
Chapter 7. In this chapter, a description of these
institutional services will be presented, and emphasis will be given to how these services have assisted
in agricultural progress.

Educational Facilities

The regular educational facilities of the Venezuelan Government provided through the Ministry of
Education have made significant strides in increasing
primary school education facilities during the last
few years, as pointed out in Chapter 2. Some of these
improvements have reached rural areas but to a lesser
degree than in cities and towns. A... o, as previously
indicated, it was estimated in 1965 that 23 per cent
of the total population of primary school age (7-14)
still did not have schools available. This amounts
to approximately 450,000 young people who are not
studying because of lack of schools. The total number
of rural residents of primary school age is estimated
at 550,000. About 56 per cent (300,000) were, in
1965-66, attending primary schools available to them,
leaving 250,000 unable to study because of lack of
schools or other reasons. The majority of these
schools provide only parts of the usual six grades
included in the primary level and are usually limited
to three grades. There are practically no secondary
schools in rural areas, and only the more affluent
farm families can send their children to boarding
schools in the towns and cities. Organized transportation services to carry children to school are also
practically nonexistent in rural areas. A great deal

of additional investment and development is necessary
before rural school facilities are adequate to the
need. At the time of the census in 1961, there were
8,642 rural schools with 10,697 teachers. Only 4 per
cent of the schools provided more than three primary
grades. Between 1961 and 1965, a considerable consol-
idation of rural schools took place, and their number
was reduced to 7,717, with 11,968 teachers. Approximately 6 per cent of the rural schools in 1965 provided a full six primary grades.[1]

Technical Schools of Agriculture

There has been a significant increase in technical schools that prepare subprofessional-level
technicians since 1960. During the decade from 1950
to 1960, there was only one practical school of agriculture operated by the Ministry of Agriculture and
Livestock at La Providencia, state of Aragua, and one
private school of this nature at Naguanagua in the
state of Carabobo, together with one home demonstrator's school at Gonzalito in Aragua, operated by the
Ministry of Agriculture and Livestock, that were in
operation on a continuous basis. At the present time,
there are three practical schools of agriculture established in the states of Aragua, Portuguesa, and
Monagas, and two home demonstrator's schools located
in Aragua and Táchira, operated by the Ministry of
Agriculture and Livestock. These provide a three-
year practical course at high school, or secondary
school, level. The one private practical school of
the Salesian Fathers, similar to the public schools,
is also still operating in the state of Carabobo,
and a private school for home demonstrators is operating at Chivacoa, in the state of Yaracuy. The
Ministry of Agriculture and Livestock also operates
a practical forestry training school at Mérida, a
coffee-culture school in Táchira, cocoa-culture
schools in the states of Miranda and Sucre, and
tractor-operating schools in Aragua and Portuguesa,
all of which, with the exception of the forestry
school, provide practical training for shorter periods
than the traditional practical schools of agriculture.
There are also two private technical schools of agriculture providing short course work, located in the

states of Trujillo and Miranda, together with three
similar schools operated by the Ministry of Education
and located in the states of Monagas, Guárico, and
Táchira.

The number of graduates from the practical schools
of agriculture, the home demonstrator's schools, the
forestry schools, and the specialized short-course
training programs since the inception of these various
training facilities is shown in Table 55. Data for
1966 and 1967 is found in Table 11 of the Statistical
Appendix.

Table 55 shows a significant increase in the number of graduates from these practical schools during
1961-65. These technical aides provide most of the
staff for the Agricultural Extension Service and for
other subprofessional work, along with farmers in the
Agricultural Bank of Venezuela and the Agrarian Institute. For example, in 1965, graduates of these
schools provided 85 per cent of the staff of the
Agricultural Extension Service and 40 per cent of the
agricultural experimental staffs of the Ministry of
Agriculture and Livestock. These technicians are not,
of course, highly trained, but most of them have some
farm background (which university graduates do not
have, generally) and have proved to be effective
workers in the field work in agricultural improvement.
Their number is still too limited, but they constitute
a significant nucleus of trained personnel for future
agricultural development. A total of 1,322 agricultural technical aides (peritos agropecuarios) had
graduated by 1965, not all of whom were working in
agriculture. There was only one such aide for each
of the 242 farms in Venezuela.

In addition to the practical schools described
above, the Instituto Nacional de Capacitación Educa-
tiva (National Institute for Vocational Education,
or INCE) has carried on short vocational courses for
farmers and farm youths. The number of persons participating in these courses, according to the 1965
report of INCE, was:

TABLE 55

Graduates of Practical and Specialized Schools for Agriculture in Venezuela, 1934-65

Years	Agricultural Technical Aides (Peritos)	Forestry Technical Aides (Peritos)	Farm Home Demonstration Agents	Coffee Culturists	Cocoa Culturists	Tractor Operators
1934-56	532	--	--	--	--	--
1948-56	--	180	--	--	--	--
1957	32	5	24	9	12	24
1958	15	10	19	11	9	21
1959	23	8	16	8	12	23
1960	30	--	24	19	19	32
1961	33	22	26	18	43	24
1962	154	22	104	33	14	24
1963	196	8	87	35	36	25
1964	172	17	78	22	31	43
1965	135	15	118	--	--	49
Total	1,322	287	496	155	196	265

Source: 1965 Agricultural Statistics Annual, Ministry of Agriculture and Livestock.

Year	Number of Participants in INCE Agricultural Vocational Courses
1961	71
1962	578
1963	3,851
1964	7,546
1965	9,783
Total	21,829

The National Institute for Vocational Education is primarily engaged in training industrial workers; the number of participants in agricultural courses indicated above is only 12 per cent of the total number of persons participating in the training activities of INCE.

Higher Educational Facilities for Agriculture

University- or professional-level educational facilities in agriculture are now provided in Venezuela at the following universities, all of which are part of the national university system:

University Department	City	State
Agronomic engineering faculty	Maracay	Aragua
Agronomic engineering faculty	Barquisimeto	Lara
Agronomic engineering faculty	Maracaibo	Zulia
Agronomic engineering faculty	Jusepín	Monagas
Forestry faculty	Mérida	Mérida
Veterinary medicine faculty	Maracay	Aragua
Veterinary medicine faculty	Maracaibo	Zulia

The agronomic engineering faculties provide a five-year course in general agricultural sciences, and specialization is not encouraged during the regular university period. No facilities for postgraduate

education for specialization purposes are yet a part
of the university structure. Those who have obtained
postgraduate degrees have had to go out of Venezuela
to do so.

The faculties for agronomy and veterinary medicine
at Maracay and the forestry faculty at Mérida were
the only facilities for university-level education in
agriculture until 1960. All the other facilities in
agricultural education became operative during 1961-
65 and their number has greatly increased. The first
class graduated from the Maracaibo faculty in 1965.

The number of graduates from these agricultural
universities between 1940 and 1965 is indicated in
Table 56. Additional data for 1966 is found in Table
12 of the Statistical Appendix.

TABLE 56

Graduates of Agricultural and Forestry Universities
in Venezuela, 1940-65

Year	Agronomic Engineers[a]	Veterinarians[b]	Foresters[c]
1940-60	302	175	84
1961	25	23	10
1962	20	30	8
1963	45	30	16
1964	45	17	25
1965	120	21	18
Total	557	296	161

[a]First graduating class in 1942.
[b]First graduating class in 1940.
[c]First graduating class in 1952.

Source: 1965 Agricultural Statistics Annual, Minis-
         istry of Agriculture and Livestock.

The number of professional-level technicians has
increased significantly during 1961-65, as shown in

Table 56. In 1965, the Agricultural Investigation
Center and experiment stations provided positions for
170 technicians of these categories, and the Agricultural Extension Service of the Ministry of Agriculture
and Livestock employed 126 professional technicians.
These were the two largest groups of agricultural
technicians with university degrees. Complete data
are not available on the total number of such technicians who are still working directly in agricultural
programs, but it is believed that only a small proportion have abandoned their professional field of
work.

The ratios of the number of farms in Venezuela in
1965 to the total number of graduates in agricultural
engineering and veterinarian medicine are as follows:

    Number of farms per agricultural
        engineer   575
    Number of farms per veterinarian   1,065

There was an estimated forested area of over
220,000 hectares in Venezuela per forester graduated
from the University of Mérida up to 1965.

Although the number of professional technicians
trained in Venezuela is now becoming significant,
there is still a severe shortage, considering Venezuela's needs. The quality of the training, especially in some specialized fields, still must be
improved. However, due to lack of coordination between the educational institutions and government
agencies and other sources of employment, it is becoming difficult for recent university graduates in
agriculture to find employment readily.

The amount of government funds expended in the
education of technicians at the subprofessional or
technical aide level and at the professional or university level during the period from 1961 to 1965 is
summarized in Table 57.

There were some fluctuations between years in
expenditures for agricultural technical and professional education, as shown in Table 57, but the

TABLE 57

Funds Spent by Venezuelan Government for Subprofessional and Professional Education in Agronomy and Veterinary Medicine, 1961-65 (Million Bs.)

Year	Subprofessional Technical Schools	University-Level Schools for Agriculture			Total Technical & Professional Agricultural Schools
		Agronomy	Veterinary	Total University Level	
1961	8.1	7.5	3.5	11.0	19.1
1962	9.3	7.7	3.5	11.2	19.5
1963	8.4	8.7	4.1	12.8	21.2
1964	8.6	10.7	5.9	16.6	25.2
1965	9.9	9.5	5.7	15.2	25.1

Source: Work sheets for national planning and 1966 budget of the Venezuelan Government, supplied by Presidential Office for Coordination and Planning.

general trend was toward substantial increases in the
allocation of resources to this important activity.

Technical Agricultural Investigation
Facilities and Personnel

Various types of agricultural research and experimental facilities have existed in Venezuela for many
years and they began taking more formal institutional
shape after the Ministry of Agriculture and Livestock
was established in 1936. Most of the research carried
out has been in the biological phases of agricultural
science, and activities have been handicapped by lack
of continuity in efforts, personnel, and financing.
The establishment of the National Fund for Agricultural Investigations in 1961 has resulted in more
serious coordination of research activities and in a
reshaping of these efforts toward more practical and
applied research to meet the needs for modern technological practices in agriculture. A special report
entitled La Investigación Agrícola en el MAC sponsored
by this Fund and published by the Department of Research of the Ministry of Agriculture and Livestock
in May, 1965, provides a good summary of accomplishments and problems in agricultural research. It also
provides both strong recommendations for reorienting
the nature of such research and important guides for
determining priorities and the nature of research to
be carried out. These recommendations focus, to a
large degree, on the need for a more economic orientation of research projects and imply the need for
agricultural economic technicians as an integral part
of research staffs--a need that has not yet been met.
This report does indicate an important change in the
attitude of research technicians toward applied research and problems of agricultural production and
distribution activities, and it should eventually
strengthen these efforts to a great extent.

In 1965, the principal agencies doing agricultural
investigation work in Venezuela were the following,
according to the aforementioned special report:

1. Department of Investigation of the Ministry
    of Agriculture and Livestock.

    a. Agricultural Investigation Center in Maracay, plus seven experimental stations, one substation, and one field research camp in other locations in Venezuela.

    b. Veterinary Investigation Center in Maracay.

    c. Fish Industries Investigation Center at Cumaná.

2. Faculties of agronomy and veterinary medicine of the Central University of Venezuela at Maracay.

3. University of the Andes at Mérida.

4. University of Zulia at Maracaibo.

5. University of the East at Jusepín.

6. The Shell Foundation agricultural service installations and demonstration centers in Cagua and in the states of Zulia and Falcón (a private entity effort).

7. The Consejo de Bienestar Rural, Caracas (a combined private and governmental effort).

8. The Ministry of Public Works (Department of Irrigation.

The universities listed above are not very deeply involved in agricultural research.

The number of technicians engaged in agricultural research in the official agencies of the Ministry of Agriculture and Livestock are summarized in Table 58.

The significant increase in technical staffs involved in research activities essential for the future progress of agricultural development is evident in the figures in Table 58, which shows the increased attention that is being given to this work. In the 1950's, the staffs of research centers suffered from a great deal of turnover in key personnel because of low salaries and other factors. In recent years,

salary scales have been raised and the turnover rates
have been much lower. A high proportion of the research staffs have ten years or more of experience in
their present organizations. A significant scholar-
ship program that has been in operation in recent
years is slowly improving the total number of staff
members with advance degrees in their specialties.

TABLE 58

Agricultural Research Personnel in Venezuela's
Ministry of Agriculture and Livestock,
1955 and 1960-64

Year	Professional-Level Technicians[a]	Professional Aides[b]	Administrative and Office Services[c]
1955	35	39	36
1960	113	75	60
1961	122	60	62
1962	129	71	74
1963	141	74	77
1964	170	115	81

[a]Includes agronomic engineers, veterinarians, chemical engineers, mechanical engineers, chemists,
biologists, bioanalysts, library technicians, and
other high-level technicians, department heads, and
advisers. Also includes personnel contracted for by
the National Fund for Agricultural Research and the
Department of Plant Sanitation of the Ministry of
Agriculture and Livestock and others.

[b]Includes professional aides (peritos agropecuarios),
cultural practitioners (practicos cafeteros y
cacaoteros), laboratory aides and assistants, sur-
veyors, statisticians, and so on.

[c]Principally, the office service staffs. Field labor-
ers are not included; these numbered 573 in 1965.

Source: La Investigación Agrícola en Venezuela, Ministry of Agriculture and Livestock, May, 1965.

In Table 59 are presented data on the annual budgets of the Ministry of Agriculture and Livestock's research agencies for the period 1962-65.

TABLE 59

Annual Budgets of the Branches of the Agricultural Investigation Department of Venezuela's Ministry of Agriculture and Livestock, 1962-65 (1,000 Bs.)

Branch	1962	1963	1964	1965
General Supervision (Caracas)	939	1,592	1,935	1,544
Agronomic Investigation (CIA)	9,068	9,347	10,301	15,798
Veterinary Investigation (CIV)	3,168	3,318	4,024	7,598
Fishing Industries Investigation (CIP)	0	545	782	2,624
Total	13,175	14,832	17,042	27,564
Per Cent of Total Budget of Ministry of Agriculture and Livestock	3.2	3.8	3.3	4.7

Source: La Investigación Agrícola en Venezuela, Ministry of Agriculture and Livestock, May, 1965; and Presupuesto-Programa 1966 of the Venezuelan Government.

Significant increases in financial resources for agricultural investigation are shown in Table 59, although the proportion of the total budget of the Ministry of Agriculture and Livestock assigned for research was still relatively low. Many observers feel that research activities should be one of the major activities of the Ministry of Agriculture and

Livestock, and these activities clearly have not reached that status as yet, although total appropriations for agricultural research more than doubled between 1962 and 1965.

An important activity of the research centers is the production and certification of seed, especially for corn, cotton, sesame, beans, and rice. Also, in the Veterinary Research Center, a significant activity (which in some years overbalances other research activities in livestock sciences) is the production of serum for disease control, especially for foot-and-mouth disease, Newcastle disease and others. The production of these important items for agricultural and livestock operations probably is not a direct function of research agencies and probably could be performed more effectively by private interests (this will be commented on in the next chapter) but essential products are being provided in this manner.

Besides the research facilities for agronomy and livestock located at Maracay, experiment stations for product research are located in the following areas:

Location of Experiment Stations	Product Specialties
Mucuchíes, Mérida	potatoes and wheat
Carrasquero, Zulia	native cattle selection and care
Calabozo, Guárico (Los Llanos)	beef, pasture management, and rice
Bramón, Táchira	coffee
Yaritagua, Yaracuy (Occidente)	sugar cane
Caucagua, Miranda	cocoa
Araure, Portuguesa	rice, corn, sesame
Barquisimeto (El Cují) Substation for arid areas	sisal, pineapple, grapes
San Tomé, Anzoátegui (Mesa de Guanipa camp)	peanuts

The above-described facilities for agricultural research provide a sound base for developing more effective work in this important phase of agricultural development. Also, as mentioned, recent efforts to coordinate these activities and to orient them toward solving real problems of the agricultural sector should result in more effective service in this respect.

Agricultural Extension Facilities and Personnel

Efforts in the training of farmers in modern agricultural technology and in the circulation of technical information began in Venezuela between 1920 and 1929. Real significance was given to this activity in 1934, when a Section of Agricultural Development was established. This was incorporated into the Ministry of Agriculture and Livestock when that ministry was formed in 1936. Demonstration farms and rural youth club ("5-V") activities were initiated soon thereafter. Veterinary services were established in some locations by the Ministry of Agriculture and Livestock in 1941 and 1942. A slow increase in these activities continued until 1946, when there were 93 extension offices operating in Venezuela, although they had the general reputation of being mainly seed sales offices. After 1946, there was a decline in support of extension activities, and by 1958, only 23 extension offices remained throughout Venezuela. After 1958, some additional impulse was applied to this activity, but not until 1961 were concrete steps taken to upgrade the technical personnel in these activities and plans made gradually to increase the services to form a real national network for organizing training and technical services for farm adults and youths. The methodology and organization employed in considering rural problems and designing services to meet farmers' needs have steadily improved in recent years, although there is a serious shortage of dedicated and well-trained technicians for this work.

At the end of 1965, the Agricultural Extension Service of the Ministry of Agriculture and Livestock had 183 field offices or extension agencies; the number of technicians is indicated in Table 60.

TABLE 60

Personnel of the Agricultural Extension Service of Venezuela's
Ministry of Agriculture and Livestock, 1966

National and Regional Supervisory Office		Field Extension Agencies	
Type of Technician	Number of Technicians	Type of Technician	Number of Technicians
Agronomic engineers	82	Agronomic engineers	44
Economists	2	Veterinarians	2
Sociologists	2	Coffee culturists	121
Anthropologists	1	Cocoa culturists	65
Technical agricultural aides (peritos)	2	Poultry specialists	6
		Beekeeping specialists	5
Home demonstration agents	32	Technical agricultural aides	258
Other technicians	32	Home demonstration agents	243
Subtotal	153		744
Total	897		

Source: Special unpublished report to the author from Extension Department, Ministry of Agriculture and Livestock, November, 1966.

163

Only in the last few years have significant numbers of professional-level technicians been included in the agricultural extension program, when the number of available university graduates made this possible and when salary scales were adjusted to attract professional-level technicians. As indicated in Table 60, professional-level technicians (agronomic engineers, veterinarians, economists, sociologists, and the anthropologist) numbered 133 persons, which was only 15 per cent of the total technical staff. Additional upgrading in the technical training requirements for extension agents is obviously needed, but an institutional structure is functioning and can be rapidly improved as more highly trained technicians become available.

In addition to the Agricultural Extension Service, as such, the special practical schools described previously in this chapter, which provide the major portion of the extension agents, are operated under the jurisdiction of the Agricultural Extension Department of the Ministry of Agriculture and Livestock. These schools take a considerable portion (in 1962-66 about 37 per cent) of the total funds made available to this department. This school operation should probably be incorporated into the regular school systems of the Ministry of Education, now that regular school facilities have been greatly increased. Such an alternative is under discussion and awaits a final decision. The Ministry of Agriculture and Livestock assumed the obligation in the past because secondary school facilities were generally unavailable to farm youths, and a complete, subsidized program had to be established.

The budgets available to the Agricultural Extension Service of the Ministry of Agriculture and Livestock for 1962-66 are shown in Table 61.

A steady increase in the amounts appropriated for Agricultural Extension Service activities is shown in Table 61. The low percentage of the total Ministry of Agriculture and Livestock budget assigned for the Agricultural Extension Services, which, together with research, should be the most important activity of

TABLE 61

Budgets of the Agricultural Extension Service of Venezuela's
Ministry of Agriculture and Livestock, 1962-66
(Bs. 1,000)

Year	Agricultural Extension Service	Practical Training Schools	Total	
			Amount	Per Cent of Total Ministry of Agriculture and Livestock Budget
1962	17,406	8,106	22,512	6.3
1963	19,919	8,306	28,225	7.4
1964	22,479	8,400	30,879	6.0
1965	25,830	8,571	34,401	5.9
1966	26,794	9,906	36,700	6.8

Source: Presupuesto-Programa 1966 of the Government.

this Ministry, is partially due to the fact that funds
for the autonomous agencies of the Agricultural Bank
of Venezuela and the Agrarian Institute are included
in the Ministry of Agriculture and Livestock budgets,
as shown previously in Table 25. With these funds
excluded, the proportion of the Ministry's budget assigned to extension was about 13 per cent in 1962-66,
which is still less than is necessary to provide this
essential service for the development of the agricultural sector.

An important activity of the Agricultural Extension Service is the sponsorship of youth clubs for
rural boys and girls called 5-V. Significant progress
has been made in this activity, and Venezuela is among
the leading Latin American countries in the scope of
this activity. The work of the Agricultural Extension
Service is complemented by a private "Society for 5-V
Youth Clubs" organized in Venezuela, which provides
premiums, travel scholarships, and credit for individual member projects and constitutes a valuable
stimulus for this program. Also, the Inter-American
Program for Rural Youth Clubs, sponsored by the American International Association for Economic and Social
Development (AIA) and the Inter-American Institute of
Agricultural Sciences of the OAS (IAIAS), provides a
significant backing for the Venezuelan youth club program with premiums and exchange programs. A recent
corn-growing contest, sponsored by this organization
in Latin America with the collaboration of the International Chemical Company, was participated in by the
5-V Club program in Venezuela with outstanding results
The winner of the national contest produced the equivalent of 9,800 kilograms of corn per hectare, and he
successfully participated in international competition
for further premiums.

The number of 5-V Clubs organized in Venezuela
and their total membership between 1963 and 1965 is
shown in Table 62.

Product Regulation and Control Services
in Agriculture

In both the Agronomic and Veterinarian Investigation Centers of the Ministry of Agriculture and

Livestock at Maracay, laboratory services are maintained for testing agricultural chemicals and meci-
cines that are to be distributed and sold in Venezuela.
Also, the Department of Vegetation Sanitation has been
established in the Ministry of Agriculture and Livestock for the protection of the public with respect
to vegetative matter brought into Venezuela. However,
this agency has a very small staff and operates only
in the principal ports of entry. Quarantine stations
for livestock brought into Venezuela are being built
by the Ministry, and all imported animals are required
either to have sanitation certificates from the point
of origin or to pass through these stations. Venezuela has maintained a foot- and-mouth disease vacci-
nation and control program for more than fifteen years
that occupies a large portion of the available veterinarians.

Minimum and maximum price controls are in effect
for some products and will be commented on in a later
section of this chapter.

TABLE 62

5-V Youth Clubs Operating in Venezuela, 1963-65

	Boys' Clubs		Girls' Clubs		Total	
Year	Number of Clubs	Members	Number of Clubs	Members	Number of Clubs	Members
1963	293	5,579	372	6,907	665	12,486
1964	338	6,419	455	9,330	793	15,749
1965	314	5,611	425	7,641	739	13,272

Source: 1965 Agricultural Statistics Annual, Minis-
istry of Agriculture and Livestock.

The Comision Venezolana de Normas Industriales
(COVENIN) has been established in the Ministry of
Development to set grading standards and other controls for products used in industrial plants. This
body has set some preliminary standards for pork products and some other products in the agricultural field

but still has not had much impact in setting standards for agricultural products.

The basic framework for necessary regulation and control activities of the Venezuelan Government with respect to agricultural products, except in the marketing field, is now established, and needs are principally in the improvement of technical and administrative skills.

Natural Resource Development and Control Services in Agriculture

Venezuela has made significant progress in the evaluation of its natural resource base, especially at the reconnaissance level of investigation, but there is a large area for which little scientifically ordered data has been obtained. Venezuela also has detailed resource analysis data on the irrigation and drainage project areas on which a great deal of investment and activity has been applied in recent years and that are projected for continuous activity in the future.

Laws and decrees have been issued on such control activities for natural resources as forests, water, soil conservation, and wildlife, covering utilization of these resources for both economic exploitation and recreation. A cadastral survey program has been under way since 1960 but has covered only small portions of Venezuela. Nor have the other control activities been implemented sufficiently to provide adequate national coverage.

The progress made in basic resource evaluation and development (especially with respect to irrigation and drainage systems) and control activities and services is summarized below.

Evaluation of Basic Natural Resources

Reconnaissance-type resource evaluation studies including descriptive maps of soils, vegetation, land use, and other ecological conditions, together with some general economic analyses, have been prepared

for approximately 40 per cent of the land area of
Venezuela. Very few other Latin American countries
have exerted equal or greater effort in the scientific ordering of the basic resource information that
is essential for adequate analysis of resource potentials and future development.[2]

In addition, a general ecological map or Venezuela has been prepared by the Agricultural Investigation Center with the technical assistance of the
Inter-American Institute of Agricultural Sciences of
the Organization of American States. The Center has
also prepared a general map of the association of
great soil groups in Venezuela.

Medium- and small-scale (1:30,000 or smaller)
aerial photographic coverage is available for practically all of Venezuela in the Cartographic Office
of the Ministry of Development, and large-scale photo-
graphs have been taken of many of the land-development
areas involved in irrigation or industrial or urban
development.

Thus, significant progress has been made in basic
resource evaluation in recent years, and general descriptive material on the resources of Venezuela is
readily available. However, the same cannot be said
of the micro-economic and detailed information needed by farm operators to guarantee that changes in
production methods will have a reasonable possibility
of success. Research, practical trials, development
of necessary educational information in these reports,
and cadastral information are sadly lacking, as will
be described more fully in Chapter 7. The description
of land development activities in connection with the
agrarian reform program will be presented later in
this chapter.

Since 1960, several regional authorities have
been established in Venezuela to delegate some responsibility for resource development to the interior
areas of the country. The most active of these is the
Corporación Venezolana de Guayana (Venezuelan Guayana
Corporation, or CVG), which was established by the
Venezuelan Government to direct the integrated

development of the large electricity-generating systems and associated industrial complexes of steel and
aluminum, together with other resource development in
the eastern part of Venezuela (in the lower portion
of the Orinoco River basin). Other regional authorities have been established for the three Andean states
of Táchira, Mérida, and Trujillo (Development Corporation of the Andes, or CORPOANDES); for the three
West Central states of Lara, Falcón, and Yaracuy (Development Fund for West Central States, or FUDECO);
and for the state of Zulia (Planning Council for Zulia
State, or CONZUPLAN). Regional plans for the drainage of the southern part of Lake Maracaibo, roads,
and other developments have also been established with
special authorities within the Ministry of Public
Works. Similar special authorities have been established for the irrigation project of Las Majaguas in
the state of Portuguesa. Further, a special commission was established in 1965 to begin a long-range
analysis of the development possibilities of the large
Orinoco River basin area with its very limited population and means of access in the southern part of
Venezuela.

These regional authorities should provide some
additional impetus to the development of the natural
resources in the areas involved. However, with the
exception of the first one established (the CVG),
sufficient time has not passed to allow concrete results to be evident. Further, these regional authorities are dependent upon the Venezuelan Government
for funds, inasmuch as no decentralized taxing or
fund-raising authority has been given them.

Irrigation Development

It was indicated in Chapter 4 that almost one
fourth of the public appropriations made available
for agriculture during 1961-65 were expended in irrigation project development and maintenance. Large
investment in this activity is also projected for
future years. In the Plan of the Nation for 1965 to
1968, inclusive, Bs. 114.2 million are allocated to
technical studies of irrigation projects, Bs. 714.1
million are allocated to construction of such projects,

and Bs. 128.9 million are allocated to operation and
maintenance of these facilities, making a total of
Bs. 957.2 million (U.S. $212.7 million) of additional
funds included in the plan for irrigation works.

In Table 63 are presented data on the irrigation
projects and land areas under irrigation in 1965.

TABLE 63

Irrigation Systems and Land Areas Under
Irrigation in Venezuela, 1965

System	Hectares Under Irrigation	Total Irrigable Hectares in the System
El Guárico	37,200	110,000
El Cenizo	6,000	8,000
Suata-Taiguaiguay	8,000	8,000
Cumaná	2,000	2,500
San Carlos	3,000	4,000
El Tuy	1,340	1,340
Cojedes-Sarare (Las Majaguas)	9,700	30,000[a]
Guanare	1,000	7,700
Guanapito	4,000	4,000
Total	72,240	175,540

[a]Additional development in later steps could reach
90,000 hectares.

Source: 1965 Agricultural Statistics Annual, Ministry of Agriculture and Livestock.

As shown in Table 63, 72,240 hectares were under
irrigation in 1965 in the nine irrigation systems
then in operation. Over half this area had been developed for irrigation during the preceding five
years. (In 1961, the total area under irrigation was
34,574 hectares.) For the three-year period from
1966 to 1968, inclusive, additional areas of 149,900

hectares were projected in the <u>Plan of the Nation</u> for irrigation development, including 80,000 hectares to be reclaimed by drainage projects in the southern Maracaibo Lake basin and in the Orinoco River delta areas.

Irrigation development is a costly process in Venezuela, and operating procedures and management for the operating facilities still have not been worked out on a basis of self-liquidation of either construction or operating and maintenance costs; therefore, these projects constitute a continuing drain on the national treasury. However, because of the climatic conditions in most tropical areas, which are characterized by a well-defined wet season fol-lowed by a dry season of from four to seven months' duration in most of the more level areas, irrigation is essential for intensive continuous use of the land for agricultural production. Generally speaking, the physical basis exists for many economically sound irrigation systems that will assist materially in in-creasing agricultural production and the use of modern production techniques. At the same time, some observers have expressed the opinion that too much emphasis is being given to this phase of agricultural development in Venezuela and that all the technical facts are not available to justify fully all the large investments currently being applied to this ac-tivity.

Natural Resource Control and Conservation Services

Educational, research, and administrative control services with regard to natural resources are some-what dispersed among several different governmental entities. Some of these services have been in opera-tion for two or three decades, but none of them has had adequate support, either in funds or trained personnel, to allow them to give national coverage. However, institutional services are available that would be expanded rapidly to provide national cover-age when public conscience and demand required that more attention be paid to the rational use and pro-tection of natural resources. Unfortunately, some animal species and some picturesque natural wonders

will probably be destroyed before the public conscience demands their protection for future generations.

The educational, research, and administrative
control agencies concerned with natural resources in
Venezuela are the following:

Soil Management and Conservation

Ministry of Agriculture and Livestock, Department of Natural Resources, Soil and Water Conservation Division, for general control and conservation
projects.

Land Department, National Agrarian Institute, for
colonization and land development activities related
thereto.

Ministry of Public Works, Department of Hydraulic
Works, Division of Pedology, for land development in
irrigation projects.

Forest Conservation and Control

Ministry of Agriculture and Livestock, Department
of Natural Resources.

a. Division of Forest Management for Control of
   Forest Exploitation.
b. Division of Investigation for research in
   silviculture.

National Laboratory of Forest Products at Mérida,
maintained by the Ministry of Agriculture and Livestock and the University of the Andes.

Inter-American Forest Institute at Mérida, maintained by the government of Venezuela and the Organization of American States.

Corporación Venezolana de Guayana, Department
for Land Reclamation and Agricultural and Forestry
Development, for projects in the lower Orinoco River
basin in eastern Venezuela.

Water Resource Control and Development

Ministry of Public Works, Department of Hydraulic Works, Divisions of Planning, Hydrometeorology, and Edafology.

National Institute of Sanitary Works for urban water systems.

Ministry of Agriculture and Livestock, Section of Agricultural Engineering for well and dam development on individual farm units.

Ministry of Defense, Air Force Command, Hydro-meteorology Service.

Inter-American Center for Water and Land Resources, which engages in research and higher education activities, is maintained by the Organization of American States and the government of Venezuela.

Wildlife and Recreation Services

Ministry of Agriculture and Livestock, Department of Renewable Natural Resources.

   a. Fauna Division, Biological Station at
      Rancho Grande.
   b. Section for National Parks.

Ministry of Development, Corporación Nacional de Hoteles y Turismo for sponsoring conservation and use of scenic resources.

Distribution and Market Facilities

Although Venezuela is far ahead of many other Latin American countries in establishing good roads and other facilities and in attracting significant investment to some food-processing industries, Venezuela's food distribution from producers to consumers is characterized by few strong points and many weak ones. (The principal discussion of this subject will be in Chapter 8, which examines obstacles to Venezuela's agricultural development.)

Marketing of agricultural products is a critical
problem in most areas of the world, and clear-cut
paths leading to the solution of these problems as
they occur in varying circumstances have not been
found. Over-all policies and methods of implementing
them must be developed; in the meantime, piecemeal
efforts or the undue influence of some special interest groups in attempting to protect their control of
certain aspects of the distribution process create
more inequities and problems than are eradicated.

A great deal more research and application of high-
level technical and administrative skills are required
in the food distribution fields. At the same time,
some positive progress is evident in certain aspects
of marketing and the development of facilities necessary for efficient food distribution, summarized below.

Road Facilities

As mentioned previously, there are over 14,000 kilometers of paved roads in Venezuela, uniting all the
major population centers. Additional rural access
roads are needed, and continuous work on construction
of such penetration roads has been going on. Road facilities and construction activities between 1959 and
1965 are summarized in Table 64.

Agricultural Cooperatives

The activity of agricultural marketing cooperatives has not reached significant proportions,
although some consumers' cooperatives and marketing
cooperatives, together with some production cooperatives, have been established since 1958. The number
of cooperatives registered with the Ministry of Agriculture and Livestock, according to the Agricultural
Statistics Annual of that Ministry for 1965, are as
follows: 1960 and before, 7; 1961, 3; 1962, 4;
1963, 4; 1964, 5; and 1965, 7. All of these cooperative organizations are not directly concerned with
marketing or other distribution activities, but it is
probable that the major portion are involved in some
aspect of marketing. However, their influence in
improving general marketing efficiency for agricultural
products is not yet clearly evident.

TABLE 64

Main Roads in Service and Rural Access Roads
Constructed in Venezuela, 1959–65
(Kilometers)

Builder	Type of Road	1959	1960	1961	1962	1963	1964	1965
Ministry of Public Works[a]	trunk roads	-	-	-	8,398	7,880	8,220	8,295
Ministry of Public Works[a]	freeways	-	-	-	165	209	239	307
Ministry of Public Works[a]	local roads	-	-	-	5,713	5,496	5,652	5,719
Ministry of Public Works[a]	other national roads	-	-	-	2,369	2,852	3,991	4,125
Cooperatives[a]	local access	-	-	-	-	1,293	1,539	1,829
Individuals[a]	local access	-	-	-	3,556	4,257	3,170	3,227
Ministry of Agriculture and Livestock[b]	rural access	1,553	1,809	874	840	835	1,087	728
National Agrarian Institute[b]	rural access	-	602	307	457	2,160	614	526

[a]Roads in service.
[b]Kilometers constructed during the year.
Source: 1965 Agricultural Statistics Annual, Ministry of Agriculture and Livestock.

176

Market Facilities for Agricultural Products

Some sort of market place exists in practically all of the 635 municipal (municipio)[3] political subdivisions in Venezuela that are open usually one day or more per week for the purpose of concentrating the agricultural products and other products for sale at both wholesale and retail levels. The nature of these markets and their facilities vary considerably, with some operated as farmers' free markets and others operated by regular commercial concessionares who rent space from the municipality on a permanent or temporary basis. In the larger population centers, there are several of these municipal markets. In Caracas, there are sixteen of these market places, operated by the government-sponsored Markets, Silos, and Cold Storage Corporation (MERSIFRICA), which also operates the large wholesale Coche Market, which serves the many retail grocery stores of the city. The city of Maracaibo is the only other city that has a semblance of a wholesale market, and a new location and new buildings are projected for construction. The city of Barquisimeto is also planning the construction of a specialized wholesale market facility.

The aforementioned municipal markets are the traditional urban and town outlets for agricultural products. Most of them lack adequate sanitary and space facilities. Consequently, they are not attractive to see and constitute traffic bottlenecks in most cities, but they apparently still provide the consumer with the type of service demanded at present.

In recent years, several large chains of supermarkets have been established in the cities of Venezuela. Some of these are starting to buy directly from producers on a contract basis and are establishing transportation and storage facilities to accommodate these arrangements.

With respect to the marketing of animal products, the slaughter facilities are under the control of the municipalities, which, in practically all cases, provide only rudimentary facilities. Only at Turmero, in the state of Aragua, and the Frigorifico Industrializado de

Bolivar slaughterhouse in the state of Zulia have facilities been established for large-scale handling of
slaughter and meat processing with some utilization of
by-products. The Venezuelan Development Corporation
plans to build a network of six integrated meat-packing
plants, but these plants are not yet in service.

The facilities for the marketing of milk products
are tied in with nineteen large pasteurizing and five
powdered milk processing plants, with total capacities
of 102,000 liters of milk and 6,500 kilograms of powdered milk per hour, respectively. The industry is
subject to a great deal of government control with
respect to a producers' subsidy program and maximum
price control for consumers' prices. The pasteurizing plants are relatively new and have fairly modern
facilities. However, the subsidy program policies,
although inducing a fairly significant increase in
milk production, have tended to permit continuance of
high-cost producing units because of lack of application of the true principles relating to investment
aimed at improving production systems. Moreover,
there is a constant crisis with respect to policies
to be followed, and widely differing arguments are
presented by the various interests involved.

As stated in the beginning of this section, the
lack of organization and clear-cut policies with respect to marketing and distribution constitutes one
of the greatest present obstacles to agricultural
development in Venezuela. It is clear that research
and management resources and talents must be greatly
increased in this important phase of the agricultural
economy.

Agricultural Credit Facilities

The Venezuelan Government has provided a prepon-
derantly large proportion of the credit made available
to agriculture on a formal and institutionalized basis.
The amount of such credit has been relatively large
on a per farm basis in comparison with other Latin
American countries but is still considered to be far
short of the real needs for a progressive agricultural

sector. Private banks and other institutionalized
lenders have not entered the agricultural credit
field to any significant extent because they have
found that urban and industrial uses provide higher
returns and greater security than agriculture could
provide in the past. Also, the banking laws in existence greatly restrict the private banks, in such
items as length of repayment schedules and types of
guarantees required. The needs of agriculture do not
fit within these restrictions, so agricultural loans
are usually not considered by these private institutions.

Private lenders, of course, do operate in rural
areas and are principally storekeepers who advance
food and supplies to farmers on the storekeepers'
terms (which are seldom made public, so no quantification of the amounts involved has been made). In
recent years, increasing amounts of credit have been
provided by machinery dealers, processing plants, and
feed suppliers. These amounts have not been quantified by any global statistics but are not believed
to have reached significant amounts in relation to
the amounts loaned by the Venezuelan Government
through the Agricultural and Livestock Bank (BAP) and
other special programs, including the Rural Housing
Service, described later in this chapter. Since 1960,
the BAP has been encouraging private institutions to
get into some agricultural financing by guaranteeing
loans made by private institutions. These loans have
been utilized, to some extent, in financing such industrial crops as tobacco, sesame, and cotton, and,
in 1965, amounted to to 12 million bolivars (mostly
for cotton, which accounted for about 3 per cent of
total loans authorized by the BAP). Private credit
institutions have also collaborated in partially
financing machinery purchases, where BAP provides the
purchaser with a down payment and a guarantee for the
balance. Such transactions amounted to Bs. 20 million
in 1965, as shown in the annual report of the BAP.

The following summary of the credit made available to agriculture covers only the credit activities
of the BAP.

Practically all of the regular loans of the BAP
to farmers in Venezuela are limited to annual production loans, in accordance with the expressed policy
of the bank directors that, with the limited credit
funds available (the demand for loans from the bank
far exceeds the funds available each year), it is
better to restrict their use to annual operating
loans than to tie up large sums in medium- and long-
term loans. The amounts loaned each year have been
increasing during 1961-65, with large increases evidenced in 1964 and 1965, when total amounts of loans
approved were over 350 million bolivars. However,
the number of farmers receiving loans did not substantially increase in 1964 and declined in 1965,
even though amounts of loans approved were almost 90
per cent more than the previous three years.

In Table 65, the number of loans approved and the
total amounts approved for the period 1961-65 are
shown for all types of loans processed through BAP,
including its "own account" loans and those authorized by special government programs.

TABLE 65

Total Number and Amounts of Loans Approved
by Venezuela's Agricultural and
Livestock Bank, 1961-65

Year	Number (1,000)	Increase Per Cent	Amount (Million Bs.)	Increase (Per Cent)
1961	70.5	–	186.4	–
1962	76.0	7.8	198.5	6.5
1963	73.8	-2.9	191.1	-3.7
1964	75.2	1.9	351.6	84.0
1965	61.7	-18.0	350.9	-0.2

Source: Annual reports of the Agricultural and Livestock Bank of Venezuela for 1961-65.

Assuming that each recipient of BAP loans received
only one loan during the year, approximately 22 per
cent of the farm units of Venezuela received credit

from the BAP, which is a large share for one credit
institution to extend.

Three main categories of loans are made by the
BAP to farmers in Venezuela:

1.   Campesino Loans.

These are small loans made to family farmers
under the agrarian reform program and are limited
generally to Bs. 5,000 each, with the exception
of loans made under the supervised credit program,
which will be described later. During 1961-65,
an average of almost 90,000 loan requests were
received by the BAP, for a total amount of almost
Bs. 200 million per year. However, the BAP approved loans to an average of only 71 per cent of
those soliciting loans each year and in amounts
of 66 per cent of the sum asked for. The average
loan approved amounted to only Bs. 1,167 per borrower, of which only 76 per cent was actually
paid out to the borrower. These loans were practically all for annual operating expenses; little
financial assistance was provided for adjustments
in the productive structure of the farms. Interest was generally 3 per cent, as prescribed by
the Agrarian Reform Law, but there were some exceptions.

2.   Empresarial Farm Loans.

These are production loans made in amounts
of more than Bs. 5,000 each to farmers with more
commercial operations. During 1961-65, an average of 7,848 loan applications were received for
an amount of about Bs. 183 million per year. The
BAP approved loans to 83 per cent of these appli-
cants and approved 63 per cent of the amount
solicited, of which 93 per cent was actually paid
out to the borrower. The average loan paid out
by the BAP to each borrower was Bs. 16,490. These
loans also included only very small amounts for
basic adjustments in the productive structure of
the farms. Principally, they were loans for annual production costs for specific products.

Interest rate varied with the size of the loan in an ascending scale but generally it was 6 per cent.

3. Special Government Credit Programs.

These programs make available, through the Ministry of Agriculture and Livestock, special long-term loans for adjusting the basic productive structure of the farms, in order to further livestock development, fisheries and coffee and cocoa farm reorganization, and the production of such items as fruits and sisal. Special funds were deposited in the BAP by the Ministry of Agriculture and Livestock to cover these loans. During the period 1961-65, an average of 1,467 coffee and cocoa loans were made and advanced, for a total of Bs. 10.1 million per year or an average of Bs. 6,914 per loan. During the same period, an average of 137 livestock development loans were made and advanced in the amount of Bs. 40 million per year, or an average of Bs. 292,270 per loan. Interest rates for livestock loans were 4 per cent, and for coffee-cocoa loans, 6 per cent. Repayment of principal can be extended over sixteen years.

A special supervised credit program was started in Venezuela in 1963, through an international loan from the United States Agency for International Development (USAID) of Bs. 45 million, which was matched by the BAP. The Consejo de Bienestar Rural provided a training program for the BAP credit technicians in conjunction with this program. The loan program provided possibilities for integrated farm financing for annual operating expenses, medium-term financing for livestock and machinery purchase, and long-term financing for permanent farm improvements. As indicated previously, the regular BAP credit activities practically excluded financing for medium- and long-term farm improvements, which are badly needed by farmers to improve the efficiency of their production efforts. These loans are limited to Bs. 34,000 for individual loans

and Bs. 68,000 for cooperative associations. The
statistics for these loans (made since 1963) are
included in the campesino category above. However, the importance of a more integrated credit
service to meet all the needs for adjusting the
productive patterns of farm units is well demonstrated, and this special program is considered
a good start in providing complete credit service
to family farmers. The supervised credit loans
made since the initiation of this program are
summarized in Table 66.

TABLE 66

Supervised Credit Program Agricultural Loans
Made in Venezuela, 1963-65

Year	Number of Loans Approved	Amount Approved (Bs. 1,000)	Amount Actually Advanced to Borrowers (Bs. 1,000)[a]
1963	471	8,729	2,253
1964	1,861	39,889	23,677
1965	2,397	47,066	34,331
Total	4,729	95,684	60,261

[a]Loans approved provide for delayed disbursement of
 credit funds as needed by the borrower for permanent
 improvements and purchases.

Source: Annual reports of the Agricultural and Live-
         stock Bank for 1963-65.

Approximately one half of the supervised credit
funds advanced was utilized for medium- or long-term
farm improvement purposes. The other half was for
annual operating expenses, including some items for
family subsistence during the production cycle.

A summary of BAP credit related to principal crop
and livestock enterprises is included later in this

chapter in connection with material presented on
prospects for development of specific agricultural
products.

The BAP has had many problems of a policy and
administrative nature that have adversely affected
its service to Venezuelan farmers. Due to such factors as frequent shifts in management, a multiplicity
of responsibilities for administering programs not
directly concerned with agricultural credit that tend
to divert resources and management from the credit
business, and inadequate business systems and management, a significant portion of the capital that has
been made available to BAP by the Venezuelan Government has been lost. Most of the old uncollectable
accounts are carried on the books of the bank, and
they have achieved a size that will require a major
campaign to bring the records up to date and remove
the dead accounts. The authorized capital of BAP
was initially Bs. 30 million, which was provided by
the Venezuelan Government when the bank was organized
in 1928. The authorized capital was increased over
the years to a total of Bs. 167 million, where it has
remained for many years. However, the amounts of
annual appropriations to the bank, in excess of operating costs, together with assignment of funds for
special credit programs of the Ministry of Agriculture and Livestock, have increased the total loan fund
account or loan portfolio to more than Bs. 1.1 billion
This is made up of what the bank reports as its "own
account" and the special deposits from the Ministry
of Agriculture and Livestock for the mentioned development programs for livestock, coffee, and cocoa. In
Table 67 is presented the distribution of these funds
and their accumulation from 1961 to 1965.

Virtually all of the "own account" funds of the
bank have been utilized only for annual operating loan
purposes during the last thirty years. Consequently,
if the accounts were properly maintained, if uncollectable loans were written off periodically and if
efficient collection methods were utilized, practically the entire amount of the indicated "own account"
funds theoretically should be available as a revolv-
ing fund for annual production loans each year for

TABLE 67

Total Funds in the Loan Portfolio of Venezuela's Agricultural and
Livestock Bank, 1961-65

Year	Total Loan Fund Portfolio at End of Year (Million Bs.)	"Own Account" Portfolio[b]		Special Venezuelan Government Funds[c]	
		Amount (Million Bs.)	Per Cent of Total	Amount (Million Bs.)	Per Cent of Total
1961	631	466	74	165	26
1962	730	519	71	211	29
1963	832	567	68	265	32
1964	1,002[a]	682	68	320	32
1965	1,146[a]	751	66	395	34

[a]Figures were adjusted downward in official reports for the totals for 1964 and 1965 but "own account" and special government fund items were not adjusted downward. Totals shown in Table 67 are for the sum of the two parts and are slightly higher than those appearing in the Annual Reports of BAP for 1964 and 1965.

[b]Includes funds for campesino loans, including supervised credit loans, empresarial loans, and other miscellaneous portfolio accounts of BAP.

[c]Includes loans made for livestock and coffee and cocoa development under the special plans of the Ministry of Agriculture and Livestock and BAP.

Source: Annual reports of the Agricultural and Livestock Bank for 1961-65.

185

campesino and empresarial loans. However, this is
not the case. Almost half of the loan funds advanced
during 1961-65 were made from new injections of money
from the Venezuelan Government or from loans from
USAID and the Inter-American Development Bank. This
fact is illustrated in Table 68.

As shown in Table 68, campesino and empresarial
loans have decreased from 27 per cent of the portfolio
of these accounts in 1961 to 18 per cent in 1964 and
19 per cent in 1965. However, the amounts collected
were reloaned only in 1962 of the five years presented in the table. It is clear that from 75 per cent
to 80 per cent of the total "own account" loan fund
portfolio of the BAP is immobilized in delinquent
loans, a large portion of which are uncollectable.

Further, the direct cost of credit activities
provided by the BAP is considerably higher than interest income, although the handling of interest income
is obscure in the bank's annual reports. The official
bank statements show losses of Bs. 10 million or more
per year during 1961-65. Although a reserve for bad
debts of Bs. 158 million is carried in the bank financial statements, this was not adjusted in 1961-65,
and bad debt write-offs are not included in the loss
figures reported. The total annual direct administrative costs of credit operations of the BAP is compared with the total portfolio and other factors for
1961-65 in Table 69.

It is clear that the administration and results
of the operations of the BAP do not meet reasonable
expectations for a business operation and that a reorganization of the capital and loan fund structure
is called for. Legislation was enacted in 1968 to
assign the empresarial loaning function to an agricultural development bank, leaving the campesino loans
and other more sociologically oriented activities to
the BAP. Also, a law has been proposed to set up a
marketing corporation to take over the commodity
storage, price-support, and other marketing activities
of the BAP. However, there has been considerable
public reaction against the proposed marketing law.

TABLE 68

Source of Loan Funds Utilized by Venezuela's Agricultural and Livestock Bank for "Own Account" Loans, 1961-65

Year	Total "Own Account" Portfolio at End of Year (Million Bs.)	Principal Recuperation on "Own Account" Loans		Total Amount of These Loans Advanced During the Year (Million Bs.)	Source of Funds Loaned Each Year			
		Amount (Million Bs.)	Per Cent of Portfolio		New Appropriations of the Venezuelan Government (Million Bs.)	External Financing (Million Bs.)[a]	From Existing Portfolio	
							Amount (Million Bs.)	Per Cent of Portfolio
1961	466	125	27	128	59	0	69	15
1962	519	123	24	175	51	0	124	24
1963	567	115	20	152	35	64	53	9
1964	682	124	18	219	32	56	131	19
1965	751	143	19	215	42	78	95	14

[a]Loans from USAID and the Inter-American Development Bank.

Source: Annual reports of the Agricultural and Livestock Bank for 1961-65.

187

TABLE 69

Comparison of Total Administrative Costs of Credit Operations of Venezuela's
Agricultural and Livestock Bank with Total Loan Fund Portfolio,
Loan Funds Advanced, and Amounts Collected, 1961-65

Year	Total Administrative Costs of Credit Operations (Million Bs.)	Percentage Relation of Costs to:		
		Total Loan Fund Portfolio	Total Loan Funds Advanced During Year	Total Principal Collections
1961	33	5	18	26
1962	27	4	12	22
1963	30	4	14	26
1964	33	3	12	25
1965	37	3	14	24

Source: Calculated from annual reports of the Agricultural and Livestock Bank
for 1961-65.

Agrarian Reform Services

The Venezuelan Agrarian Reform Law, which became effective in March, 1960, provides that the National Agrarian Institute (IAN), an autonomous government agency established as a branch of the Ministry of Agriculture and Livestock, will be the executing agency for this law. However, the law also specifies participation of several other government agencies in this activity and provides certain coordination functions required to utilize the services of these various government entities. Many of the activities of the Ministry of Agriculture and Livestock and the Agricultural and Livestock Bank are directly related to agrarian reform activities and are so indicated in their annual budgets. Also, Article 162 of the Agrarian Reform Law directs that the Board of Directors of IAN will meet in November of each year with members of the Ministries of Treasury, Development, Public Works, Education, Agriculture, Sanitation and Social Assistance, Labor, and Justice, along with the director of the National Office for Planning and Coordination, the presidents of the Central Bank of Venezuela and the Venezuelan Development Corporation, the managing directors of the Agricultural and Livestock Bank, the director of the National Nutrition Institute, and representatives of any other organization as may be necessary for the purpose of projecting and coordinating the budget planning for the coming year for investments and activities related to agrarian reform.

The aim of the law is to provide broad authorizations for adjustments in the agrarian structure (concerned principally with redistribution of land resources to people who work the land) and for integrated development of agricultural methods to improve production, productivity, income levels, and general welfare of families operating medium- and small-sized farm units. These goals were implemented with significant government funds both before and after the law became effective in 1960.

The agrarian reform program has been the subject of considerable controversy, and some observers have stated that it has been utilized as a tool to pacify

rural areas with inadequate technical advances, scientific analysis, and planning with respect to the ecological and economic factors in the work and projects
attempted.

During the first few years after the law was
passed, a large amount of the funds appropriated was
utilized for land acquisition from private individ-
uals and the purchase of improvements from squatters
on publicly owned property to provide a land base for
the ambitious colonization programs and the relocation
of farm people into rural communities. During 1963-
65, the policy of IAN was to hold down new acquisitions and projects and to concentrate on consolidating
the projects already started, providing improvements
and facilities necessary for the production efforts
of the families who were assigned new farm parcels
before these facilities were available.

Since 1958, the annual budgets of IAN have varied
between 100 million and 200 million bolivars per year.
From July 1, 1958 to the end of 1965, the total expenditures of IAN were more than 1 billion bolivars.
(At the exchange rate of 4.50 dollars, this amounts to
$233,380,000.) In addition, substantial funds have
been applied directly to the agrarian reform program
by the Ministries of Agriculture and Livestock, Public
Works, Education, and Sanitation and Social Assistance,
along with the Agricultural Bank of Venezuela, for
which complete quantification is not yet possible with
respect to actual application to agrarian reform.
Also, the Agrarian Institute issued government bonds
in the approximate amount of Bs. 195.7 million during
1960-65, the proceeds from which have been utilized
for land and permanent improvement acquisitions, in
addition to annual budget figures. Table 70 presents
a summary of expenditures by IAN for land acquisition
and the purchase of permanent improvements, together
with rural community investments and sums spent for
land development on the farm parcels.

The total shown in Table 70 for investments by
IAN in land acquisitions and various types of permanent improvements since 1958 amounts to Bs. 728.5
million. Deducting the bonds utilized for land purchase in the amount of Bs. 195.7 million leaves Bs.

532.8 million for these purposes, which is 49 per
cent of the total appropriated funds available to IAN
during the period. (The other 51 per cent was apparently utilized in administration expenses.) Included
in operating costs are contributions to the Federation
of Farmers' Syndicates (Federación Campesina), which
receives substantial support from IAN.

TABLE 70

Expenditures of Venezuela's National Agrarian
Institute for the Physical Resource Base
for Land Settlements, 1959-65
(Million Bs.)

Year	Land Improvements and Purchases[a]	Community Infrastructure Development	Land Development	Total for Land and Improvements
1959	N.D.	N.D.	N.D.	1.1
1960	108.0	13.0	6.6	127.6
1961	82.2	37.5	25.2	144.9
1962	48.6	15.1	53.5	117.2
1963	71.3	6.6	8.9	86.8
1964	67.7	14.6	8.0	140.4
1965	52.7	34.4	23.4[b]	110.5
Total	-	-	-	728.5

[a] Includes amounts obtained from Venezuelan Government
agrarian bonds issued for land acquisitions in the
following amounts (Bs. million): 1960, 66.5; 1961,
42.4; 1962, 25.4; 1963, 15.9; 1964, 17.4; 1965, 28.0.

[b] Includes, for 1965, Bs. 13.7 million from a loan
from the Inter-American Development Bank.

Source: Annual reports of National Agrarian Institute
and Ministry of Agriculture and Livestock for
1959-65.

As indicated in Chapter 5, IAN reports that
118,737 farm families have been directly benefited by

agrarian reform activities during the period 1959-65.
The total budget of IAN during this period was
Bs. 1,090 million plus Bs. 195.7 million in agrarian
bonds, which indicates an average cost to IAN of almost Bs. 11,000 per family settled up to the end of
1965. This, of course, does not include the substantial costs of other government agencies applied directly to these items. For example, the principal
costs of housing and large contributions for main
roads and irrigation and drainage works that were
provided by the Rural Housing Service of the Ministry
of Sanitation and the Ministry of Public Works, respectively, are not included, nor are the annual production loans provided by the Agricultural Bank of
Venezuela, a large proportion of which have not been
repaid.

Surveys made in sixteen states between 1963 and
1965 in connection with the supervised credit program
indicated that less than 10 per cent of the farm parcels on land settlements were in adequate condition
for reasonably efficient family farm operations. The
others were deficient because of inadequate size, lack
of access roads, lack of sufficient deforested areas
or good soils, lack of essential irrigation and drainage facilities, title problems, and other reasons.
Although the production on farms of these settlements
has not reached the degree of intensity originally
planned, efforts have continued to consolidate these
settlements and to provide them with essential facilities. The agricultural production on these farms,
according to official IAN Annual Reports, is summarized
in Table 71 for the period from 1961 to 1965.

As shown in Table 71, the average value of total
farm production per family in 1964 and 1965 of
Bs. 4,015 and Bs. 3,791, respectively, is less than
half the average farm production of Venezuela, which
was over Bs. 8,000 in 1965. In fact, the gross value
of farm production shown in Table 71 for these two
years is only slightly higher than the average net
income per farm family in Venezuela, which, as shown
in Chapter 5, was about Bs. 3,500 in 1965. Also,
there was a reduction between 1964 and 1965 in the
value of production per family in the IAN settlements.

TABLE 71

Value of Agricultural Production of Farms in Settlements Established
by Venezuela's National Agrarian Institute, 1961-65

Year	Hectares Harvested (1,000)	Value of Crop Production (Million Bs.)	Value of Livestock Production (Million Bs.)	Total Value of Production (Million Bs.)	Cumulative Number of Families[a]	Value of Production Per Family (Bs.)
1961	161	106	9	115	42,169	2,727
1962	208	137	17	154	56,772	2,713
1963	254	182	20	202	66,426	3,041
1964	287	242	71	313	77,955	4,015
1965	347	352	97	449	118,737	3,791

[a]Number of families benefited since 1958.

Source: Annual reports of the National Agrarian Institute and Ministry of Agriculture
and Livestock for 1961-65.

The value of production from these settlement farms,
according to the IAN figures, constituted 13 per cent
of the total agricultural production of Venezuela in
1965, whereas the number of farms on settlements constituted over one third of the farm units of Venezuela.

The average amount of land in production per farm
unit in the agrarian reform settlements in 1965 was
2.9 hectares, which definitely is too limited in view
of the fact of the general lack of intensive production practices and of intensive crops on these farms.
On the other hand, the total amount of land included
in farm parcels in 1965 was over 2.6 million hectares,
which is 22.6 hectares per parcel, on the average.
With only 11 per cent of this area in production, the
land selection process apparently has not resulted in
a reasonable proportion of good productive land and
land development for production has lagged excessively
behind needs of the families already located on these
parcels.

It is clear that the families on IAN settlements
still have not achieved sufficient production levels
for satisfactory standards of living, as intended by
the Agrarian Reform Law, but some progress is starting
to become evident.

PRIVATE SERVICES OF AN INSTITUTIONAL NATURE
AVAILABLE TO FARMERS

In addition to the description of private services
and facilities available to agriculture that is presented in Chapter 4 and in Tables 34 and 36, some
additional private agency services have made and are
making important contributions to agricultural development in Venezuela. Available information is not complete in this respect, but some indicators of private
agency activities can be presented.

Private Research and Extension Agencies

The Shell Foundation, through its Service to Farmers, which has been located at Cagua in the state of

Aragua since 1950, has been carrying on significant
work in both research and demonstration in connection
with improved agricultural production practices. A
large number of farmers from various parts of Venezuela have been included in demonstrational tours.
Technical bulletins and more popular farmers' bulletins have also been produced by this agency. In
recent years, an intensive demonstrational extension
service, working with farmers in land settlement colonies and adjacent areas, has been initiated in the
states of Zulia and Falcón. These states are showing
favorable results in improving incomes and living
levels among subsistence farmers, who are the most
difficult to reach with extension programs.

    The Consejo de Bienestar Rural (Rural Welfare
Council, or CBR), which has been operating as a private
nonprofit agency in Venezuela since 1947, has made
significant contributions to agricultural development
in both the research and extension fields and has established demonstrational action programs in rural
areas. This agency was initiated by the American
International Association in 1948 and soon developed
into a mixed government- and private agency-financed
organization. It has participated over the years in
many of the technical assistance programs for the
principal official agricultural agencies of Venezuela
and is now largely financed by them. Training programs for farmers and agricultural technicians that
have been conducted by CBR have included demonstrational action programs in supervised credit, direct
extension, community center development, circulation
of technical information on agriculture, and mechanization (both motorized and animal drawn). Also, CBR
has provided a steady flow of technical information
bulletins, pamphlets, and leaflets for its sponsoring
agencies, together with technical manuals in credit,
home economics, agricultural economics, and agricultural mechanization. The CBR provided most of the
significant research and analysis reports of an agricultural economics nature that have been prepared
since 1950, and these are available to important agricultural industries and to organizations concerned
with general and specific agricultural problems. It
initiated, in collaboration with its sponsoring

agencies and some other government agencies, an effective system of making basic interdisciplinary regional agricultural resource surveys to assess the agricultural potential of these resources. Such surveys were planned and executed by CBR for eight important regions in Venezuela, and the first reconnaissance-type land use, soil, forestry, and ecological maps were prepared for these regions as part of these surveys. Many of the leaders in the agricultural agencies of Venezuela now have gone through a training process with this agency, either as employees or as participants in special study and training programs. The mixed financing arrangements between government and private entities and the fact that CBR is a private, nonprofit organization have enabled it to remain free from political implications that could have diminished CBR's effectiveness.

The Mendoza Foundation and some other business organizations of the Mendoza family have contributed to the research and informational aspects necessary for agricultural development in Venezuela. These entities have participated in the development of improved corn varieties and recently have been working in determining and selecting adapted soybean varieties for Venezuela. In 1966, the Foundation established an economic analysis section to carry on private investigations, independently and in collaboration with official agencies, into several important development and marketing aspects of the economy, including a survey of the implications of the Latin American Free Trade Association for Venezuelan products.

PROGRESS IN ADOPTION OF IMPROVED AGRICULTURAL TECHNOLOGY

The increased production of agricultural products in Venezuela is mainly due to the development and planting of additional land areas. Improved technology and methods of productivity have played a secondary role, as indicated in Chapter 5. However, approximately 5 per cent of the farms, which have 25 per cent of the crop land in Venezuela, use relatively advanced technology. Most of these farms are producers of crops for industrial use (sesame, cotton, sugar cane, and tobacco). Also, potatoes and such vegetables as tomatoes are produced with modern practices predominating in the total area cultivated.

Few quantitative measures are available for determining the extent of improvements in agricultural technology during 1961-65. In the following paragraphs, available data will be presented and will be followed by an evaluation of the status of technology by important crops and crop groups.

Mechanization in Agriculture

There is a wide range of modern farm machines and implements in use on farms in Venezuela, from simple pack-back spray rigs to large self-propelled harvesters for rice and cotton. Track-layer tractors are quite common, but the number of these imported into Venezuela has declined notably in the last four years compared to the last decade, dropping from 300 to 600 per year during the period from 1955 to 1959 to less than 100 per year during 1961-65. However, the number of wheel-type farm tractors and their implements has increased substantially, with importations running from 683 in 1961 to 1,009 in 1962; 1,954 in 1963; 2,039 in 1964; and 1,176 in 1965. Tractor plows imported varied between 400 and 1,360 per year between 1961 and 1964 but fell off to 173 in 1965. Disc harrows imported varied between 450 and 1,680 per year. Harvesting machines (principally for rice) were imported in numbers ranging from 55 to 123 per year.

Determination of the number of tractors existing on farms since the 1961 agricultural census, which showed 14,667 tractors on farms, can only be done by estimate. By adding the number of tractors imported each year after that date and deducting those imported seven years previously (on the assumption that tractors generally become inoperative after seven years), the estimates of tractors in use on farms between 1961 and 1965 were arrived at and are presented in Table 72.

The average annual rate of increase in the number of farm tractors between 1961 and 1965 was about 7.5

per cent, which is approximately the same rate that
agricultural production increased.

TABLE 72

Number and Types of Tractors in Use
on Venezuelan Farms, 1961-65

| Type of | Number of Tractors in Use | | | | |
Tractor	1961	1962	1963	1964	1965
Wheel and garden types	11,873	13,047	13,872	15,224	15,474
Annual increase, wheel tractors (per cent)	–	9.9	6.9	11.4	2.1
Track-layer types	2,794	2,349	2,053	1,473	1,299
Total	14,667	15,396	15,925	16,697	16,773

Source: Figures for 1961 from the agricultural
census. Other figures are estimates based
on adding number of tractors imported each
year and deducting those imported seven
years previously.

The Plan of the Nation 1965, prepared by the
CORDIPLAN, estimated that 26.18 per cent of the total
crop land was worked with machinery in 1965. Applying this same percentage to total crop land shown in
Table 45 for 1965 yields a figure of 411,800 hectares
as the total area tilled with machinery. The
CORDIPLAN source also provides a proportional distribution by major crop groups, which, applied to the
total crop land tilled with machinery, provides the
results shown in Table 73.

TABLE 73

Land Tilled with Machinery in Venezuela,
by Major Crops, 1965
(1,000 Has.)

Crop	Total Hectares Cultivated	Number of Hectares Tilled with Machinery	Per Cent of Total
Cereals	569.1	206.7	36.3
Legumes	108.2	1.2	1.1
Roots and tubers	69.7	14.4	20.6
Industrial crops[a]	241.4	176.7	73.2
Fruits and vegetables	174.7	12.8	7.3
Cocoa and coffee	410.0	b	b
Total	1,573.1	411.8	26.2

[a]Includes cotton, sesame, sugar cane, and tobacco.
[b]Only negligible areas have machinery for tilling the soil.
Source: See explanation in preceding text.

Some of the farms that have tractors have a pro-
fligate number of machines in order to perform land
preparation in a very short period so that they may
take advantage of most favorable climatic conditions;
the machines may be largely idle during the remainder
of the year. However, field observations have indicated that, on the average, each tractor is utilized
on 40 hectares of crop land each year. Applying this
figure to the total crop land worked with machinery,
the total number of tractors utilized is calculated
at 10,295. The balance of the tractors shown in Table
72 for 1965 is thus 6,478 (16,773-10,295), all of
which are assumed to be operated on the cultivated
pasture lands on cattle ranches. These pasture lands
amounted to 2,748,800 hectares, according to 1965
estimates. Utilizing these figures, the following
rates of tractor can be calculated for 1965:

Number of hectares of crop land worked
per tractor   40.0
Number of hectares of crop land in all
farms per tractor on crop farms   152.8
Number of tractors on crop farms per
1,000 hectares of crop land   6.5
Number of hectares of cultivated
pastures per tractor on livestock ranches   424.2
Number of tractors on livestock
ranches per 1,000 hectares of cultivated
pasture   2.4
Average number of tractors per 1,000
hectares of crop land and cultivated
pasture land   3.9

Use of Fertilizer

Tropical soils are usually deficient in some of
the essential nutrients necessary for plant growth
because of the generally rapid leaching of the soil
due to continuous relatively high soil temperatures
and rainfall patterns that provide excessive water
above the absorptive capacity of the soil during at
least some parts of the year in most areas. Consequently, production practices geared to high productivity per unit of land area practically always
require liberal use of fertilizers.

Venezuela had established before 1960 a
government-owned petrochemical plant (Venezuelan
Petrochemical Institute, or IVP) at Morón in the state
of Carabobo to produce, among other things, fertilizers. This autonomous institute, although beset with
many administrative and efficiency problems, has assumed the predominant role of supplying the fertitil-
izers for the crop land of Venezuela. In 1965, IVP
distributed over two thirds of the mixed fertilizer
formulas used in Venezuela; the other one third was
imported and distributed by other suppliers. However,
all of the potassium fertilizers are imported by IVP,
along with part of the phosphates. Nitrogen, phos-
phorous, and potassium, in their usual compounds for
use as specific fertilizers, were all distributed by
IVP for the first time in 1965. In previous years,
some of these individual element compounds were imported by private suppliers.

There has been a significant increase in the use
of fertilizers in Venezuela since 1960, especially
by producers of industrial crops, potatoes, and
fruits and vegetables. There has, however, been very
little development in the use of fertilizers on cultivated pastures, and there is only negligible use
of them on pastures at present.

The apparent consumption of fertilizers in Venezuela for the period 1961-65, expressed in metric tons
of the fertilizers as applied and also in terms of
the usable nutrients of the three most important elements, is shown in Table 74. As presented in Table
74, the total tonnage of fertilizers applied to crops
increased 66.9 per cent between 1961 and 1965.

As mentioned previously, the IVP claims that it
is selling fertilizers at its zonal distribution
points at less than cost, which is true, because the
annual deficits of the IVP have been made up by additional appropriations from the national treasury.
However, the petroleum-based products, especially
urea and other ammonia compounds, could probably be
produced by IVP at less than world prices. The plant
is also utilizing primary materials for part of the
phosphate products that are produced from mines in
the state of Falcón. Other materials are still imported, primarily from Germany. The prices in 1965
for the primary element compounds, sold in the form
ready for application to crops and delivered in paper
sacks (approximately 1 quintal or 100 pounds each)
to the various distribution points in Venezuela where
they are sold directly to farmers, are shown in Table
75, together with a calculation of the cost per kilogram of the principal available nutrients.

Practically speaking, in 1965 the cost of the
available nutrients combined was one bolivar per
kilogram, as shown in Table 75 (about $0.22 U.S.).
The increase in fertilizer costs during 1961-65 was
mentioned in the previous chapter as between 45 per
cent and 49 per cent, and was principally due to the
effect of the devalued bolivar on imported fertilizer
elements. Annual costs of these imports, in foreign
money, have risen about 10 per cent during the five-
year period.

TABLE 74

Use of Fertilizers in Venezuela, 1961–65

(Metric Tons)

Fertilizers as Applied to Crops

	Mixed Fertilizer Formulas		Individual Element Compounds		Total	
Year	Distributed by IVP	Distributed by Private Suppliers	Distributed by IVP	Distributed by Private Suppliers	Amount	Index of Increase
1961	23,801	18,493	15,382	11,716	69,392	100.0
1962	19,390	31,445	13,849	6,672	71,356	102.8
1963	17,310	28,594	14,299	23,905	84,108	121.2
1964	30,690	25,472	38,996	1,219	96,377	138.9
1965	47,882	22,032	45,872	–	115,786	166.9

Equivalents in Available Principal Nutrient Elements

	Nitrogen		Phosphorous		Potassium		Total Nutrients	
Year	Amount	Per Cent of Total Nutrients	Amount	Per Cent of Total Nutrients	Amount	Per Cent of Total Nutrients	Amount	Per Cent of Total Tonnage Applied
1961	8,703	37	5,930	25	8,917	38	23,550	34
1962	9,197	37	6,808	28	8,517	35	24,522	34
1963	11,592	44	5,853	23	8,695	33	26,140	31
1964	12,897	40	7,946	25	11,080	35	31,923	33
1965	15,801	43	9,301	25	11,503	32	36,605	32

Source: Unpublished data from Venezuelan Petrochemical Institute and calculations made by the author.

TABLE 75

Prices and Nutrient Content of Fertilizers
Sold by the Venezuelan Petrochemical
Institute, 1965

Product	Price per Metric Ton	Content of Principal Nutrient Elements
Urea	Bs. 438	46% N_2
Ammonium sulphate	270	20-21% N_2
Ammonium nitrate	225	20% N_2
Super phosphate	211	20% P_2O_5
Triple super phosphate	317	46% P_2O_5
Potassium chloride	401	60% K_2O
Potassium sulphate	427	50-52% K_2O

Weighted Average Price per Kilogram
of Available Nutrients

N_2	Bs. 1.32
P_2O_5	0.76
K_2O	0.77
All nutrients	0.99

Source: Special data provided by the Venezuelan
Petrochemical Institute. Price is wholesale
to farmers at distribution points maintained
by IVP.

The relation of the consumption of fertilizers
to the total crop land in Venezuela during the period
1961-65 is shown in Table 76, expressed in amounts of
available nutrients.

If cultivated pasture land (for which very little
fertilizer is utilized, as mentioned previously),
which amounted to 2,747,900 hectares in 1965, is added to the crop land for that year, the rate of use
per hectare of crop land and cultivated pastures is
8.05 kilograms.

TABLE 76

Fertilizer Nutrients Applied per Hectare of
Total Crop Land in Venezuela, 1961-65

Year	Total Available Nutrients Utilized (M.T.)	Has. of Crop Land (1,000)	Kgs. of Nutrients per Ha. of Crop Land
1961	23,550	1,307.9	18.0
1962	24,522	1,436.6	17.1
1963	26,140	1,490.4	17.5
1964	31,923	1,502.0	21.3
1965	36,605	1,573.2	23.3

Source: Special data provided by the Venezuelan
Petrochemical Institute. Unpublished data
from Venezuelan Petrochemical Institute and
calculations made by the author.

The incentives for utilizing fertilizer can be
calculated on the basis of the amount of important
crops at prices to farmers that was required to pay
for each kilogram of fertilizer nutrients. This calculation is made for the four important crops that require considerable fertilizer in Venezuela in Table 77

TABLE 77

Factors Determining Use of Fertilizer on Four
Important Venezuelan Crops, 1965

Crop	1965 Product Price to Farmers (Bs. per Kilogram)	Kilograms of Crop Required to Pay for 1 Kilogram of Fertilizer Nutrients[a]
Rice	0.60	1.65
Corn	0.38	2.60
Cotton (unginned)	1.20	0.83
Sesame	1.10	0.90

[a]Nutrient cost per kilogram is Bs. 0.99, as shown
 previously.
Source: Data from 1965 Agricultural Statistics
        Annual and calculations made by the author,
        using data from Table 75.

The above calculations can be applied in calculating the amout of increased yield that would be
required to pay for the fertilizer applied. For example, if 100 kilograms were to be applied per hectare
of rice, the yield would have to be increased by at
least 165 kilograms to pay for the fertilizer elements
only. In most cases, the margin is favorable for justifying more fertilizer use, based on available
technical data and the costs involved. However, fertilizer trials to determine optimum application rates
still have not been carried out in sufficient areas
and for all important crops by the controlled experimental methods that are needed for intelligent use of
fertilizers.

Use of Pesticides

The commercial farm operations in Venezuela utilize significant quantities of pesticides that include
insecticides, fungicides, herbicides, and various
products to treat and disinfect seeds and control and
repel rodents, as well as other disinfectants. Unfortunately, complete data on the local manufacture
and importation of these products are not available
to permit a complete quantification of the use of
pesticides in agriculture. A large portion of the
elements utilized is still imported, and some imported
items are processed into the products utilized on the
farm. There is not adequate separation of the available data to determine the quantity of imported products that is utilized in local manufacture and that
appears in the statistics as nationally manufactured
pesticides. Consequently, the summation of imports
and locally produced pesticides that appears in
available statistics does not represent the actual
use of these products.

The data available on the importation of various
types of pesticides is shown in Table 78. The importation of insecticides has been diminishing because of increased national production, although the
other products are still principally imported and
show substantial increases in importation and use.

The national production of insecticides, fungicides, and disinfectants (excluding herbicides), as

reported in the 1965 agricultural statistics summary
of the Ministry of Agriculture and Livestock during
the last five years, was as follows (in metric tons):
1961, 2,133; 1962, 4,015; 1963, 3,351; 1964, 5,754;
and 1965, 8,270.

It is clear that the use of herbicides increased
substantially in 1961-65, although, as stated previous
ly, precise data are not available. Insecticide and
fungicide use more than doubled during this five-year
period, whereas the use of herbicides has increased
tenfold during the same period.

TABLE 78

Importation of Pesticides into Venezuela,
1961-65 (Metric Tons)

Pesticide	1961	1962	1963	1964	1965
Insecticides	6,122	3,665	1,395	2,133	1,499
Fungicides	151	374	385	853	728
Herbicides	335	1,976	1,295	3,292	3,869
Other (rat poison, seed-treating products)	139	184	79	813	209

Source: 1965 Foreign Trade Statistics Annual, General
          Statistics Office, Ministry of Development
          (customs statistics).

Improved Seed Use

Improved seed development and control have been
carried out by the Ministry of Agriculture and Livestock for a limited number of field crops. Reproduction and certification of such seeds were usually
carried out on the agricultural experiment stations,
but since 1964 private producers, through Protinal,
C.A., a private corporation, have been collaborating
with the Center of Agricultural Investigation (CIA) in
the reproduction of improved varieties developed by
CIA. This agency makes the inspections of and certifie

the seed requirements. The industrial crops of cotton
and sesame have a fairly high incidence in the use
of certified seed (more than 70 per cent of total
planted areas), but for most other crops, the use of
registered or certified seed is low (less than 30
per cent of total planted areas). Significant increases have been made in recent years for crops for
which certified seed is available. The production
of certified seed during the period 1961-65 is indicated in Table 79.

Livestock Breeding Improvements

In 1965, there were 58 privately owned, specialized cattle breeding farms with a total of 11,895
head of high-quality animals, together with two purebred breeding farms maintained by the Ministry of
Agriculture and Livestock with 1,977 head of cattle.
Also, there were artificial insemination centers in
operation in the states of Lara (Carora) and Miranda
(El Laurel) with a total of 26 purebred bulls of
dairy breeds, principally Brown Swiss. The number
of artifically inseminated dairy cows has increased
significantly in the areas served by these two insemination centers between 1961 and 1965, according
to the Agricultural Statistics Annual of the Ministry
of Agriculture and Livestock. The figures were:
1961, 7,054; 1962, 10,363; 1963, 14,509; 1964, 16,935;
1965, 20,266.

Registries of purebreds have been maintained for
many years by the Ministry of Agriculture and Livestock for cattle, hogs, and horses. The 22 breeds
of purebred cattle and 11 breeds of purebred hogs for
which registries were maintained during the period
1962-65 are shown in Table 80.

The incidence of improved cattle is still quite
low in the herds of Venezuela, but considerably more
has been done in breed improvement than in the improvement of other management practices. Limited
credit available for the purchase of high-quality
animals has also restricted these improvements. Improved hog production has achieved very little impetus in recent years, as is indicated by the purebred
registry shown in Table 80.

TABLE 79

Seed Certified by Venezuela's Ministry of Agriculture and Livestock,
1961-65 (Metric Tons)

Year	Corn	Cotton	Sesame	Black Beans	Other Edible Beans	Rice	Soy-beans	Peanuts
1961	1,253	827	4	1	1	–	0	0
1962	2,493	1,242	5	2	4	1	0	1
1963	2,241	1,019	10	15	2	1,000	1	2
1964[a]	2,300	1,418	182	101	0	2,000	0	2
1965	4,000	3,000[b]	350	100	0	200[c]	0	0

[a]In the 1964 figures for corn, cotton, sesame, and black beans are included registered seed as well as certified seed. Analyzed seed is also included in the 1964 figure for cotton and rice.

[b]Amount of cotton seed certified as indicated by the 1965 figure is considerably more than the annual requirement for cotton areas planted.

[c]Certified seed only.

Source: Agricultural Statistics Annual, 1961-65, Ministry of Agriculture and Livestock.

TABLE 80

Purebred Cattle and Hogs in Venezuela's Official Registries, 1962-65

| | Cattle | | | | | | Hogs | |
| | Zebu Breeds[a] | | Other Breeds[b] | | Total | | | |
Year	Bulls	Cows	Bulls	Cows	Bulls	Cows	Boars	Sows
1962	1,812	2,368	284	541	2,092	2,909	205	435
1963	1,612	2,216	436	889	2,048	3,105	83	125
1964	1,605	2,323	562	785	2,167	3,108	28	74
1965	1,849	2,127	486	840	2,335	2,967	5	12

[a]Eighty per cent of these were Brahma breed registries. The other 20 per cent were distributed among four other zebu breeds.

[b]Forty-six per cent of these were Brown Swiss, 26 per cent were Santa Gertrudis, and 16 per cent were Holstein for the total of the four-year period. The other 12 per cent were distributed among fourteen other breeds.

Source: 1965 Agricultural Statistics Annual, Ministry of Agriculture and Livestock.

The poultry industry, as mentioned previously, has progressed very rapidly in recent years, and some large breeding and hatching farms are now well established and are providing the preponderant proportion of the poultry stock now utilized for intensive and highly productive operations in Venezuela.

Livestock Feeding Improvements

With the exception of poultry production, which is generally carried on with modern technology, livestock production is generally characterized by extensive but unproductive operations. Feeding of concentrates and improved pasture use is generally limited to dairy operations. A limited number of hog farms (those accounting for 20 per cent of total pork production) utilize feed concentrates. The cost of feed concentrates is relatively high because large-scale feed grain production does not exist in Venezuela, and the feed-mixing industry, although it enjoys substantial protection from foreign competition through customs duties and licensing of imported feeds and ingredients, has not produced feeds at prices low enough to encourage rapid development of enterprises producing feeds for cattle and hogs. The high costs continue for domestic corn utilized in mixed feeds. This, together with lack of adequate research and trials on the economics of and animal response to feeding operations, has resulted in the low level of intensive beef and pork producing units. Also, practical demonstration of semi-intensive farm-produced forage and other feeds combined with other foods for livestock production has not gained much headway.

There has, however, been a fairly steady increase in the use of feed concentrates for cattle and hogs, a well as a considerable increase in poultry feed concentrates use during the period 1961-65, as shown in Table 81.

As shown in Table 81, the utilization of corn (which is the only nationally produced cereal of consequence suitable for livestock feed) in the feed concentrates produced has varied from about 30 per cent to 20 per cent of the total weight of feed

TABLE 81

Production of Feed Concentrates for Venezuelan Livestock, 1961-65
(Metric Tons)

Year	Cattle	Hogs	Poultry	Horses[a]	Total	Increase (Per Cent)
1961	57,609	22,053	177,708	2,011	259,381	—
1962	49,295	27,334	214,227	1,988	292,844	12.9
1963	56,752	32,940	207,531	2,212	299,435	2.2
1964	70,885	51,344	283,992	2,344	408,565	36.4
1965	70,571	59,569	306,721	2,026	438,885	7.4

[a]Principally race horses.

Source: 1965 Agricultural Statistics Annual, Ministry of Agriculture and Livestock.

concentrates during this five-year period. Actually,
the proportion diminished· from 30 per cent in 1961
and 1962 to about 22 per cent in 1965. The principal
other cereal grains utilized are bran and other by-
products from imported wheat.

Although intensive feeding operations for cattle
and hogs are still at a low level, the several feed
concentrate companies in operation are well established and are taking more active interest in and
supporting some research in the development of more
economical raw materials for livestock feed. These
companies should be able to expand rapidly to meet
demonstrated demands for such products in the future.

RURAL HOUSING IMPROVEMENTS

The only government agency working directly in
the improvement of rural housing is the Rural Housing
Service of the Malariology Division of the Ministry
of Sanitation and Social Assistance. Before 1962,
the National Agrarian Institute constructed houses
on its settlement projects, but since then, this phase
of settlement development has been managed by the
Rural Housing Service. This service was established
on an experimental basis in 1949 by the Malariology
Division after it had been successful in largely con-
trolling malaria in Venezuela and began expanding its
interest to other health problems. Another factor
involved in the establishment of the Service was the
discovery that the thatched huts, which were common
·as rural housing, harbored the hosts for Chagas disease, which is a serious problem in Venezuela. After
ten years of studies and experimental work, a definite
program was started with very limited funds, based on
labor supply furnished by the recipients, plus a
skilled foreman and materials provided on a long-term
credit (twenty years) provided by the Rural Housing
Service with no interest charge. Since 1958, this
service has directed the construction of the following numbers of rural houses, according to annual reports of this agency:

Year	Houses Constructed
1959	605
1960	2,011
1961	2,214
1962	5,900
1963	8,531
1964	11,312
1965	12,613
Total	43,186

Most of the housing has been constructed in rural
communities (or in the nuclei of agrarian reform settlements) with very few houses constructed on individual farm units. This concentration of housing
into nuclei or in already established communities follows the policy of the agency that other public services of water supply, schools, and road access must
be available to the families in housing units and
that these services could be provided more economically in communities. This policy has created problems
from a farm management standpoint because it has
greatly limited the types and intensity of farm operations that could be carried on in cases where the
farm families do not live on the producing unit, but
where the sociological aspects of community participation were considered more important by the policy-
makers. The 43,186 houses constructed between 1959
and 1965 involved an investment of Bs. 204 million on
the part of the Rural Housing Service, which amounts
to Bs. 4,726 per house. The unit cost is considered
to be quite reasonable, considering the cost of materials in Venezuela and the type of structures built.

The progress achieved is significant but is over-
shadowed by the large volume of inadequate housing.
The 1961 census indicated that, of the 1,462,000
housing units in Venezuela, 511,350 or 35 per cent
of the total were classified as shacks or huts, and
a large proportion of these were located in rural
areas. Consequently, only limited progress is being
made in solving the housing problem in relation to

the total need, with less than 10 per cent of the indicated need covered in the seven-year period 1959-65.

The Rural Housing Service has utilized international financing from the Inter-American Development Bank of two loans amounting to a total of $22 million U.S. (Bs. 98.6 million), all of which had not been disbursed in 1966.

The houses constructed by the Rural Housing Service have been located as follows:

12,593 in 241 agrarian reform settlements
30,593 in 790 other rural communities

The results of the lending activities in connection with the rural housing program show problems similar to other government lending programs in Venezuela. Credit management skills have not been applied sufficiently to carry out the programs on a completely businesslike basis, especially with respect to collections. Although data are not available as to the amount of repayment quotas that have matured, the total amount collected on the more than Bs. 200 million invested between 1958 and 1965 was only Bs. 14.8 million, whereas the amounts due and payable are estimated at three times that amount. The history of government loans that result in being grants rather than loans is apparently well known to Venezuelans, and collection of payments due in any government lending program is a special problem. Sound and continuous businesslike procedures and administration will be necessary to correct this custom of not repaying government loans. This well-established custom strongly militates against the proper development of successful credit programs, to which assignment of additional funds to fill the real need for credit could be justified. Carrying out lending programs without reasonable collection efficiency may be a way of distributing government funds to certain segments of the population, but it is not sound policy for increasing agricultural production and productivity.

Prior to 1962, the National Agrarian Institute (IAN) constructed 5,793 houses and remodeled 5,881

houses in colonies and settlements, with investments
made both before and since 1962, in work directly
related to services for housing units. Among these
services, constructed in settlement projects during
the last fifteen years, were 4,057 storage sheds,
650 wells, 64 community water systems, 2,901 septic
tanks, 469 water tanks, 31 schools, 6 medical dispen-
saries, 41 electricity-generating plants, 318 water
pumps, and 1 public market. Total investment by IAN
in housing and related services is reported at
Bs. 58.3 million during 1951-65.

Because of a mild climate throughout most of Venezuela, protection from the elements is not a critical problem in design of housing facilities. However,
providing sanitary conditions so that the rural families can enjoy good health to permit them to carry
out the arduous work involved in farming is necessary.
Also, decent housing serves as a stimulus to rural
residents for cultural development and civic responsibility. Solving the housing problem will require
more ingenuity and investment than has yet been demonstrated in rural areas.

SUMMARY OF IMPROVED TECHNOLOGY AND ECONOMIC
STATUS BY PRINCIPAL CROP AND LIVESTOCK
ACTIVITIES

In the foregoing sections of this chapter, general
descriptions of the institutional services, technological advances, and other factors contributing to
agricultural progress in Venezuela have been presented. In order to provide a more specific evaluation
of the effects of these various factors on the increases in agricultural production and productivity,
a summary by the most important crops and livestock
enterprises is presented herein to reflect the status
of development in each of these enterprises. This
summary is presented in a series of tables that are
largely self-explanatory as to the methodology utilized and the criteria applied in determining the evaluation arrived at for each crop or livestock activity.

Tables 82, 83, and 84 provide a summary evaluation
for thirteen important crops, indicating relative

improvements in crop production (Table 82); effectiveness of institutional services related to research
and extension, transport services, market outlets, and
credit (Table 83); and the influence of modern technology on factors of production and management skills
(Table 84). Tables 85, 86, and 87 provide a similar
evaluation for five important Venezuelan livestock
products.

These evaluations, of course, are generalizations,
and there are exceptions to most general categories
applied. However, by following the criteria and assumptions indicated in the footnotes to the tables,
a picture emerges of the technological and economic
developments in these specific enterprises between
1961 and 1965.

A summary of these eighteen enterprises is given
in Table 88 and includes information on supply
and demand, per capita consumption, and prices. The
last column, which represents wholesale prices of
these products in external markets, is not, of course,
directly comparable to the preceding column on local
prices received by farmers. However, these external
wholesale prices are shown to indicate the possibility,
or lack of it, of considering foreign sales of some
products that could be produced beyond national needs.
For example, such products as corn, rice, potatoes,
sesame, and poultry, which have farm prices that are
higher locally than the world market wholesale price,
would have no chance of competing on an unsubsidized
basis in these markets. The only products in the
table that have a significant margin (50 per cent or
more) between the local farmers' price and a world
market price, indicating a competitive possibility,
are bananas and plantains. Some exports are now made
of these products and are expected to increase in the
future.

Table 89 presents a final evaluation of the economic results for ten important annual and semipermanent crops in 1965. The data available on costs of
production allow only an approximation of net income
because several indirect cost items are not fully
taken into account. Consequently, the evaluation is

TABLE 82

Improvements in Venezuela's Crop Production Methods, Rate of
Productivity, and Agronomic Practices from 1961 to 1965

Crop	Increase in Total Hectares Planted	Increase in Productivity (Yield per Hectare)	Use, in Relation to Total Planted Area, of:			
			Selected Seed	Fertilizers	Pesticides	Mechanization
Corn	medium	small	medium	small	medium	medium
Rice	large	large	large	large	large	large
Black beans	small	small+	small	small	small	small
Potatoes	large	small	large	large	large	large
Mandioc (yucca)	small+	small[a]	small	small	small	small
Sesame	large	large	large	medium	large	large
Cotton	small+	medium	large	medium	large	large
Bananas	medium	small	small	small	small	small
Plantain	large	large[b]	small	small	small	small
Cocoa	small	small	small	small	small	small
Coffee	small	small	small	small	small	small
Sugar cane	medium	large	large	large	large	large
Tobacco	small	small	large	large	large	large

[a] Official statistics of the Ministry of Agriculture and Livestock show a large increase in yield between 1961 and 1962, but this was probably an adjustment from previously inaccurate figures and not an increase in productivity.

[b] Increased productivity is probably due to bringing into production newly deforested lands of good fertility and not to improved practices.

Note: "Small" represents less than 10 per cent (+ indicates actual decline). "Medium" represents 10 per cent to 40 per cent. "Large" represents more than 40 per cent.

Source: Based on various tables presented previously in this book.

217

TABLE 83

Effectiveness of Functioning of Certain Institutional Services with Regard to the Production of Selected Crops in Venezuela, 1966

Crop	Research and Extension Services				Transport Services			Market Outlets			Production Credit Services[b]		
	Biological Science		Farm Management								BAP Loan Distribution: Proportion Applied in Relation to Share of Agricultural Product		Other Production Credit Available[c]
	Adequate	Inadequate	Adequate	Inadequate	Well Organized	Partially Organized	Inadequate	By Contract or Quota[a]	Fairly Definite Outlets	No Contract or Pre-arrangement	Higher	Lower	
Corn	x			x		x			x		x		scarce
Rice	x		x			x			x		x		scarce
Black beans		x		x			x		x			x	scarce
Potatoes	x			x	x				x			x	scarce
Mandioc		x		x			x			x		x[d]	scarce
Sesame	x			x	x			x					scarce
Cotton	x			x	x				x		x		adequate
Bananas		x		x		x				x		x	scarce
Plantains		x		x		x				x		x	scarce
Cocoa		x		x	x				x		x		scarce
Coffee		x		x		x			x		x		scarce
Sugar cane	x			x	x			x			d		adequate
Tobacco	x			x	x			x				x	adequate

[a] Subject to government purchase under minimum price support program.

[b] Limited to production credit, principally that available from BAP. Credit for medium- and long-term investments generally not available for crop farms except through special program for coffee and cocoa. Relationship with the total value of agricultural production refers to the percentage distribution of BAP funds by products.

[c] Generally very limited (scarce) except for the few crops indicated with adequate supplies where the processing industry (or the CVF, in the case of sugar cane) has organized special production credit facilities.

[d] Not directly financed by BAP.

Source: Based on previous data in this study and subjective evaluations by the author.

TABLE 84

Influence of Modern Technology on the Production of
Selected Crops in Venezuela, 1966

Crop	Natural Resource Utilization		Scientific Information Regarding Improved Practices		Capital Supply and Utilization		Status Level of Management Skills Applied		
	Cultivation Adapted to Ecological Limitations	Destructive Practices Still Common	Adequate and Reasonably Applied	Inadequate[a]	Reasonably Adequate	Inadequate	Advanced	Fair	Rudimentary
Corn	x	x		x		x		x	
Rice			x		x		x		
Black beans	x	x		x		x			x
Potatoes	x		x		x		x		
Mandioc (yucca)		x		x		x			x
Sesame	x		x		x		x		
Cotton	x		x		x		x		
Bananas	x			x		x		x	
Plantain	x			x		x		x	
Cocoa	x			x		x			x
Coffee	x			x		x			x
Sugar cane	x		x		x			x	
Tobacco	x		x		x		x		

[a] In the case of such products as coffee and cocoa, technical information is available but has not been applied.

Source: Subjective evaluation of previous tables.

219

TABLE 85

Effect of Improved Animal Husbandry Practices on Venezuelan Livestock Production Between 1961 and 1965

Livestock Product	Increases in Production	Breed Improvements	Increase in Use of Imported Breeding Stock	General Feeding Practice Improvements	Increase in Use of Feed Concentrates	Increase in Use of Artificial Insemination	Use of Veterinarian Services	Improvements in Animal Sanitation Practices
Beef	medium	medium	high	low	low	low	low	low
Dairy products	high	medium	high	low	medium	low	low	high
Pork	low	low	high	medium	high	low	high	medium
Poultry	high	high	high	high	high	low	high	high
Eggs	high	high	high	high	high		low	high

Note: The three adjectival classifications refer to increases in incidence of use of the indicated factors between 1961 and 1965 according to the following scales for the five-year period: low, less than 10 per cent; medium, 10 per cent to 40 per cent; high, over 40 per cent change with respect to the situation in 1961.

Source: Based on data from Agricultural Statistics Annual, Ministry of Agriculture and Livestock, 1961-65.

220

TABLE 86

Effectiveness of Functioning of Certain Institutional Services with Regard to Selected Livestock Production Activities in Venezuela, 1966

Livestock Product	Research and Extension Services				Development of Processing Industries			Market Outlets			Credit Services		
	Biological Science		Farm Management										
	Adequate	Inadequate	Adequate	Inadequate	Adequate	Partially Deficient	Deficient	By Contract	Fairly Definite Outlets	Indefinite	Adequate	Some Available	Very Limited
Beef		x		x			x		x			x	
Dairy products		x		x	x				x			x	
Pork		x		x		x		a	x			x	
Poultry	x		x			x			x			x	
Eggs	x		x						x			x	

a For limited industrial use of pork products, the processors contract with producers for certain quantities as a basis for obtaining the contingency license for imports.

Source: Based on subjective evaluation of data in this study.

221

TABLE 87

Influence of Modern Technology on the Production of Selected
Livestock Products in Venezuela, 1966

Livestock Product	Natural Resource Utilization		Scientific Information Regarding Improved Practices		Capital Supply and Utilization		Level of Management Skills Applied		
	Use Adapted to Ecological Limitation	Destructive Practices Still Common	Adequate and Reasonably Applied	Inadequate	Reasonably Adequate	Inadequate	Advanced	Fair	Rudimentary
Beef		x		x		x			x
Dairy products	x		x		x			x	
Pork	x			x	x				x
Poultry	x		x		x		x		
Eggs	x		x		x		x		

Source: Subjective evaluation of data in this study.

TABLE 88

Supply and Demand, Consumption, and Prices of Selected
Agricultural Products in Venezuela, 1965 and 1966

Product	Level of Supply and Demand, 1965 — Production Related to Consumption				Consumption per Capita, 1965 (Kg. per Year Unless Otherwise Indicated)		Price to Farmers (Bs. per Kg.)		Wholesale Prices in World Market, 1966 (Bs. per Kg.)
	Less than Consumption	Approximately Equal to Consumption	Exceeded Consumption — Foreign Market Established	Foreign Market Indefinite[a]	Urban	Rural	Minimum Price Support, 1965	Average Price Received, 1965	
Crops									
Corn	x				19.7	46.9	0.40	0.38	0.28
Rice (paddy)				x	9.9	9.3	0.60	0.60	0.47
Black beans	x				6.6	7.3	1.10	1.09	0.40
Potatoes				x	18.6	9.5	0.40-0.35[b]	0.52	0.29
Mandioc (yucca)		x			10.7	27.1	None	0.20	N.D.
Sesame	x				5.3	0.7	1.20[c]	1.10	0.80[c]
Cotton (unginned)	x				6.0[d]	6.0[d]	1.36-1.45[b]	1.20	0.94
Bananas				x	40.2	43.1	None	0.25	0.91
Plantains				x	128.4[e]	68.3[e]	None	0.10[e]	0.70
Cocoa			x		0.2[f]	0.05[f]	1.45	3.61	2.67
Coffee			x		3.0	2.4	1.48	3.36	4.06
Sugar									
Refined				x	25.0	11.9	None	0.87[g]	0.45[g]
Crude					8.5	8.5			
Tobacco				x	1.5	0.7	None	5.20	5.72
Livestock Products									
Beef	x				19.3	14.4	None	1.70[h]	2.08[h]
Milk	x				89.7[i]	30.7[i]	0.87[i]	0.78[i]	N.D.
Pork	x				3.7	1.5	3.15[j]	2.35[j]	2.48[j]
Poultry		x			5.7	1.2	None	3.04[k]	2.79[k]
Eggs				x	84.7[l]	40.0[l]	None	0.17[l]	N.D.

(Continued)

TABLE 88 (Cont.)

^aMarkets for bananas and plantains in the Caribbean islands and the U.S. are being developed and increased. Cocoa export markets are established but limited and are not governed by the international quotas that exist for coffee. However, Venezuelan cocoa is of good quality and has had a premium market. No outlet is immediately available for the surplus accumulation of the other products listed in this column. Sugar has a quota on the U.S. market of about 8,000 metric tons, but this amount is less than surplus production and is subject to change.

^bQuality grades account for range in prices.

^cBs. 1.20 is a contract price and not a support price. Also, Bs. 0.80 for external market is the value of sesame imported into Venezuela in 1965-66.

^dData not available to distinguish between urban and rural consumption.

^eNumber of individual fruits and price per unit.

^fConsumption of chocolate.

^gRepresents wholesale price, not price to farmer for sugar. Price per ton of sugar cane to farmers was Bs. 38.00 in 1965.

^hWeight of live cattle.

ⁱWhole milk and all other milk products converted to liters.

^jBs. 3.15 price applies to certain industrial uses only. Bs. 2.35 is price to farmer of live hogs. as world price is per kilogram of dressed carcass.

^kPrice of Bs. 3.04 to farmers is for live poultry. World price indication is for dressed poultry meat.

^lNumber of eggs in consumption column and price per egg in price column.

Source: Long Term Forecasts of the Supply and Demand of Agricultural Products in Venezuela (Caracas: Consejo Bienestar Rural, 1965; 1965 Agricultural Statistics Annual, Ministry of Agriculture and Livestock; annual report for 1966, International Monetary Fund; 1965 Statistical Yearbook, United Nations Food and Agricultural Organization.

TABLE 89

Economic Feasibility of Production of Selected Venezuelan Crops in 1965

Crop	Estimated Direct Costs of Production (Bs.)	Price per Kg. Received by Farmers (Bs.)	Yield Required to Equal Costs of Production (Kg./Ha.)	Average Yield in 1965 (Kg./Ha.)	Margin of Actual Yield that Covered Indirect Costs, Management Return, and Profits			Economic Feasibility of Production
					Amount of Production (Kg./Ha.)	Value of Production (Bs.)	Per Cent of Direct Costs	
Corn (irrigated)	499	0.38	1,313	1,128	Neg.	Neg.	Neg.	unfavorable
Rice (irrigated)	1,434	0.60	2,390	3,191	801	480	33	unfavorable
Rice (upland)	625	0.60	1,041	1,596	555	333	53	favorable
Black beans	434	1.09	398	401	3	3	1	unfavorable
Potatoes	2,237	0.52	4,302	8,403	4,101	2,132	95	very favorable
Mandioc	812	0.20	4,060	12,290	8,230	1,646	203	very favorable
Sesame	509	1.10	463	621	158	206	40	favorable
Cotton	877	1.20	731	941	210	252	29	unfavorable
Sugar cane	1,986[a]	0.038	52,263	62,908	10,542	401	20	unfavorable
Tobacco	3,735	5.20	718	1,391	673	3,499	94	very favorable

[a] Average of planting and ratoon crop cycles.

Note: As explained in Chapter 5, estimates of direct costs are not considered averages or representative of present production costs because some technological inputs, including mechanization, use of fertilizers, pesticides, and other modern practices, still are not utilized extensively in all crops listed. The lack of data on the amounts of indirect costs (interest costs on borrowed capital and interest return to land and other capital, depreciation of permanent improvements, and so forth) makes a more precise evaluation impossible. The final column, economic feasibility of production, is largely subjective because it takes into account the factors indicating degree of risks, as presented in the immediately preceding tables, and assumes that indirect costs amounted to at least 40 per cent of direct costs for irrigated rice, potatoes, sugar cane, and tobacco, and 25 per cent for other crops. In addition, there should be at least a 20 per cent margin above direct costs to cover management return and profit.

Source: Calculations based on data previously presented.

made by a process of eliminating the direct costs, represented by a corresponding quantity of the product at farmers' prices, and estimating indirect costs and a management and profit margin, as indicated in the footnote. The resulting evaluation shows that five of the ten important crops had economically unfavorable results in 1965, two had favorable results, and three had very favorable results.

The main purpose of presenting the analysis in Table 89 is to indicate the lack of micro-economic (individual farm management) analysis and planning in agriculture. Although the data on costs of production are not completely accurate or representative, it is clear that there are extreme differences between the economic feasibility of production based on modern technological and that based on traditional subsistence methods. However, there is practically no evidence of shifts in production pattern to indicate that producers are adjusting their production to profit by short-term or long-term advantages that occur in market prices and demand.

Of course, some products are affected by factors outside the farmers' control, such as area quotas (for sugar cane) and lack of an accessible market, which make shifts from one crop to another difficult. This, however, does not explain the great rigidity in production patterns that is well demonstrated in some of the more permanent crops, such as coffee and cocoa, where production has continued at a loss and for which accumulating and impossible debt situations have developed without consequent adjustments in production methods or patterns. It is clear that a great deal more attention must be given to the problems and viewpoints of the individual farmer in order to increase efficiency and to adjust production to national needs and price incentives.

NOTES

1. Plan of the Nation, 1965 (Caracas: CORDIPLAN, 1965).

2. Eight regional or area studies of this nature have been carried out by the Consejo de Bienestar Rural at the request of its sponsoring agencies of the Ministry of Agriculture and Livestock, the Agricultural Bank of Venezuela, and the National Agrarian Institute. The most recent studies of this nature, which reached more detailed study levels than previous efforts, were the Cojedes and Motatán River watershed studies, completed in 1966. These were sponsored by the United Nations Special Fund and the Ministry of Agriculture and Livestock, with CBR acting as coordinator and operating agency. Regional resource studies for the states of Apure, Zulia, and Falcón have been carried out by other private groups sponsored by the Ministry of Agriculture and Livestock.

3. The standard political subdivisions in Venezuela are made up of states and federal territories, districts (distritos), and municipalities (municipios) in a descending order of area covered.

CHAPTER 7 PROBLEMS AND OBSTACLES

Previous chapters of this study have mentioned several problems and obstacles and have presented, where possible, quantified estimates as to the extent of these problems. This chapter will attempt to organize and summarise these problems and present them in a manner relating them more directly to the factors of production and other considerations essential to agricultural development in Venezuela.

In this study, some general categories of problems and obstacles have emerged that influence many aspects of Venezuelan agricultural development. There has been a lack of sufficient attention, investment, or effort to adequately develop the resources and skills needed for an aggressive and balanced development in accordance with needs and possibilities.

First, sufficient skills in analysis, management, and execution have not been developed at the micro-economic level, or at the farm level (where decisions for change in methods of production are made), to permit a rational and aggressive attack on the obstacles to increasing productivity. This is reflected in the apparent lack of, or limited, correlation between price and demand factors and the production picture. The inadequacy is indicated in the wide disparity in possible profit margins between several important types of products with very little apparent shifting by producers from one activity to another that appears to be more remunerative. On the other hand, there are outstanding examples in which special campaigns of financing and technical assistance have resulted in spectacular increases in productivity, as in the case of rice and sesame. More micro-economic efforts and resources are needed to make possible the maximization of any economic advantages and to determine means for overcoming disadvantages in the development picture.

Second, the general chaotic condition of distribution and marketing facilities for most perishable crops and products (as well as for some that are not so perishable) is a critical problem. This situation makes it extremely difficult for a farm operator to justify the cost of the larger inputs required for modern technological production of these goods because he has no reasonable assurance of increased returns at market time from the larter volume produced. The result is a slow growth in the farm units, both as producers of food (for which demand increases steadily) and as consumers of products from other sectors--a process that is essential for the balanced development of the Venezuelan economy.

These two general problems, of course, affect the lack of some factors, shortages of others, and efforts that should be exerted in many aspects of the development activities in Venezuela. General government policies, education and research efforts, priority assignments of capital, and many other factors can help to remove these two general obstacles. In the section that follows, organized on the basis of factors of production used in traditional economic analyses as well as some supplemental factors, many of these problems will be pointed out. In a later chapter, some ideas on alternative solutions will be presented.

OBSTACLES RELATED TO LAND AND OTHER NATURAL RESOURCE UTILIZATION

Several important problems and obstacles to development are related to knowledge of and use practices with respect to land, water, vegetation, and other ecological aspects of natural resources.

The first of these is the present limited scientific description, analysis, and evaluation of these basic resources. This, together with a tendency on the part of some administrators of programs involving

development of natural resources to plan and execute
large-scale, expensive projects without an adequate
analysis of the resource base involved, has resulted
in considerable waste of scarce capital and some
projects have not resulted in increased net value of
the production of Venezuela. Although considerable
progress has been made in general descriptive studies
of basic resources, adequate scientific data in the
detail required for specific development project
planning are still scarce and often are not organized
in a manner that renders them readily usable for
project-planning purposes.

Some of the more important types of basic resource
inventories, accurate and continuous registries for
an adequate period of time, and classification of
these data for effective use that are seriously lacking or incomplete for agricultural development programs are listed below.

1. Soil studies and maps at the semidetailed and
detailed levels required for scientific intensification of the use of the land resources cover only small
areas of Venezuela. Further, there is no continuous,
organized program to provide coverage of all important
land areas prior to or as a prerequisite to important
changes in land use purposes. This is of critical
importance to the agrarian reform program, especially
with its tendency to acquire land for the establishment
of land settlements composed of small, individual farm
units in order to foster intensive land use practices.
Too many mistaken judgments have already been made
regarding the productive capacity of the soil in many
settlements due to lack of adequate and scientifically
described soil information, and exorbitant prices
have been paid for some land for the same reason.

2. Surface and subterranean water resource inventories, together with long-term records of climatic
factors of precipitation, winds, soil temperature,
river flows, and sedimentation, cover only certain
areas. Such inventories of these resources, specifically for agricultural considerations, are practically nonexistent. Several very expensive gravity
water schemes have been developed without taking into

consideration the underground water supplies and possibly could have been developed to supply irrigation
needs at much less cost in some areas. Furthermore,
destructive land clearing in critical watershed-
production areas will have increasing adverse effects
and will continue uncontrolled until water resource
inventories are completed.

    3. Forest resource inventories and scientific
descriptions that would permit both development of
integrated exploitation on a sustained-yield basis
and adequate control and management of this important
resource for the general welfare cover less than 15
per cent of the forested areas of Venezuela. As a
result, most of the existing exploitation is irrep-
arably destructive.

    4. Very little in the way of resources, manpower,
and search for modern methods of performing cadastral
surveys has been applied to this essential activity,
which is a prerequisite to sound agricultural development. The Cadastral Office, which has been in existence for many years in the Ministry of Agriculture
and Livestock, still had not covered even 5 per cent
of the land area of Venezuela by 1965. Without the
establishment of a real estate tax system or the application of resources and ingenuity to this activity
to spur more rapid coverage by cadastral surveys, this
problem will continue to be a serious obstacle to agricultural development, especially with regard to the
efficient implementation of credit programs to finance
basic adjustments in real estate resources and improvements. This inefficiency is one of the reasons
why adequate credit for such permanent farm improvements has not been made available.

    In addition to the scarcity of inventories, maps,
and other scientific description of basic natural
resources, there is a serious need for legislation
providing for adequate management and control of basic
resources for agricultural use. A recent law dealing
with forests, soils, and water represents some improvement over previous legislation. However, many
important considerations are still missing from this
law that limit its effectiveness. For example, laws

dealing with the establishment of water rights, use, and conservation are presently very deficient. Wildlife protection and control laws and regulations are also inadequate.

Laws and procedures dealing with land title transfers are inadequate and archaic. The existing system is so complicated and slow that little progress has been made in issuing titles on farm parcels in the land settlements of the agrarian reform program. Land titles have been established and transferred on fewer than 6 per cent of the land parcels established and assigned to farmers between 1958 and 1966.

Several observers have commented that a land tax law should be established in Venezuela; otherwise, cadastral surveys will never be adequately organized, and such a tax would be worthwhile for this purpose only, even if not for other revenue-raising purposes. Even a nominal land tax would be a strong incentive to use land more in accordance with its true productive potential.

OBSTACLES RELATED TO LABOR AND LABOR SKILLS

Serious underemployment and unemployment are evident in rural areas of Venezuela. Also, the per capita income of rural residents is less than Bs. 700 per year, which is only about one fourth of what is needed to provide rural people with a decent living standard, according to home economists. The value of production per worker in the agricultural sector of the economy is less than one fifth that of persons employed in other sectors, indicating a low level of agricultural skills and productivity. These and other factors indicate a serious obstacle to development of the agricultural and other sectors because the agricultural sector, constituting more than 30 per cent of the total population, should be producing more food and fiber and at the same time consuming more of the products from other sectors as agricultural inputs, rather than participating in the national economy at such a low level.

There are, of course, many factors contributing
to the low productivity of rural workers. Some of
the most important factors are the following:

1. Continuing high rates of illiteracy are
caused by lack of opportunity of many rural residents
to participate in formal education services, making
it very difficult for such persons to understand and
adapt their work methods to the goal of increased
productivity.

2. The public school curriculums and operating
methods are the same for rural areas as they are for
urban areas and are more oriented toward urban needs
than rural needs. Consequently, school attendance
is low and drop-out rates are high in rural areas,
not only because of distance and other problems of
getting to school but also because of the lack of
adaptation of curriculums and regulations to real
rural needs. Only very recently have any special efforts been started to design and institute practical
vocational teaching in rural schools through a special
training program in a center located near Turmero,
state of Aragua.

3. Secondary and higher education facilities are
generally unavailable to rural residents, so it is
very difficult for such persons to develop leadership
and other skills in order to provide a strong and co-
herent force to bring about the necessary adaptation
of the school system to rural needs. This also is a
problem with respect to management skills for farm
units (treated later as a supplemental factor of production).

4. Many of the special technical and vocational
school facilities that have been established and made
available to rural youths to a greater degree than
regular secondary schools are dead ends as far as
further technical training is concerned. The existing institutional structure makes it impossible for
outstanding graduates of most of these practical
schools to further their education.

5. No university courses or facilities are available for the study of home economics. Consequently, no high-level technicians are being trained in Venezuela to assist in improving rural home management, nutrition, and other fields. Also, no local nutritional or textile technicians are being trained to assist in research and development for more industrial uses of agricultural products or to provide scientifically based inspection service for the protection of the public in connection with manufactured products. The relatively low nutritional level of farm workers limits their capacity to work and to be more productive, yet the home economics field is sadly neglected and could, if more adequately developed, be a strong force in improving the health and working abilities of rural workers.

In addition to educational deficiencies in rural areas, some other problems that are of a long-term nature and are inherently costly to resolve because of the dispersed location of rural populations are those related to medical services, social security benefits, and labor laws, which so far have had very limited application to rural workers.

OBSTACLES RELATED TO CAPITAL SUPPLIES AND UTILIZATION

As indicated in this volume, Venezuela has been more favorably endowed with capital supplies for development than many other Latin American countries, due to its intensive and valuable petroleum exploitation activities. Some of the capital thus generated has been utilized in the development of road networks, school systems, and irrigation works of benefit to the agricultural sector of the economy. However, to improve the basic productive structure of agriculture and to bring into the dynamic economy of Venezuela a large portion of farm families and farm units, there remains a serious capital shortage. Also, the utilization of capital in such large development activities as irrigation project development and land settlement, as well as in special campaigns and in financing programs for individual farm development and specific

commodity production, has shown many faults. Consequently, large amounts of invested capital have not
increased production, especially that related to units
of capital, land, or manpower utilized. Many of the
problems of misuse of capital are closely related to
the low level of management skills, which is further
discussed in the next section of this study, with respect to both farm management and larger institutional
management problems.

The agricultural sector is at a competitive disadvantage in most countries in attracting sufficient
capital from both government and private sources because of its usual limited ability to pay returns on
capital or to provide the more realizable guaranties
at the same rates as industrial and commercial sectors
of the economy. However, because agricultural production is a primary economic activity and provides essential food and fiber for the people, the government
necessarily concerns itself with providing a large
share of the capital in the form of credit services
and other production inducements for agriculture. As
indicated previously, the government of Venezuela is
providing a large amount of the available agricultural
credit and is financing many other services considered
important for agricultural development. This function, of course, has both a positive and negative side.
It is necessary that the government encourage agricultural development and responsibility in such fields
as research, education, product control and regulation
for the protection of the public is clearly within the
appropriate sphere for government action programs.
However, when public agencies attempt to engage in direct commercial services for important segments of the
economy, efficiency is usually less than that achieved
by private interests. The "public trust" requirement
in government agency operations that prevents them
from taking usual calculated risks in daily business
affairs, together with the bureaucratic unwieldiness
that traditionally develops, place public agencies at
a less efficient level than private firms in providing
direct commercial services. This problem has, in some
instances, militated against sound development in the
agricultural sector. In the case of facilities for
grain storage, for example, the government has tended

to involve itself in the direct development of these
essential facilities instead of limiting itself to
encouraging private business to assume more responsibility. Government agencies have become involved
in direct production or commercial services activities by providing financial arrangements to private
business firms but retaining government control of
the business or by establishing specific programs
and facilities for some commercial service needed in
the agricultural sector. Greater efforts are needed
to place these direct services and development facilities in the hands of private business. Such an ac-
complishment in some instances would probably lower
costs for the services and would stimulate production.

The Agricultural and Livestock Bank (BAP) is the
principal source of agricultural credit for Venezuelan
producers and provides many essential services for
producers. In fact, too many functions are grouped
in the institution, thus impairing the efficiency of
its services to the farmers and diverting essential
capital that should be used to build up an increasingly larger credit fund for agricultural development.

Some of the principal problems of this institution
have a vital bearing on the pace of Venezuela's agricultural development. With the exception of the first
few years after its founding in 1928, when all of its
funds were loaned for long-term real estate mortgage
credit, the BAP has dedicated practically all of its
regular loan funds during most of the last thirty
years to the financing of annual production costs of
certain crops and livestock activities. This policy
decision, made by the bank directors and continually
renewed, may have been sound in the past. However,
the frequent turnover of bank management personnel
and the lack of a continuing technical improvement in
credit management skills have resulted in substantial
losses rather than in the build-up of a larger re-
volving fund for agricultural credit. The preponderant portion of loans made during recent years has
come from new money injected into the bank from government sources. Consequently, with its "own account"
fund, the bank has made no headway in developing the
integrated credit program that is essential for

significant improvement in the structure of the producing farm units. Also, the failure to eliminate
from records all the old uncollectable accounts,
which continue to show that the bank has a very large
(but unusable) loan "portfolio" prevents the bank
from clearly justifying its need for additional capital.

The lack of reasonable sources of substantial
amounts of capital for basic farm resource adjustment
and reorganization to incorporate semipermanent and
permanent improvements that would lead to increased
productivity is a serious omission in the credit picture. The special credit programs for livestock development and the coffee-cocoa program with funds
and loan-making services provided by the Ministry of
Agriculture and Livestock have provided some basic
adjustment capital. However, the lack of application
of sound loan principles in the processing of these
loans has also greatly diminished the programs' effectiveness. The same is occurring in connection
with the rural housing program. Other special development loan programs, such as those for rice, sugar
cane, and dairy production, which were carried out by
the Venezuelan Development Corporation in the past,
also provided substantial capital for machinery purchase, land clearing and leveling, farm building,
fencing, and other permanent improvements. Skill in
making loans was also deficient in these programs,
but early losses were ignored and sufficient capital
was made available to make increased production possible. There is no regular credit available under
any reasonable and institutionalized terms for the
purchase of rural land. The agrarian reform program
is distributing land without direct cost to the settlers. However, the lack of credit for land purchase
has greatly restricted the transfer of land to persons who wish to make more intensive use of this resource. Further, the lack of credit for medium- and
long-term investment has tended to cause diversion of
annual-type loan funds for use in permanent improvements by the borrowers and has generally resulted in
serious delinquency and hopeless debt situations because of inadequate terms of repayment for these
types of investments.

The credit laws specify that only the BAP can grant crop and chattel mortgages. Private lenders cannot make available formal and legal crop and chattel mortgages, which is another reason why private capital sources have not become involved in agricultural credit operations. Machinery dealers have been able to operate some credit operations with conditional sales contracts wherein title to the machine or other chattel is reserved by the seller until the item is completely paid for. However, this type of contract is not adaptable to other farm improvement needs and there is no official register outside of the BAP for crop and chattel credit transactions that would serve as a bona fide notice to third parties that a crop is covered by a lien. Further, the legal procedures for processing real estate mortgages are very archaic, resulting in extreme time and cost requirements for such transactions. This problem is closely related to the lack of cadastral surveys and records previously mentioned.

The BAP is charged with responsibility for several government programs not directly related to agricultural credit, including social improvement programs that involve advances of funds that should not be called loans, together with price-support, commodity storage, and food and machinery importation programs. It is clear that a significant reorganization of the bank is essential and that the bank should receive special authorization to clear out the large volume of uncollectable accounts and to establish more business-like operating procedures for the future.

The large investments in the agrarian reform program and the Rural Housing Service during recent years have channeled significant capital into agricultural development, especially for housing, access roads, land clearing, and so on. However, the management of these investments has not been properly coordinated with the real economic need for development in a large proportion of the projects that have been started. As a result, a large number of settlement areas are only partially developed, but parcels have already been assigned to settlers. Production efficiency cannot be rapidly achieved because of the lack of such

basic facilities as water systems, roads, and markets.
However, a large proportion of these settlers have
received production capital based on intensive operations that cannot yet be achieved--capital that cannot be reimbursed from the limited or extensive
production activities that could be carried on. Consequently, an impossible debt situation has developed
that will affect these operations for many years.
This situation, coupled with inadequate economic and
physical planning of many of the settlement areas, is
causing a serious loss of scarce capital needed for
agricultural development.

OBSTACLES RELATED TO ORGANIZATION AND MANAGEMENT
OF THE BASIC FACTORS OF PRODUCTION

Some utilization and management problems with
respect to the three basic factors of production have
been mentioned in previous sections of this chapter.
However, as indicated in the beginning of the chapter,
the deficiencies in management skills at all levels
of the agricultural sector provide one of the most
serious obstacles to balanced agricultural development. Consequently, additional comments on this subject are deemed appropriate in this section of the
study.

Limited management skills are, of course, due to
deficiencies in many aspects of the institutional
facilities that are necessary to develop such skills
together with lack of public demand for more efficiency and less waste in the use of resources for
production. This applies to educational, research,
and experience requirements for the execution of government programs, private supply and marketing services for agriculture and, of prime importance,
individual farm management.

With respect to the more general aspects of management deficiencies that constitute serious obstacles
to agricultural development and in connection with
the larger institutional structures involved in the
agricultural sector, a number of problems are discernible.

A general fault of most agricultural development programs is the lack of clearly stated goals and objectives established on a relatively long-term basis and in practical terms. This results in considerable vacillation in the types of activities designed to implement the programs, as well as considerable changing of policies and activities selected for emphasis from year to year. Consequently, momentum is lost, work is wasted, and opportunities are lost due to failure to follow through to the necessary stage of development for continuous operation of many projects. Changes in top management personnel, which have also been too frequent, result in changed policies and direction of efforts with little regard to the high cost involved in abandoning partially completed activities or projects. Also, the lack of clear-cut goals and objectives makes it very difficult to coordinate implementing action on a reasonable and measurable basis so that adequate judgment can be applied as to the degree the implementing action is contributing to progress. This permits abuse in the utilization of capital and other resources applied to program activities without any possibility of determining definite responsibilities on which disciplinary action could be based among the executives at the various levels of the organization. Dedicated and efficient performance is difficult to achieve under these circumstances.

There is a strong tendency among many organizations to budget and execute programs on the basis of expenditures for personnel salaries, without adequate provision for other essential inputs of supplies, materials, and transport that would make it possible for the employees to do effective work. This has been an especially critical problem with regard to agricultural research and extension services. Considerable progress has been made in research activities in this respect, but it is still a critical problem in many other service activities.

Some individual agencies have established relatively uniform personnel policies, including pay scales, seniority rights and other personnel incentives. However, there is a general problem in the government because of the lack of a civil service

system that would provide continuous incentives for
good performance and attract people who wish to provide dedicated service and enjoy some career protection. The existing fairly liberal labor law does
not cover most government employees, although some
autonomous agencies and ministries have collective
contracts with lower salaried employees.

The lack of management skills at the farm unit
level constitutes one of the most critical obstacles
to increased agricultural development; it is at this
level where the final implementing decision is made
for changes in agricultural production methods and
organization. As pointed out in the previous chapter,
there is little evidence of any correlation between
market prices or price changes and the production of
many of the agricultural products produced in Venezuela. This is a strong indication that the preponderant proportion of the farm managers do not apply
analytic skills in adjusting their farming operations
to take advantage of either short-term or long-term
favorable price situations that may exist for certain
products or to take action to change production volume or practices to ameliorate unfavorable price effects. There are, of course, several factors beyond
the control of individual farmers that affect this
lack of adjustment but these do not explain the relatively rigid pattern that exists in the organization
of resources for production or the lack of effective
demand on the part of farm operators for the types of
input services and information that would make individual farm production activities more dynamic.

It is particularly significant in this respect
that with seven important crops enjoying relatively
liberal price-support programs and five other products enjoying certain price protection and incentives
through export and import controls and subsidies,
Venezuelan farmers would have more definite price
targets with which to work than in most other countries and could increase the precision of their analyses, if such analyses were made.

Farm management is a very neglected discipline in
educational institutions available to farmers, and
the low educational level of the great majority of

farm operators has made it impossible for them to
develop, on their own, necessary analytic skills so
that they can appreciate the economic benefits of modern technology. In recent years, some farm management
courses have been made a part of the curriculums in
the agricultural universities. However, in the research department staffs provided by the government,
there are no agricultural economic or farm management specialists participating, on a full-time basis,
in research activities or projects. The same shortage of this type of technicians exists in the agricultural extension services. This is a serious
limitation on the development of economic practicality
in the technological services available to farmers.
It is reflected in the shortage of practical empirical data and analysis of costs of production, even
though most of the price-support programs are based
on alleged cost of production factors but lack a
technical research foundation to the degree required
for effective administration of these programs. For
this reason, in some products, such as rice, the
production incentive has caused surpluses, whereas
in others, such as beans, which apparently have similar favorable prices, there has been inadequate response in production.

Further, lack of farm management skills and research information is one of the reasons why the
marketing services for many products, especially
perishable products, have continued in such chaotic
conditions for long periods. Economically oriented
analysis and information have not been adequately
developed at the farm level and in the intermediate
steps of distribution on a realistic enough basis to
permit development of convincing programs for improving the marketing services. Marketing and other
supplemental services and conditions that constitute
obstacles for agricultural development are subjects
of the next and final section of this chapter.

OTHER IMPEDIMENTS TO AGRICULTURAL DEVELOPMENT

Some auxiliary or supplemental categories of activities and services are involved in the agricultural

production picture on which comments need to be made
in connection with impediments to agricultural development. All of these are related, of course, to
the basic factors of production, on which observations have previously been made. However, the char-
acter of these problems and their importance in the
global development picture make it desirable to present them as special points in the discussion.

Marketing and Distribution of Agricultural Products

As indicated in the beginning of this chapter,
the lack of organization in the marketing and distribution services available to agriculture, especially for the more perishable products, is one of
the most critical impediments to more rapid agricultural development. There are, on the one hand,
several products with minimum price-support programs
(corn, rice, beans, potatoes, sesame, cotton, and
sisal fiber), together with others for which special
price protection devices are provided by export or
import controls and subsidies (sugar, coffee, cocoa,
milk, and some pork products), for which fairly definite market channels are established, and with regard to which the Venezuelan Government plays a large
role in purchase, storage, and distribution. On the
other hand, the marketing processes of many products
are unorganized and are subject to a wide variety of
problems ranging from too many steps and too many
intermediaries handling very small volumes to near
monopolies at the wholesale level for some products,
such as meat. Even with regard to the products with
established market channels and protected prices, the
subdevelopment of management skills and the lack of
adequate micro-economic data and analysis, especially
cost data at the farm level, to permit efficient management of these programs results in widely varying
response or lack of response in the production picture due to these alleged production incentives and
market protection devices. All of these factors
mitigate against the producer's receiving a reasonable and fair price and force the consumer to pay
more than he should because of inefficiencies in the
marketing and distribution processes. Consequently,

the correlation between production quantities and
price changes is almost nonexistent for most agricultural products in Venezuela.

Products sold for direct consumption without any
processing, such as most vegetables, fruits, and
legumes, still have no organized assembly points in
producing areas. Such assembly points are necessary
to permit not only more effective transportation arrangements but also the establishment of an effective
system of product grading, uniform packing, and large
lot shipment to consuming centers. Now, individual
truckers, often without adequate specialized equipment for adequate care of the products, pick up products from individual producers in a wide variety of
containers and carry these products to local or central markets without grading or sorting them. Consequently, later purchasers at the wholesale or
retail levels must inspect every container and carry
on price negotiations in very small lots, a procedure
that involves some unnecessary costs. The lack of
grading and uniform packing has also limited attempts
at establishing a market price and quantity reporting
system for important market areas on a current enough
basis to serve as a guide for shipment of products
from the producing areas to alternative market outlets. Packing sheds have been established in the
plantain-producing areas for the purpose of packing
fruits for the newly developed export market in the
U.S., from which some experience in this respect hope-
fully will be gained that can be applied to other
products.

Specific market development activities for perishable products, utilizing marketing specialists on a
full-time and continuous basis, have received very
little attention in the agricultural sector. Commodity groups and government research and extension programs have not dedicated any significant resources
to this activity. There is a need for the development
of knowledgeable market searchers which involves aspects of research and applied action programs to work
on problems of improving marketing efficiency along
commodity lines.

Recent efforts have progressed toward the establishment of industrial meat packing plants, including
integrated slaughtering and utilization of all products, where such services were not available in the
past. Livestock producers have had to carry their
animals for sale to municipal slaughterhouses, pay
the slaughter fees and taxes, and then sell the car-
casses to meat wholesalers or retailers. There are
still no regular stockyards or public market facilities where producers can sell live cattle on an auc-
tion or contract basis. In the larger consuming
centers, the wholesale meat distribution activities
have tended to consolidate into monopolies that will
probably have adverse effects on the interests of
both producers and consumers. The wholesalers have
also developed transportation services for live and
slaughtered cattle and, in recent years, have been
buying live animals in producing areas but with considerable bargaining advantages over the producers
with regard to prices.

Joint or cooperative efforts among producers to
assure that they receive fair returns on products for
sale through pooling of products and utilization of
skilled marketing personnel have had little development in Venezuela. This is a field where cooperative
effort can show some of the quickest and most spectacular results in benefit to producers and consumers,
but the lack of well-trained and dedicated leaders
among the farmers themselves has made cooperative
development from within the groups most needing it
very difficult to achieve.

General Government Policies and Services with Respect to Agricultural Development

As mentioned previously, there is not sufficient
development of clear-cut policies and goals for many
agricultural agencies. Further, the underdevelopment
of management and technical skills among the executives of several well-intentioned programs to enable
them to assist in solving agricultural problems and
provide incentives for greater production in accordance with Venezuela's needs has produced negative
results, or at least less progress than should be

expected. This is tied in with problems of research
and experience in many of the key factors, especially
at the micro-economic level, needed for rational administration of these programs. One of the programs
with serious deficiencies in clear-cut goals and implementing action relates to minimum price-support
and market protection activities. These activities
often are considered primarily as marketing devices
rather than as production incentives or controls.
Most price-support activities are allegedly aimed at
providing producers with at least a return greater
than reasonable costs of production. However, no
continuous and scientifically ordered research and
data collection activities are carried on to determine real production costs and to keep such information up to date. Consequently, the response to these
price-support activities has been very variable and
subject to frequent crises that nullify some of the
expected beneficial effects in providing order in
the production response. Some of the protection devices and price supports have resulted in development
of surpluses (sugar and rice) and have (in the case
of milk) tended to maintain high production costs.
Due to lack of adequate technical information and
administrative skills, these devices are very slow
to be adjusted to changing situations.

The government has been assuming an increasingly
larger direct operating responsibility in connection
with such service and business operations as storage
for corn and rice, processing of sugar and importing
of grains, machinery and other items that have dis-
couraged or prevented private interests from entering
these fields of business. It is believed by many
observers that the government should utilize its resources in encouraging more participation on the part
of private business in these activities rather than
to attempt to provide the facilities completely. This
would probably result in less cost to the public and
a service more effectively geared in the needs of
producers and consumers.

Considerable improvement has occurred in both
the quantity and the quality of technological services through the research and extension services of

the Ministry of Agriculture and Livestock, but there
is still a serious lack of adequate resources and
practical results from this work to enable it to have
the needed impact on agricultural development. The
improvement in technological skills is, of course,
a long-term process, but services to assist in these
improvements should have high priority in allocation
of resources on a continuing basis. This is especially important because of the relatively low education level of the majority of rural residents and
the low income levels prevalent at this time.

There are, of course, many detailed items in the
agricultural sector that have constituted impediments
to agricultural development in Venezuela. Most of
them are tied into the types of problems included in
the foregoing paragraphs, and additional detail is
not considered as essential for the purposes of this
volume.

CHAPTER **8** PROJECTIONS TO 1975

The information presented in the previous chapters provides a basis for projecting the future of agricultural development in Venezuela, as well as the progress of some of the institutional services and facilities related to this growth. This will be done for 1966-75 for crop and livestock production, anticipated demand, and the export and import situation for important products up to 1975. Interim data for 1970 will also be presented when possible. General economic and demographic forecasts were included in Chapter 2, so the material in this chapter will be limited to the agricultural sector.

FORECASTS OF SUPPLY AND DEMAND OF IMPORTANT PRODUCTS FOR 1970 AND 1975

The specific forecasts for the production, demand, and export-import situation for the important agricultural products will be based principally on the study previously completed by the Consejo de Bienestar Rural for the Economic Research Service of the U.S. Department of Agriculture entitled <u>Long Term Forecasts of the Supply and Demand of Agricultural and Livestock Products in Venezuela</u>. This study provided historical data up to the end of 1961 for most products analyzed, and projections were made for 1965, 1970, and 1975. In addition to utilizing the historical time series data on products, together with information on population growth and institutional and government policy influence, an extensive consumer survey was conducted as an additional basis for the future forecasts. The consumer survey permitted, for the first time in Venezuela, calculation of several elasticity relationships, separated for urban and rural residents, on a

per capita basis for important products, indicating
changes in demand with respect to changes in incomes
of consumers and changes in prices of products that
were taken into account in the forecasts.

The forecasts are the most complete available.
Additional historical data up to 1965 indicated that
some minor adjustments were needed in the forecasts
for 1970 and 1975. This is done in the following
analysis for some items; adjustments are generally
based on the differences between the forecast figures
for 1965 and the actual figures registered. The basic
annual changes forecast for the period between 1965,
1970, and 1975 have not been changed because the
bases for projecting the rates of change utilized in
the original study are still valid.

A summary of the supply and demand situation together with import and export estimates as projected
for 1970 and 1975 is presented in Table 90. The
bases for these forecasts and the annual rates of
change assumed in their calculations are summarized
in the following paragraphs for products with significant production in Venezuela.

Exports

The rate of growth calculated on the basis of
the historical trend, population growth, and elasticity factors determined for bananas and plantains
for the period from 1965 to 1975 was at the compound
annual rate of 3.2 per cent--just 0.2 per cent more
than the projected population growth. The recently
established export market has been increasing significantly for these products, especially in the case
of plantains. This was difficult to quantify for
projection purposes because of the short period that
banana and plantain exports have been significant.
An amount of 15 per cent more than domestic consumption was assumed to cover possible growth of this
export outlet, which indicates the possibility of
reaching 151,000 metric tons of exports of bananas
and plantains by 1975. This is probably high and
will only be achieved by very vigorous market development activities and strict cost and quality control.

TABLE 90

Projection of Supply and Demand and Export and Import Possibilities
for Selected Venezuelan Agricultural Products, 1970 and 1975
(1,000 Metric Tons)

Product	Apparent Demand (Production plus Net Trade) 1970	1975	Domestic Supply 1970	1975	Imports 1970	Exports 1975
Exports						
Bananas	466	527	535	606	69	79
Plantains	585	673	651	745	66	72
Cocoa beans	11	11	22	22	11	11
Coffee	40	48	56	57	16	9
Imports						
Wheat and products	652	848	1	1	651	847
Corn	666	793	490	530	176	263
Barley and malt	66	92	0	0	66	92
Oats and products	27	31	0	0	27	31
Beans and peas	72	85	50	59	22	26
Dairy products (milk equiv.)	988	1,229	654	825	334	404
Beef	214	251	208	261	6	10
Pork	47	58	46	58	1	0
Vegetable fats and oils	104	129	54	67	50	62

Seed potatoes	18	24	0	0	18	24
Lint cotton	25	29	15	18	10	11
Other Products						
Rice (milled)	105	124	105	124	0	0
Sugars	373	444	373	444	0	0
Food, potatoes	164	201	164	201	0	0
Mandioc	400	464	400	464	0	0
Eggs	39	48	39	48	0	0
Poultry	49	60	49	60	0	0
Tobacco	11	14	11	14	0	0

Source: Long Term Forecasts of the Supply and Demand of Agricultural and Livestock Products in Venezuela (Caracas: Consejo de Bienestar Rural, 1965). The following adjustments from this source were made for supply and demand columns: Plantains, up 20 per cent; cocoa, up 7,000 tons; wheat, up 14 per cent (for demand and imports); barley, down 15,000 tons; beans, down 30,000 tons; milk, demand down 250,000 tons; supply down 90,000 tons; seed potatoes, down 9,000 tons in demand and imports; cotton, up 7,000 tons in demand and imports; tobacco, down 3,000 tons.

251

The exports in 1965 amounted to only 12,000 metric
tons.

The rate of growth in production and demand for
cocoa beans is calculated at 3.9 per cent compounded
per year between 1965 and 1975. This is based principally on increased domestic demand; the margin for
export remains fairly constant. The cocoa produced
in Venezuela is of high quality and is not involved
in international marketing agreements. However, productivity is relatively low on existing farms. The
government has established a special development program for cocoa plantations that have been deteriorating and are heavily debt-ridden. Technological
information is available for greatly increasing
yields, but the general surplus supply of cocoa beans
in the world market is a serious restricting factor.

An annual compounded rate of growth of 3.6 per
cent for coffee production and demand are foressen
for the period 1965 to 1975. Venezuela is a signa-
tory of the International Coffee Agreement but has
not been filling its quota of 475,000 sacks of 60
kilograms each in recent years. Available technological information clearly demonstrates the possibilities of greatly increasing productivity per hectare
of coffee land. However, the coffee industry has
been stagnant for many years because of world market
surplus conditions, an accumulated debt situation on
producing units, and the very large capital requirements for improving production methods, which producers have not been able to assume.

Imports

An annual compound rate of increase of 3.9 per
cent is calculated for corn production and demand.
Although technological information is available that
would permit tripling or quadrupling existing average
yields, it is assumed that because of the widely dispersed distribution of corn production, with the small
subsistence-type farms contributing over 75 per cent
of the production, growth in corn production will be
slow. More industrial uses are developing but not
yet covering a large part of the total product.

The forecasts of increase in bean imports amount
to the compounded rate of only 2.5 per cent per year,
which is less than population growth. The deteriorating production and productivity evident in the
historical data for beans is the principal basis for
this forecast. Research and extension in connection
with food legumes have been sadly neglected and disease problems are serious. However, recent interest
in solving the technological problems in connection
with food legumes could bring about a more rapid
growth, but no concrete results are evident to date.

For dairy products, the compounded annual rate
of increase indicated for 1966-75 is 3.7 per cent.
Milk subsidy programs to encourage local production
to substitute for imported dried milk have greatly
increased milk production since 1950. However, efficiency and productivity have not been emphasized in
these programs and expensive production methods still
prevail. The subsidy programs and other government
policies have been in constant crisis, and spectacular increases are not foreseen for this industry in
the near future, although per capita consumption
from a dietary need standpoint is still very low.

The growth forecast for beef imports is at the
compounded rate of 3.3 per cent per year. The cattle
production industry is generally considered to have
the ecological base for much greater production and
productivity, and additional applied technology and
investment in improvements could bring about spectacular increases in production. However, lethargy
in responding to special development financing programs has dimmed hopes for more rapid growth.

A 4.4 per cent rate of increase in pork imports
is indicated by the forecasts. High feed costs for
intensive hog production is one of the principal
limiting factors.

The principal nationally produced products included in the category of vegetable fats and oils
are sesame, cotton seed, and copra. The rate of
growth indicated is 4.5 per cent compounded annually,
which is one of the highest rates indicated in this

section. This rate is based on the already initiated improvements in productivity that have been demonstrated for sesame and cotton but that were offset partially by lower rates of growth in coconut production. Also, with a well-established demand for vegetable oils in excess of national production and with technological information available that will make possible greater productivity and reduced costs, greater-than-average growth expectations are reasonable for these products.

The rate of increase in cotton imports is estimated at 4.0 per cent. Imports of this crop are limited to long staple cotton at the present time. Efforts have recently been initiated to produce this type of cotton on lands bordering the Orinoco River basin, a procedure that may increase rate of growth and reduce imports even more. Technology applications are already fairly advanced but a margin exists for additional improvements in productivity.

Other Products

This category is comprised of products with an approximate balance between production and consumption or with temporary surplus.

The rate of increase of the production of milled rice is forecast at 3.3 per cent, compounded annually. Rice technology is fairly well advanced already, and currently there is surplus production that has not been marketed. High costs of production limit possibilities for export. The emphasis on increasing irrigated areas substantially in Venezuela is based largely on eliminating upland rice production and substituting therefor irrigated rice production, which has higher yields per hectare. However, unless costs can be lowered to permit sale in international markets or some export subsidy program is adopted, production will be limited to internal demand. Problems of surplus disposition are definitely evident for this product.

A 3.5 per cent annual compounded rate of growth is foreseen for sugar cane. The description above

for rice applies to sugar cane, except that practically all sugar cane is now on irrigated land.

A 4.1 per cent annual rate of growth is forecast
for potatoes. Seed potatoes are still imported, and
some efforts are being initiated to supply some seed
locally. The technological and market situation for
potatoes is similar to that for rice. The higher
growth rate for potatoes is based on the assumed
higher incomes and the corresponding substitution of
potatoes for some other starch foods, which is justified by the demand-income elasticity data.

The rate of growth for mandioc (yucca) is shown
at 3.0 per cent per year, which is equal to the population growth forecast. Data available on this crop
are not considered to be very reliable, and production
is dispersed among the large number of small subsistence farms that apply very little modern technology.
It is, however, an important food item in Venezuela
and will continue to be so, although per capita consumption is expected to reduce because, as average
income increases, there is a tendency to substitute
potatoes for mandioc.

A relatively high growth rate of 4.2 per cent is
projected for egg production, which has had spectacular increase during the last few years; large imports
have been eliminated, and prices are generally lower.
Eggs have a fairly high quanity-income elasticity,
which justifies the higher than average growth estimate in demand. The technological methods already
demonstrated should make it possible for production
to keep up with this demand.

The compounded rate of growth in poultry production is projected at 4.0 per cent. The poultry situation is similar to that for eggs described above.

The compounded annual rate of growth of tobacco
production for the 1965 to 1975 period is 3.7 per cent.
The modern technological base already established for
tobacco justifies the prediction that production can
keep pace with demand. It is assumed that the high
cost of tobacco production limits significant entry
of this product into international trade.

There are several other products for which possible growth possibilities may be important in the future for Venezuela, such as tropical fruits, some vegetables, forest products, and fish products. However, lack of sufficient data and analysis have not permitted precise forecasts of future production and demand probabilities. Efforts are increasing to develop export markets for such products as tomatoes and watermelons in order to supply some off-season demand in the U.S. but are not expected to constitute a significant influence on the global agricultural picture. Special research and development activities recently initiated for the fishing industry should mean that a greater contribution will be made by this industry to the gross national product in the future. The same possibility exists for forest products but the implementing forces for a major breakthrough in development in this industry are not yet discernible.

PREDICTIONS OF IMPROVEMENTS IN INSTITUTIONAL SERVICES FOR AGRICULTURAL DEVELOPMENT

No analytic data are available that would permit a quantified forecast for the structure and adequacy of the institutional services that will be available to agriculture. However, some activities already started and present and future indications of financial support for the public institutions concerned with agriculture give some basis for observations and comments on what can be expected in this respect. Of course, changes in policies and appropriations, together with other factors, can cause immediate change in the prospects and would require continuing reappraisal; but this is the recognized risk in all economic forecasts. The following observations can be presented with respect to the probable future growth in the major categories of institutional and technical services for agriculture and include a consideration of both quantity and quality aspects when possible.

Institutions Involved in Technological Improvement Activities

Included in this category are the various types of educational and research services together with supply services providing the input factors required for modern technology in agriculture.

The impetus achieved in increasing school facilities in rural areas throughout Venezuela during the last few years is expected to continue at the same or at a greater rate in the future. It is not expected that school facilities will be increased in rural areas sufficiently to provide complete coverage, but based on recent data, an increase in school facilities at the rate of between 3 per cent and 4 per cent per year can be expected. In rural areas, where absolute population numbers are expected to remain quite constant (even though rural areas are decreasing in proportion to the total population), the number of rural children of primary-school age who are served by some type of school facility can be expected to increase to 65 per cent to 70 per cent. The proportion of the rural schools that provide more than three grades of schooling should also increase substantially. The establishment of secondary schools in rural areas on a significant scale is not expected, because there is so much to be done in providing complete primary schools. However, school transportation systems probably will become established so that more rural young people can participate in urban secondary schooling facilities.

It is not expected that the large increases in technical schools and agronomic universities that occurred during 1960-65 can be continued at the same rate in the future. In the Plan of the Nation, 1965-68, seven new technical schools for agriculture are projected for construction. However, it is believed that the existing technical schools and universities will turn out more graduates that can be readily absorbed in the institutional services now existing. This means, not that the need for agricultural technicians will be met, but that coordinated and adequately planned utilization of these technicians will not be fully achieved and that a higher proportion of those graduating consequently may not find opportunities to apply their technical training in agriculture. Consequently, entrance qualifications for these schools may become more restrictive, as has already occurred in teacher-training institutions.

THE AGRICULTURAL DEVELOPMENT OF VENEZUELA

The continued and steady improvement in agricultural investigation services can be reasonably expected. The present programs of improving the professional capacities of investigation personnel are expected to start paying dividends during the next ten years. Also, the demand for more technical investigation from a developing agricultural sector is expected to make this activity assume an increasingly more important portion of the Ministry of Agriculture and Livestock's activities, as it should do. Increased participation of private investigation activities on the part of foundations, processing plants, and farm production input suppliers can be expected. An increase of 10 per cent to 20 per cent per year in financing for investigation facilities is forecast.

The Plan of the Nation, 1965-68, provides for an increase of twenty-five to thirty new Agricultural Extension Service offices each year for three years, which constitutes an annual increase of about 15 per cent. This high increase will probably not be continued. However, the supply of available technicians and the pressure for more technical assistance in connection with the agrarian reform program and increased food production activities make an estimate of a continuing 10 per cent annual increase in extension staffs and financing appear reasonable at this time. Also, the development of the Latin American Free Trade Association will require more agricultural technology.

In the few areas of Venezuela where fairly intensive farm production practices are already established (mainly in the Western, Central, and Western Plains regions), supplies of machinery, fertilizers, pesticides, and other items required by modern agriculture are expected to keep pace with demand. In other regions, there will probably be a lag in obtaining some of these services as new areas are developed for more intensive production. It is not expected that import capacity will be a serious limiting factor for obtaining the supplies that must continue to be imported for modern agricultural production, although limited management skills may cause temporary shortages.

Institutions Providing Credit and Other
Capital Services

The principal institution involved in credit services at the present time is the Agricultural and
Livestock Bank (BAP). It is believed that with the
present trends already indicated, some improvement
in credit services and amounts of credit available
will occur during the coming years. There will probably be a continued shortage of medium- and long-term
farm reorganization or adjustment capital. The present
organization of the BAP probably will be adjusted by
new laws to transfer commercial farming credit activities to a separate institution. Also, commodity
price-support and storage activities will be separated
into a specialized autonomous institution of the government. These changes should make increasingly
larger amounts of credit funds available to agriculture. The recent trend of getting more private capital for current operating costs and machinery
purchases through special guarantees from the BAP is
expected to continue, especially for products that
serve as raw materials for processing and industrial
enterprises. This could be an important factor in allow-
ing the government funds available for agricultural
credit to reach more farmers in more adequate amounts.
The administrative and technical services of the special development financing programs for livestock and
coffee-cocoa are expected to improve so that these
funds may be more effectively utilized.

There will be a continuing problem, however, of
the successful competition of the agricultural sector
with urban and industrial interests for private investment capital, and the government will have to play
a major role in organizing and supplying capital for
agricultural development.

Land Resources and Development

The availability of land for greater production
is not and is not expected to become a critical
problem. There is ample margin in undeveloped land
resources and in possibilities for intensification of
use of existing land to permit necessary increases
in production.

There will be continued problems of rational use
and management of the land resources, especially in
connection with the agrarian reform program and
the development of irrigation project facilities.
However, a steady increase in the management skills
can be expected, based on present experience being
gained and the special efforts being carried out to
improve technical abilities of professional-level
personnel. One of the most critical unknowns in this
situation is the lack of significant development in
agricultural economic and farm management skills that
are needed to influence the micro-economic development
necessary to implement the general improvement plans.
Considerably more emphasis will need to be given to
this applied science in the professional educational
institutions, in the application of these techniques
in investigation and extension work, and in the development of farm management skills among farm operators to achieve reasonable progress in land use and
management. Only limited results can be expected in
improved micro-economic analysis and planning, because of the low level of the activity at present and
the length of time required to develop necessary
skills.

GENERAL FORECASTS OF AGRICULTURAL DEVELOPMENT

From the foregoing observations and analysis, it
can be concluded that agricultural development in
Venezuela will be characterized by the following conditions and frameworks based on the present situation
and recent history.

The rate of growth of agricultural production
will probably continue at a rate slightly above that
for the rest of the economy, as occurred during
1961-65. This involves a compounded annual rate of
about 4 to 5 per cent. Inasmuch as the rural population is expected to remain constant, the per capita
increase in value of agricultural production among
the rural population and those actively engaged in
production will increase at a higher rate. However,
the average income per family, although expected to

increase by 45 per cent to 50 per cent, will still
be only about one half of what is considered a minimum income for a decent living standard.

Production of most agricultural products will be
within the framework of national demand. Higher costs
of production, compared with most other competing
countries, will greatly limit any new exports of
agricultural products unless special subsidy programs
are adopted. Exports of plantains and bananas and
some other fruits and vegetables will probably increase to about 10 per cent to 12 per cent of total
production. The traditional exports, coffee and
cocoa, are expected to decline slightly because of
the competitive situation in the world markets, although national consumption of these products is expected to increase steadily. The small amount of
meat products, mainly beef and pork, that are now
imported are expected to be eliminated by 1975, with
national production meeting the local demand. Other
products now imported, principally wheat, corn, barley, oats, powdered milk, and vegetable fats and oils,
will continue to be imported in significant quantities in order to supply part of the demand not covered by local production.

Surplus production of sugar and rice will become
more burdensome unless significant changes in the
price-support and price protection policies for these
products are made.

Present indications are that a network of integrated packing plants for beef and pork will soon be
a reality. This network would serve as an important
impulse leading to improvement in the livestock marketing channels and could lead to some public stockyards and sales lots operated on a permanent basis as
a complement to the industrial packing plants. More
adequate wholesale markets for agricultural products
are expected to be completed in Maracaibo, Barquisimeto, and San Cristobal. Other marketing improvements will be slow because of the limited numbers of
adequately prepared technicians available and foreseen for the immediate future.

Government investments in agricultural development programs are expected to continue at about 10
per cent to 12 per cent of total national budgets,
mainly due to continued plans for irrigation project
development. The rate of private investment in agriculture is not expected to increase significantly
because of the continued high demand for capital for
urban and industrial uses at more remunerative rates
than agriculture can pay.

The general outlook for agriculture is one of
steady growth at higher rates than during 1950-65
but with no spectacular breakthrough now discernible
that would rapidly remove the large gap in per capita
productivity and income that exists between the agricultural sector and other sectors of the Venezuelan
economy.

In the next and final chapter, some ideas are
presented that may assist in accelerating the economic development of the agricultural sector in Venezuela

CHAPTER **9** ACCELERATING
AGRICULTURAL
DEVELOPMENT

The picture of agricultural development that has
been described thus far shows, first of all, that
the amount of capital invested in agricultural projects intended to improve total production (especially
of some products that were not produced in sufficient
quantity to supply national needs, such as rice, sesame, cotton, sugar cane, tobacco, potatoes, corn,
meat, poultry, and eggs) has increased in recent years.

Second, there has been a considerable improvement
in the the quantity and quality of private technological services and supplies for a limited number of
producing enterprises and types of products, especially products with some industrial outlets, such as
sesame, cotton, sugar cane, and tobacco. On the other
hand, application of available technological knowledge and applied research for many other farm products
is still deficient.

The availability of land resources and the conditions of other natural ecological resources are not
yet a critical limiting factor in increasing agricultural production and productivity in accordance with
demonstrated national needs for food and fiber. Of
course, substantial shortages of scientifically ordered descriptive inventories of the basic resources,
combined with considerable destructive use of these
resources, do constitute serious problems for future
development.

Most critical is the need for competent administrative and technological management of the various
economic factors of production and services in the

agricultural sector, at all levels, to achieve rational organization of these factors and to develop complete efficiency in increasing the productivity per unit of land, capital, and manpower. Much less progress than could reasonably be expected has been made in increased production and productivity and improvement in per capita income and general welfare of the rural sector of the population. Consequently, the portion of the total population that is dependent on agriculture for its livelihood (about one third of the total) is still far behind other sectors of the economy in achieving reasonably adequate income for decent living conditions. It is clear that implementing forces for development still have not been adequately studied, designed, and applied at a micro-economic level so that individual farm operators will respond to the degree necessary in adapting their production methods to increase production in accordance with Venezuela's needs and the possibilities indicated by the land and capital resources available. This deficiency has had ramifications in all aspects of education, research, public administration, private management skills (especially on individual farms), and institutional services available to agriculture. It is clear that considerable waste of natural resources and scarce capital has occurred in development activities undertaken because of inadequate attention to cost efficiency and feasibility in relation to real potentials and alternatives for obtaining supplies of food and fiber needed in Venezuela. The lack of developed farm management skills and the analytic information needed for making intelligent decisions on changes in production methods is a critical problem. It is the individual farm operator who makes the decision and implements the changes in practices needed to achieve greater productivity. Convincing data needed to bring about change have not reached these operators to the extent necessary.

The foregoing general characterization of the agricultural situation in Venezuela sets the stage for presenting some ideas on alternative means, or fields where more emphasis is needed to accelerate the rate of agricultural development. It is quite

evident from the foregoing that most of these suggestions will be related to the most critical need
indicated--that of improving human capacities for
efficient management of the factors of economic production and technological understanding and application in the production and distribution aspects in
agriculture.

Presentation of suggestions regarding means of
more rapid improvements in agricultural development
will be organized in this chapter as follows.

1. Ideas related to activities concerning the
four factors of production: land and basic natural
resources, labor skills, capital, and organization
and management of these factors of production.

2. Ideas related to specific commodities or
groups of commodities and their development.

3. An array of projects or activities, in order
of priority according to the criteria developed in
this study, which could be undertaken to accelerate
the rate of agricultural development.

GENERAL SUGGESTIONS WITH RESPECT TO ECONOMIC
FACTORS OF PRODUCTION

The following ideas provide indications for additional activities or greater emphasis on certain
programs already started with respect to the four
basic factors of production, which would serve to
accelerate the rate of agricultural development in
Venezuela.

Land and Other Natural Resources

The following activities with respect to development and rational control and conservation of natural
resources need strengthening, and new methods and
institutional services need to be designed, tested,
and adopted to improve the utilization of these resources.

Scientific Description and Evaluation of Natural Resources

This activity requires continuous attention and implementation; efforts to date have been too dispersed and piecemeal in nature. The importance of keeping this evaluation work ahead of actual development project planning and execution justifies a permanent institutional arrangement with a continuing basic staff of natural scientists and economists to dedicate full time to this work. A properly organized and financed organization could provide essential services to several existing organizations engaged in agricultural development. With a full-time staff operating in this field, precise skills and methods in making resource inventories and evaluation at the various levels of investigation required could be developed more efficiently and economically than by using special staffs for specific projects, as has been done in the past. High-level coordination and direction in assignment of priorities would make it possible to organize this work so that essential phases could be completed prior to future planning and execution of new development projects. With a basic full-time staff of technicians engaged in this work, a flexible tool for agricultural development would be available, which could be augmented in special circumstances, for temporary periods, by additional assignments of funds and personnel from other operating agencies to do special resource inventory work in accordance with national plans and changing or emergency situations that may develop. However, a basic staff should be permanently employed, made up of representatives of at least the following scientific disciplines: agronomy, soil science, animal husbandry, forestry, and agricultural economics. Regular advisory services of geologists, sociologists, hydrologists, and wildlife and recreation specialists should be provided on a part-time basis as required.

This staff could work both independently and in collaboration with other agencies, in accordance with priorities established at the ministerial level. One of its functions would be to complete reconnaissance-level basic resource inventories and maps and a general

evaluation of soils, land use, forest types, and
farming regions, as well as zonification by types of
farming and other ecological description and classification for the approximate 60 per cent of Venezuela
that lacks this information in an ordered manner.
Both surface and underground water resource mapping
could well be a part of the duties of the group.
Semidetailed analyses and evaluation of these factors
could then be undertaken on a systematic basis in
areas of greatest productive potential. The organization would also collaborate with operating agencies
in making detailed resource investigations in specific development project areas and in advising operating
agencies on the maintenance of permanent registries
and records of essential ecological data, such as
meteorological stations and river-flow measurement.

This organization would be primarily a research
organization but would have close ties with operating
agencies, to make it possible to anticipate the need
for specific resource data in advance of projects involving adjustments in basic resource use. Such an
organization could serve as an effective vehicle to
obtain international exchange of scientific information and technicians in the basic resource field. It
would also facilitate the effective use of international financial and technical assistance, such as
that provided by the several United Nations development funds and agencies and by the special programs
and training centers of the Organization of American
States, and Resources for the Future, among others,
interested in basic resource analyses.

Such an organization could be organized within
the Ministry of Agriculture and Livestock, as a section in the Department of Renewable Natural Resources,
and the respective sections in the agricultural research centers, with participation of both animal-
science and agronomic divisions, could make the field
studies involved and participate in the elaboration
and application of specific policies relating thereto. Also, a specialized Institute of Natural Resources
to dedicate itself exclusively to this research work
could well be justified. Another means of effecting
this work would be by long-term contract arrangements,

sponsored by the Ministry of Agriculture and Livestock, with one of the private societies or companies
with economic and physical science investigation
skills that exist in Venezuela. Most of the basic
resource inventories accomplished in Venezuela in the
past have been done by such private organizations
through special contract arrangements with the Ministry of Agriculture and Livestock or with other agencies of the government. Considerable experience has
already been acquired in this aspect and the main
new items needed are a long-range charter and a financial commitment to continue such basic work on a
permanent basis instead of on a sporadic project basis. Operations on a project basis have caused considerable waste in the utilization of manpower skills
in the past because of the necessity of organizing a
new group of technicians for each project, due to
lack of continuity in the effort. An annual budget
of approximately Bs. 750,000 would enable such an
organization to maintain a basic staff and to move
ahead systematically. Such costs would be more than
made up by preventing costly mistakes in development
project selection or in more costly crash-type study
operations made after a project is selected.

Cadastral Survey Work

New methods and additional resources are critically needed to advance cadastral survey work in
Venezuela. In recent years, crash programs for cadastral work have been attempted in Chile and Panama,
from which important knowledge and experience could
be drawn. New ideas have also been developed by
aerial photographic companies. Cadastral information
and convenient registry offices are essential for
reasonable and efficient operation of several important programs and activities.

For example, an adequate analysis of land use and
tenancy structures in Venezuela, so essential for
reasonable macro-economic and micro-economic planning,
is dependent on the availability of fairly complete
cadastral information, which is now almost completely
lacking. Furthermore, effective operations of any
agricultural credit programs are seriously handicapped

by lack of up-to-date land title registries and information. The availability of bona fide land title
registries is essential for an efficient system of
land title transfers, which is an integral part of
the dynamic market for farm land that is characteristic of progressive agriculture. At present, there is
practically no market for farm land because of the
difficulties of cost and time lost in making title
transfers under the current archaic systems, together
with the lack of credit for land purchases. With
adequate cadastral information, registries could be
maintained that would provide legal prima facie evidence as to the status of land titles and liens
thereon.

Although there is no system of land taxes in effect in Venezuela, there are income taxes and other
types of taxation in effect, but all have serious
problems of application and efficient administration.
A complete cadastral survey and efficient registry
would greatly facilitate the effective application
and collection of several types of taxes.

Serious consideration should be given to proposals
for establishing a land tax.[1] Establishing such a
real estate tax system on a nominal basis could be
justified to finance the rapid completion of the cadastral survey that is so critically needed. After a
cadastral survey was completed, a means of scientific
appraisal could be developed to apply real estate taxes on the basis of productive value or market value
of the unused land kept by the landowner or other effective and equitable basis that may be selected for
revenue-raising purposes. As oil stocks become de-
pleted, other government revenue sources will, of
necessity, have to be developed, and it is not too
soon to start exploring other possibilities. Besides
supplying the impulse to complete the necessary cadastral work, a real estate tax system would provide
a strong impulse for achieving land use more in accordance with real productive potentials. It would
become too costly to maintain good productive land in
idle or extensive use categories. There are, of
course, many problems in administering a real estate
tax system. The present underdevelopment of agency

administrative skills for efficient operation suggests the need for some caution in establishing additional bureaucratic structures. However, in the case of cadastral work, which is so important and is constituting such a serious obstacle to present land use improvements because of the lack of adequate cadastral information, additional emphasis and possible additional institutional structure can well be justified. This is so, even to the point of establishing a real estate tax system as a tool to induce the completion of the necessary cadastral survey work. Such a tax system probably will eventually become a necessity for government revenue purposes.

Strengthening Other Institutional Services Related to Basic Resources

As indicated in previous chapters, omissions and weaknesses are observable in some legal authorizations and present operations of the institutionsl services related to basic resource development and management that need corrective action. Some of the more critical of these factors, together with the nature of possible corrective action, are discussed in the paragraphs below.

Water laws for regulating development, use, and conservation of both surface and subterranean water resources are needed in Venezuela, including establishment of water rights and control of pollution. A legal study of sample laws in use and proposed in other countries, together with specific justifications and ideas developed by conservation groups from several countries, should provide an adequate basis for developing such a law adequate to Venezuelan conditions.

A more modern and scientifically based law to control and protect wildlife is considered a necessity by most observers. Here again, a comprehensive study of examples available from other areas, together with the technical advice of conservation groups, should provide a sound basis for updating the present laws.

The need for land title transfer regulations and
official registries is closely related to the need
for cadastral surveys and registries previously discussed. However, the present regulations, which
generally still require handwritten documents and
other laborious procedures and clearances, could well
be modernized by authorizing the use of some of the
more modern record and registry devices available.

The several government agencies involved in
natural resource education, research, and control
were described in Chapter 6, where it was indicated
that none of them had sufficient manpower or resources to provide national coverage. Some revision in
basic laws has been previously indicated as necessary
for improvement in the operations of these institutions. Coordination and implementation of these
services could be improved by the designation of an
interdisciplinary and interagency task force, the
purpose of which would be to develop an integrated
statement of objectives and goals for such activities
and to specify more clearly the responsibilities of
each of the various entities involved in carrying
out programs directed toward achieving the stated
goals. Special emphasis should be given to developing measurable short-term and long-term goals for
each agency. Then with a periodic examination of
annual operating reports, an effective administrative
tool would be available clearly to justify requests
for additional resources. Such an analysis might
indicate the need and the basis therefor for reorganization of the institutional structure or disciplinary action on the part of the administrators
involved in the event lack of progress was determined
not to be due to lack of resources. With effective
administrative support up to the ministerial level
and with clear-cut delegation of authority at all
levels of these agencies, effectiveness of these
agencies in reaching established goals and in providing national coverage in these important activities
could be greatly improved. Such programing based on
measurable progress in annual planning and review
of results would put some "teeth" into the administrative procedures. Also, it should provide a basis
for fully justifying increases in budgetary support

from the government treasury. In addition, greater
effort in enlisting the support of private organizations interested in conservation and the recreational
use of natural resources on the part of the government agencies is justified, for it could assist in
developing more public consciousness of the importance
of the proper use of Venezuela's natural resources.

The large investment in irrigation and drainage
structures that is programed for Venezuela generally
is well justified because of existing ecological conditions and the desirability of year-round productive
effort on farms. Besides providing the possibilities
for greater productivity from the efficient use of
land and water, these structures also provide a basis
for maximizing the utilization of manpower and the
capital factors of production. There are, however,
danger signals with respect to the economic feasibility of some of these projects, indicating a possible
wastage of scarce capital resources. These danger
signals have been discussed in previous chapters,
especially with respect to large amounts of capital
that were invested in project areas before adequate
basic technological data were available. In addition,
there has been a failure to consider adequately the
alternative possibilities for obtaining the necessary
water--either in the same area or in other more eco-
logically favorable areas--together with underdevelopment of managerial skills in project operations.

The agencies responsible for irrigation development have been making progress in developing skills
for planning and executing the construction of irrigation and drainage projects, and considerable international financing, in addition to national treasury
funds, has been justified and obtained for these activities. There are, however, two important factors
mitigating against the long-range successful operation
of some of these projects, for which additional attention is recommended.

First, instead of large, expensive projects, more
attention should be given to developing several smaller
projects where construction and maintenance costs per
unit of land area would be less. In this way, the

management skills required for effective operation
would be more in line with those presently available.

Second, more consideration should be given to
the miceo-economic, or individual farm, requirements
with regard to both construction and operation. This
recommendation applies to the economic feasibility
analysis for the whole project as well as to the
efficiency of water use in individual farms. This
problem is related, of course, to the general problem
of lack of adequate micro-economic analysis and data
and to the general problem of defining objectives and
measurable goals for such projects. For such projects
to provide the expected impetus to the improvement of
agricultural production and productivity in the use
of other production factors, they should be economically sound from a cost allocation standpoint within
the budget capability of the individual user of irrigation water. This factor has not been given adequate
consideration in projects already under operation, as
evidenced by the fact that water users, for many years,
have paid nothing for the irrigation water delivered.
This problem is occurring with respect to annual operating and maintenance costs, to say nothing of
amortization of the construction costs involved. Per-
mitting projects to be constructed and operated where
the users of the water services do not or cannot pay
for their fairly allocated portions of the costs, so
that the project will be largely self-liquidating in
its financial aspects, is not sound development policy
in the long run. Policy, objectives, and performance
in this respect definitely need clarification.

Labor Skills and Their Utilization

The major suggestions that can be made for improving and utilizing labor skills are related to
continued educational efforts and adaptation of educational facilities to the needs of the rural segment
of the population.

General Educational Systems

Continued substantial government investment and
support in improving the general educational system

is expected in the future. However, because of the geographical dispersion of the rural population, progress will be slower in providing more complete coverage in rural areas than in urban centers. Continued efforts to expand rural school coverage are programed in national plans at what is believed to be the maximum feasible rate. The literacy program for adults is expected to continue. There are, however, some adjustments and additional activities directed at meeting rural needs that could be incorporated into the general educational system.

First, special study of rural school hours, subject matter requirements, and facilities is suggested to adapt these schools to the real needs of the farm population. The rules of the present system are quite rigid in these respects and are largely urban oriented. The present drop-out rate in rural schools is high and the number of rural children who go on to secondary schools and institutions of higher learning is very limited. Consequently, some adjustments in rural school activities could well be justified to provide more practical training in accordance with agricultural needs.

Second, development of more prevocational and vocational training in rural primary schools is suggested. As indicated previously, the preponderant proportion of rural youths have the opportunity of attending only primary schools, and that is the only place that formal prevocational or vocational training can reach them. A recent program in Chile sponsored by the American International Association, USAID, and the Ministry of Education has demonstrated a practical method of providing special vocational training facilities for rural schoolteachers and could serve as a reference guide.[2] A recently established school at Guaraguta near Turmero, in the Venezuelan state of Aragua, is developing a vocational training program for teachers that could serve as a model for future efforts.

Third, as rural access roads are being improved at a significant rate, special studies and efforts should be directed to providing more organized public

school transportation systems so that more rural
youths can be given the opportunity to attend urban
secondary schools. A significant portion of the
rural youths who have an opportunity for secondary
or higher education leave the agricultural sector to
earn their living. However, the result of more widespread secondary school training may be an increase
in the number of dedicated leaders who are involved
in the solution of rural problems.

Additional efforts should be made to tie the
practical agricultural schools operated by the Ministry of Agriculture and Livestock and some private
groups into the regular educational system. If school
curriculums were adjusted to correspond more closely
to high school level requirements, which would mean
an additional year at least in these schools, many
more potential agricultural leaders could be developed. The outstanding graduates could then go on to
university training and could increase the supply of
agricultural technicians with a real farm background.
Attempts have been made in this respect in the past
but without satisfactory results. An agreement between the Ministry of Education and the Ministry of
Agriculture and Livestock is strongly recommended to
solve this impasse.

Arrangements should be made to establish
university-level training facilities for home economists in Venezuela. Although the present graduates
of schools for home demonstrators (below the high
school level) are providing significant assistance
in improving rural living conditions, higher education facilities are needed in the home economics
field to make possible continued improvement in rural extension work. Also, such university-trained
technicians are needed in nutrition and textile specialties to assist in developing more industrial outlets for agricultural products. Specific proposals
for establishing a home economics department within
the agronomy faculty have been made on at least two
occasions in recent years, but they have not pros-
pered to date. A re-evaluation of this important
development would be well justified.

Agricultural Extension Service

The plans for increasing the Agricultural Extension Service of the Ministry of Agriculture and Livestock in 1966-68, according to the Plan of the Nation, are substantial and greater increases cannot reasonably be expected. However, this is the principal activity directly concerned with improving the skills of farm operators and workers, and the need for such improvements justifies a greater emphasis and support of this activity. Several observers maintain that the Agricultural Extension Service, together with the services of agricultural investigation that are needed to provide the technical information to be disseminated, should constitute the major activities of the Ministry of Agriculture and Livestock and should utilize a major portion of its funds. These two services absorb about 10.6 per cent of the total budget of the Ministry; after excluding the budgets of two autonomous agencies of IAN and BAP, the Extension and Investigation Departments have about 21 per cent of the funds utilized for direct Ministry operations. A much greater proportion of the funds of the Ministry of Agriculture and Livestock funds could be justified for extension and investigation activities, because of the low educational level of a large proportion of the rural population. The demands for intensive and practical work to assist these people in improving agricultural productivity and rural living standards are very great.

The Agricultural Extension Service should adapt research results on improved farming practices so that they have a farm-management orientation and provide more convincing arguments to induce farmers to improve production practices. Advance planning, in collaboration with the agronomy faculty, to encourage a certain number of students to become interested in farm management work, and the awarding of postgraduate scholarships to prepare specialized technicians for farm management work in the Agricultural Extension Service would be prerequisites for assuring the availability of the necessary number of technicians in the future.

In addition, the Agricultural Extension Service should collaborate with the investigation centers in providing a regular flow of requests from extension agents to these centers for practical research and trials leading to answers on problems of increasing productivity of important farm products within economic and physical possibilities. For example, scientifically controlled research data on methods and quantities of fertilizers and herbicides that can be applied economically on various types of crops and in different localities are not available in Venezuela. This type of information is essential in order for the extension agent to convince the farmers with whom he works to adopt suitable technology in this respect.

With the greater numbers of agricultural technicians graduating from the institutions of higher learning now and in the future, a specific program needs to be developed by the Agricultural Extension Service to incorporate more of the professional-level technicians into the extension work and thereby to upgrade the technological service made available to farmers. Advance arrangements, similar to those indicated above with regard to farm management, are suggested to assure the entry of more professionals in the field.

Additional suggestions on extension work requirements in connection with specific farm-product development are included in a later section of this chapter.

Agrarian Reform Program and Farm Labor Skills

To date, the agrarian reform program, both in Venezuela and elsewhere, has demonstrated that the step from subsistence farming methods to more intensive commercial farming on the part of the major portion of the farmers with low educational levels is very difficult to accomplish. Providing land ownership security to these farmers, who have been generally operating as squatters on land, has not proved sufficient, in itself, to induce improvement in their

welfare on the basis of greater agricultural productivity. Consequently, income levels of families
benefited by this program have not increased as rapidly as is needed to incorporate this large segment
of the population into the economic structure of
Venezuela. The small land units per farm parcel that
are generally distributed in the settlement projects
require intensive land use with products that bring
significant returns in order to achieve adequate incomes for the family. This type of management requires refined skills and experience on the part of
the farm opeators, which generally are lacking, and
learning them is a slow process. In the meantime,
the high degree of underemployment, loss of valuable
manpower, and inadequate farm incomes continue. This
condition has been well demonstrated in the program
in Venezuela, and although a large amount of capital
and effort has been expended in this activity, the
goals of rapidly increasing agricultural production
and improved rural family welfare in connection with
the land redistribution activities and other services
developed for these people have not been achieved.
This situation, together with the ambitious program
for developing irrigation facilities for large land
areas that is generally tied into the agrarian reform
program, leads to the following suggestions for re-
orientation of at least part of the agrarian reform
program and adjustment of policies and methods related thereto. Adjustments in land distributing
policies are justified at present, not only to provide a more economically sound basis for increasing
agricultural production but, at the same time, to
provide a more reasonable basis for improving the
welfare of the significant number of people who have
heretofore contributed very little to the economy,
either as producers or consumers. Such adjustments
would result in greater earnings for large numbers
of rural residents, who have practically no assets,
other than their ability to work, to offer in achieving greater productivity and earnings. It would be
hoped that eventually the major portion of rural
residents could develop the entrepreneurial skills
necessary to efficiently manage productive farms,
but it is clear that this process will be slow and
will reach into decades of time. The suggestions

presented in the following paragraphs relate to how
this labor force can be more effectively utilized to
achieve greater agricultural production and, at the
same time, provide greatly increased earnings for
these people during the long interim that these people, or their children, will need to develop the
skills necessary to be effective modern farm operators or to work effectively in other segments of the
economy.

In connection with the lands irrigated by the
Venezuelan Government as part of the agrarian reform
program, it is suggested that the present farm size,
which varies from less than five hectares to fifteen
hectares per unit, be increased to larger units of
from forty to sixty hectares, a size that constitutes
a sound economic basis for intensive farming. Thus,
a sufficient land base would be provided for diversified, year-round farming operations.

Consequently, the number of farms to be assigned
to farmers as owners would be greatly reduced. However, each of these farms would provide remunerative
labor for from four to six additional specialized
workers (depending on the type of products) on a contract basis. This type of work opportunity, which
could be supported by reasonable wage regulations if
necessary, would greatly increase the earnings of
present squatter farmers and workers. It would also
provide them with the steady income they need to improve their housing and to increase educational and
cultural opportunities for themselves and their families. Such work opportunity would also expose these
workers to modern farming methods without assuming
the full responsibility and risk of managing a farm
themselves. Thus, better utilization and fewer losses
of agricultural credit funds would be achieved.

More careful selection of farm operators would
be necessary in connection with assignment of parcels. However, with a greatly reduced number of farm
units, farmers with the experience and skills necessary to manage these commercial farms could be selected. Also, these larger farm units could produce
income to justify the significant government expenses

for education and would attract more of the techni-
cally trained people, from both the practical schools
and universities, who would be interested in becoming
farm operators but who generally lack inducement and
opportunity at the present time. In addition, agricultural extension and credit services could be much
more efficiently provided under this pattern of land
distribution.

A more effective agricultural ladder would thus
be provided for rural people to move upward from
farm worker to owner of a farm run on a commercial
basis. In a generation, the development of labor
skills and the establishment of a stable land ownership system would more likely be achieved by the distribution of larger farm units. Many of the families
that were placed on small units before they were
skilled enough to operate these farms efficiently
already find themselves in an impossible debt situation and still do not have sufficient skills to make
a success of farming operations on the small units
available to them. Their financial difficulties have
been aggravated, in part, by delays in developing
adequate technical assistance facilities and essential
community facilities, such as roads, drainage projects, and marketing services.

The case for establishing larger units on irrigated lands involved in the agrarian reform program
is presented in only brief form here. There are many
other arguments and reasons, from the standpoint of
the welfare of the individual family as well as the
welfare of Venezuela as a whole, that favor this pattern over the pattern of small units being established
at present. Modern agriculture requires units larger
than five to fifteen hectares to justify all of the
inputs of machinery and materials involved in such
production. At the same time, the utilization of labor supplies would be more effective and the net
outflow of people to urban areas should not be significantly increased. Other patterns of distributing
land, including the idea presented herein, are well
worthy of consideration and adoption in Venezuela's
agrarian reform program.

Capital Supplies and Their Utilization

The material presented in Chapter 7 indicated the shortage of capital for the agricultural sector, especially investments in items needed to improve farm organization for more efficient production. Other problems mentioned were the underdevelopment of administrative and management skills for credit programs as well as for individual farm management and capital utilization. It was indicated that agriculture can attract very little private capital because of the competitive advantage that industrial and urban development activities have in the private capital markets. Consequently, the Venezuelan Government will be required to continue as the principal institutional source of credit for agriculture. Because of this, most of the suggestions that can be made in connection with capital supplies and utilization concern government policies and programs. Proper utilization of capital on farms is, of course, part of the farm management skills that need improvement. Such aspects are covered in the next section on management of the factors of production.

The preceding discussion of problems with regard to capital supplies and utilization presented ideas on corrective action that was seen as necessary and possible. In this section, these ideas will be summarized with limited discussion, for the sake of brevity.

The necessity of reorganizing the institutional structure of the Agricultural and Livestock Bank (BAP) is well demonstrated in order that this institution can carry on effective service as the principal source of credit to farmers. Separation of marketing, price-support, and storage services from the BAP into a specialized marketing and commodity service organization should be accomplished as soon as possible. Also, special authorization is needed to make it possible for the bank to clear out of its credit portfolio the large volume of uncollectable accounts that are still carried in the books. This will involve assignment of special resources to make possible a case-by-case review to determine the reasons for uncollectability and adjustment of the accounts according to specific criteria developed for this purpose.

Experience in developing such criteria is available in connection with agricultural credit programs elsewhere that would serve as adequate guides. Such adjustment of the largely inoperative loan portfolio of the BAP is a prerequisite to the establishment of sounder business procedures in this institution and to the operation of this agency as a real credit organization.

Separation of the larger commercial farmer loaning function from the BAP is recommended. However, the establishment of an entirely new institutional structure to handle these types of loans, as prescribed in the Agricultural Development Bank Law, passed in 1968, is not believed to be essential. One alternative for providing this type of credit service without a completely new institutional structure would be to establish a section in the Venezuelan Development Corporation. This agency has operating programs in connection with sugar cane production and has had previous experience in other agricultural loaning programs in connection with livestock and rice. Another possibility might be to establish a mixed government and private bank capital and management arrangement with one of the private banks of Venezuela having well-distributed branch offices.

The supervised agricultural credit program started in Venezuela in 1963 has provided some experience in the utilization of integrated credit to cover all types of agricultural credit needs of individual farmers. This program has considerable educational objectives for the owners of medium-sized and small farms. Consequently, costs of such programs are higher than interest income from loans made. However, the principle of providing a line of credit to cover not only annual operating expense credit needs but also farm structural adjustment credit for medium- and long-term periods must be expanded to cover most types of credit programs operated by the Venezuelan Government.

Reorganization of the farms to make it possible for
farmers to adapt to modern farm production methods
requires large investments in machinery, in improved
breeding stock for livestock, and in such permanent
improvements as buildings, fences, land leveling, and
establishment of permanent tree crops. The unavail-
ability of credit for these medium- and long-term
investments, which is the general case in Venezuela,
is an obstacle to improving efficiency in farm operations and proper utilization of annual inputs leading to greater productivity. Adaptation of loaning
programs to this principal of integrated credit service and larger credit supplies need to be given high
priority.

A special commission should be established, with
representatives from the Ministry of Agriculture and
Livestock and the Ministry of Justice, to study and
develop ways and means to establish a general crop
and chattel law and procedures to make possible more
credit activities by nongovernmental agencies in the
agricultural sectors.

The recently developed arrangements for providing
production credit for certain industrial crops, such
as cotton and sesame, made possible by the collaboration of the BAP with private banks in guaranteeing
and providing other facilities needed to interest
private sources of capital to participate in the agricultural sector, should be encouraged and increased.

Marketing processes and channels will, of necessity, become oriented to larger scale handling of
agricultural products to accommodate the larger urban
centers that are developing so rapidly. This will
entail a larger need for commodity credit to finance
the marketing organizations and facilities involved
in product distribution. Processing plants apparently have access to credit now so that they can purchase
products from farmers and then carry the products in
their own inventories for considerable periods until
they are processed and sold to retailers and consumers. However, as systems of product assembly, classification, and uniform packing develop, some of which
will be part of producers' organizations, there will

need to be a significant line of credit available so
that at least part of the purchase price can be paid
to the producer on delivery of his products. Ordinar-
ily, short-term credit only is required for such
marketing activities, and private banks will probably
be interested in providing this type of service. However, advance planning is needed in this respect to
facilitate the development of this type of credit
service so that such organization of marketing activities can progress.

Management of the Factors of Production and Distribution of Products

Improvement in the managerial skills at all levels of the agricultural sector has been indicated as
one of the most critical needs for increasing rates
of agricultural development. This applies from institutional management at the government level down
to management of individual farms. It especially has
application to marketing and distribution activities
for agricultural products. Such improvements are,
of course, dependent on long-range educational processes and upgrading of administrative and technical
skills. Ideas are presented herein with regard to
possible means of speeding up the requisite educational process as well as to specific actions leading
to improvements in the organization and management of
the factors of production.

Micro-Economic Studies, Training, and Orientation

One of the critical bottlenecks in the agricultural development picture is the lack of adequate
information regarding proper farm management as a
means to improving farm productivity and data needed
for the proper administration of government programs
such as agricultural extension, credit, price support
and marketing. Greater emphasis on this important
phase of technology requires action in the higher
educational institutions, as well as in the investigation, extension, and economics departments of the
Ministry of Agriculture and Livestock, and among
farmers themselves and their commodity organizations.
Also, processing industries involved with agricultural

products and businesses supplying machinery, fertilizers, and other supplies to farmers should be encouraged to assist in improving the technical
information both about and for the individual farm
units. Some empirical information and experience
is being utilized in determining production methods
of individual farm units. However, very little is
being done with regard to keeping organized records
or analyzing results to indicated adjustments needed
to increase productivity and profits. The following
suggestions are made for the development of farm
management skills and the procurement of essential
data relating thereto for use in the several organizations needing such information.

First, agricultural economics training facilities
in the agricultural universities of Venezuela need to
be augmented and improved, and postgraduate scholarships need to be emphasized in the following subjects:

1. Farm management
2. Animal husbandry (Responsibility for
        teaching this subject is presently
        divided between two faculties.)
3. Farm production economics
4. Agricultural credit
5. Marketing principles and practice,
        including price analysis, product
        classification, packing, and dis-
        tribution facilities
6. Cooperatives
7. Land economics
8. Industrial uses of agricultural products
        and processing techniques

As rapidly as possible, full-time agricultural
economists, especially those who have specialized
in farm management, should be incorporated into the
Agricultural Investigation Department of the Ministry of Agriculture and Livestock. At least one
well-qualified agricultural economist should be included in the directive staff for research to assist
in incorporating more economic considerations into
a great majority of the individual crop investigations, even though such investigations deal with

specific natural science research, so that the results can be more readily interpreted and prepared
for use by farm operators. Also, agricultural economists of varying degrees of preparation should be
added to the Agricultural Investigation Center staffs
or should be incorporated into the Department of Economics and Statistics of the Ministry of Agriculture
and Livestock to undertake a series of farm management and cost-of-production studies on a continuous
basis. A staff of three or four such technicians
could be well justified to carry on farm management
and farm-cost analyses for several purposes--partic-
ularly to provide the technical information needed
for agricultural price-support programs. Such studies
should be worked out based on a collaborating arrangement with farmers in several different types of
agricultural production. The keeping of exact records
by the farmers could be supervised by the research
staff, and reliable and accurate information on farm
management problems and solutions would, in time, be
available. These results would go a long way to indicate what is needed to make farmers respond to demand factors in production patterns, as well as
indicate the possibilities for adjustments in farm
organization and production practices that are needed to yield more net income. This sort of information and its application are essential for dynamic
agricultural development.

Agricultural economists are needed in the Agricultural Extension Service, in both the national
office and the zonal offices, to advise on methods
of developing convincing economic material in support
of the technological information being communicated
to farmers. A feedback of ideas to the investigation
centers on management and practices needing research
and trials with respect to specific products or com-
binations of products would thus be facilitated.
After additional agricultural economists were incorporated into the Agricultural Extension Service, specific training materials and interpretation of farm
management study results for use by farmers could be
developed for effective direct training programs.
The development of farm management training projects
could then be incorporated, with high priority, in

the annual plans for the national and local extension
programs.

Clarification of Objectives in Establishment of Measurable Goals for Agencies Administering Agricultural Development Programs

The development of administrative and technical
skills for management of government programs has been
commented on frequently in this volume. This process
has resulted in wastage of funds, lack of continuity
in essential program activities, and failure to follow sound and efficient organization and business
practices. One of the reasons for these problems is
the lack of clearly stated and understood objectives
for the various programs involved, together with a
lack of measurable goals that can be reviewed and
evaluated periodically to determine progress made toward objectives for the particular work being done.
This deficiency has greatly weakened the process of
budget justification and has permitted abuses in the
use of funds and personnel without adequate basis for
administrative control or disciplinary action against
those responsible for abuses. The time has arrived
to establish clearly stated objectives and measurable
goals and to put some "teeth" into administrative
methods so that better performance of personnel can
be achieved. In addition, greater delegations of
authority in carrying out program operations could
be safely accomplished in this way.

In the macro-economic planning done for the plans
of the nation, significant progress has been made in
setting over-all objectives and measurable goals and
in instituting a system of periodic evaluation of
progress. Generally, the failure to reach established
goals can be traced to the failure of the agencies
involved to gear their work performance in accordance
with national goals. Consequently, the various agencies involved should make a more complete and realistic evaluation of what is expected of each program
and activity and interpret these into stated goals,
which can be measured, for the furtherance of the
work in agricultural development. This should be
done both on a long-range basis and in connection with

annual budget preparation. Special task forces
should be appointed within each of the major agencies
involved in agricultural development to prepare such
statements of objectives and to develop convenient
criteria for establishing the measurable goals to
give administrative force to performance. Such task
forces should be coordinated by the Ministry of Agriculture and Livestock with the technical collaboration of CORDIPLAN. Also, the task forces should have
resources to employ outside consultants as necessary
in the field of public administration and business
methods. The agencies involved should be endowed
with legally defined authority to make adjustments
in their executive organization in accordance with
both the needs indicated by this review and the working objectives and goals after they are approved by
the Ministry of Agriculture and Livestock.

Establishing a Civil Service Law for Public Employees

Considerable study has been made of the need for
a basic civil service law in Venezuela, and proposals
for such a law have been under consideration for many
years. Such a law is essential in order to overcome
the institutional underdevelopment in public agencies
that has prevented many of them from providing efficient and necessary services for the economic development of Venezuela. In order to attract and maintain,
with reasonable continuity, the more dedicated and
effective administrators and technicians, such a law
is needed to provide a basis for reasonable professional and economic advancement and protection from
unwarranted pressures from groups working against the
general welfare. The number of agricultural technicians is increasing rapidly so that more personnel
can be selected in the future on a merit basis. At
the same time, without a civil service law, this
greater number of persons seeking professional positions will also increase the pressures and influence
of interest groups attempting to disrupt the public
services for their own gain without regard for the
general welfare.

Greater efforts and new methods are needed with
respect to several other aspects of management of the

factors of production. Several of these aspects
will be brought out in the next section of this study,
which deals with recommended action in connection
with specific products leading to an increased rate
of agricultural development.

IDEAS FOR INCREASING RATE OF GROWTH FOR SPECIFIC AGRICULTURAL COMMODITIES

As previously pointed out, there is a great deal
of variation in the technological level which has
been reached in the development of important crops
and livestock enterprises. Relatively efficient
methods are not used throughout the production and
distribution process of all products. In this section, ideas will be presented on possibilities for
increasing the rate of production for important agricultural products or product groups.

From an ecological standpoint, several products
should be able to be produced in relatively large
volumes. Low yields that may now exist are due to
problems of management and costs of input factors,
for which solutions should be found by determined
efforts and methods aimed at increasing the volume
of production, until it is at least adequate to supply national demand. The principal products in this
category are corn, rice, beans, roots and tubers,
sesame, cotton, peanuts, sisal, tropical fruits, vegetables, coffee, cocoa, sugar cane, tobacco, copra,
beef, pork, poultry, milk, and eggs. Ecological conditions and other factors will continue to limit national production of wheat, feed grains, and most
deciduous fruits.

In Table 91, an attempt is made to show the long-
range production possibilities of Venezuela's major
agricultural products, classified in accordance with
the possibilities of providing substitutes for imported
products, supplying national demand, and providing
an export outlet. These possibilities are presented
in ascending order from left to right in the table,
with the assumption that the production covers all
the production categories to the left of the column
checked in the table for each product. The last two

TABLE 91

Suggested Long-Range Production Possibilities for
Important Venezuelan Agricultural Products

Product	Long-Term Goal or Possibility						Status of 1966 Production in Relation to Goals	
	Substitute for Greater Portion of Imports	Supply Total National Demand				Cover National Demand and Allow Exports in Significant Quantities[b]		
		At Present per Capita Consumption Levels	For Increased per Capita Consumption Because of:				Defi-cit	Similar to Goal
			Greater Dietary Need	Additional Uses Indus-trial	Animal Feed			
Cereals								
Corn		x		x			x	
Rice					x			x
Grain sorghums (new)	x						[a]	
Legumes								
Edible beans		x	x				x	
Other edible legumes		x		x			x	
Soybeans (new)					x		[a]	
Roots and tubers								
Mandioc (yucca)		x						x
Potatoes		x						x
Other roots & tubers		x						x
Textiles & oilseed crops								
Sesame						x	x	
Cotton		x					x	
Peanuts				x			x	
Coconut (copra)	x			x			x	
Sisal							x	

290

Fruits and Vegetables				
Bananas		x			x
Citrus		x	x	x	
Other tropical fruits	x				
Tomatoes		x	x	x	
Other vegetables	x		x	x	
Other crops					
Coffee		x			x
Cocoa		x			x
Sugar cane		x			x
Plantain		x			x
Tobacco		x	x	x	
Livestock and Products					
Beef		x		x	
Pork	x		x	x	
Poultry	x		x	x	
Milk	x		x	x	
Eggs	x			x	

a Practically no production.

b It is estimated that the export products indicated, besides the four now exported regularly (bananas, plantain, coffee, and cocoa) could be competitive in foreign markets. The high cost of production excludes many of these products from foreign sales, and national demand for sesame, citrus fruits, and beef is not presently being met. Competition in international markets for these products would be dependent on an increase in productivity sufficient to substantially lower present costs per unit of each product.

Source: Subjective evaluation by the author, based on previously presented material.

291

columns present an evaluation of the status of production in relation to the long-range possibility
category indicated. As can be seen in the table,
twenty of the products are being produced below the
long-range possibility in varying degrees and the
other nine products are now in the long-range possibility category and will grow only with the increase
in population or as additional export markets may be
developed.

Supplementing Table 91 is a summary of the items
needing greater capital investments and efforts to
achieve the production possibilities indicated in
Table 91, with indications of the products involved
with respect to each item of action indicated.

This summary is largely self-explanatory. One
item in connection with the market service needs that
is not included in the summary statement is storage
facilities for grains. A great deal of capital has
been invested in these installations by the Venezuelan
Government and by private interests, and this service
is probably past the critical stage as far as investment in facilities is concerned. However, as far as
operations are concerned, greater efforts should be
made in working out suitable arrangements for the
government to turn the management of these facilities
over to a private agency on a lease or sale basis.
This would free the government of a large responsibility for funds and for the management of these services, with its high annual demand on the natioal
treasury. This sort of business can be more efficiently managed as a private activity and it should
be attractive to private capital, especially if suitable contracts for storage of products acquired by
the government in its price-support programs are made
available to the private storage companies. Storage
costs to the government would definitely be less under
such an arrangement than under the present directly
managed storage program.

Another factor not included in the list is development of additional processing industries for
agricultural products, especially fruits and vegetables. Additional facilities will be needed, but

canning and processing industries now established
with private capital will probably grow to meet this
demand as increased volume justifies new facilities.

Items Needing Greater Investment of Capital and Human Resources to Achieve Production Possibilities Indicated in Table 91

Item	Products and Factors of Production to Which Applied
1. Use of land and other natural resources	
a. Increase in irrigated land areas	Corn, beans, cotton, peanuts, beef, and milk
b. Adjustments in on-farm use of irrigation water	
(1) On-farm distribution systems improvements	All irrigated crops and pastures
(2) Land leveling	" " "
(3) Study and determination of optimum rates of application	" " "
c. Control of destructive practices due to planting crops on steep slopes and burning of vegetation	Corn, beans, mandioc, and pastures
d. Development of more suitable crop rotation systems to assist in maintaining fertility and controlling diseases	Corn, rice, potatoes, cotton, and vegetables

Item	Products and Factors of Production to Which Applied
2. Institutional service improvements	
a. Critical research items needing attention to obtain greater productivity	
(1) Variety development and testing	Grain sorghums, beans, soybeans, bananas, tree fruits, plantain, forage grasses, and legumes
(2) Seed selection and sanitation	All annual crops except corn, sesame, and cotton
(3) Determination of optimum fertilizer use practices	All crops and pastures
(4) Determination of optimum pesticide use practices	All crops and pastures
(5) Land preparation and cultivation practices, including plant spacing (with and without mechanization)	All crops and pastures
(6) Farm management research by types of farming and regions	All farms, especially cattle and hog farms

Item	Products and Factors of Production to Which Applied
(7) Livestock feeding feasibility experiments	Beef, pork, and milk
(8) Marketing facilities and practices	All products, especially fruits and vegetables
(9) Determination of additional industrial uses for farm products and the feasibility of their development	Corn, rice, soybeans, mandioc, peanuts, fruits, and vegetables
(10) Development of new products	African oil palm, castor beans, other fiber crops, spices and medicinal plants, mutton, and milk goats

b. Credit supplies and services

  (1) Larger supplies of credit needed for:

(a) Annual production input costs	Beans, bananas, plantains, beef, and pork
(b) Purchase of machinery and breeding livestock, and other medium-term adjustment credit	Corn, beans, sisal, bananas, tree fruits, vegetables, beef, and pork

Item	Products and Factors of Production to Which Applied
(c) Such permanent farm improvements as buildings, development of permanent crops, fencing, and water facilities	All products except rice, sesame, cotton, sugar cane, tobacco, and poultry
(d) Lines of credit for commodity purchases during the marketing process	Fruits and vegetables, beef, pork, and sisal

c. Market facilities and service improvements

(1) Production area assembly, classification, and packing facilities (these are almost completely lacking)	All fruits and vegetables, including roots and tubers
(2) Public livestock markets (preferably tied in with or contiguous to integrated meat packing plants under construction, plus other markets in major producing areas)	Beef and pork

Item	Products and Factors of Production to Which Applied
(3) Terminal wholesale market installations in major consuming centers	Fruits and vegetables, roots and tubers, poultry, and eggs
(4) Price and market quantity reporting system from major consuming centers on a current basis to assist in channeling products to markets	Practically all products
(5) Market development and consumer research and education services	Practically all products

(Agricultural Extension Service improvements are closely related to the research items indicated in the previous section. Development of suitable materials and communication aids, together with specific training programs for each of the items 2-a-(1) to (8), are needed to permit effective extension of technology to farm operators. The following items should receive additional emphasis in the extension program: home management, including home improvements, nutrition, clothing, money, management, and cultural improvement among farm families.

PRIORITY ACTION PROJECTS LEADING TO HIGHER
RATES OF AGRICULTURAL DEVELOPMENT
IN VENEZUELA

From the foregoing sections of this chapter,
major points requiring action are extracted and ar-
ranged in the folowing paragraphs in a subjective
order of priority based on an appreciation of the
present obstacles to agricultural progress. Solution of each problem is proposed by the project activity indicated. Separate activities that could
be undertaken by government or private agencies interested in improving agricultural development are
also indicated.

The development of facilities for increasing
micro-economic research, training, and application
in improving administration of development programs
in agriculture and in increasing farm management
skills is critically needed. Such techniques of
micro-economic analysis are essential at all levels
to implement rational development, to improve productivity, and to confront and solve the many complex
production and distribution problems involved in
modern agriculture. Also, agricultural economic
technicians, especially those with specialization
in farm management research and training, are very
scarce in Venezuela. Limited facilities now exist
for preparing technicians in this discipline of applied science. Several segments, which involve different institutional agencies and which require several approaches to bring about the needed improvements
in this respect, are discussed below.

University-level educational facilities for preparing agricultural economic technicians are seriously
deficient. Only introductory courses in agricultural
economics are included in the curriculums of the agricultural faculties of the Central University of Venezuela. The professorial staff should be strengthened,
and additional courses provided, to study means of
maximizing utilization of the factors of production,
farm management, and market analysis. Also,
university-level facilities for education in home management are urgently needed.

Although an extensive postgraduate facility in
agricultural economics would be difficult to justify
at the present time because of the limited number of
graduates in this field, scholarships for postgraduate
study in foreign universities should be established
to encourage more agricultural university graduates
to specialize in this area of study.

Arrangements for employing more agricultural
economists in Venezuela's agricultural research and
extension agencies need to be implemented. This
could be done by utilizing the few Venezuelans trained
in this field at the present time and also by arrang-
ing with international technical aid organizations to
furnish such technicians until additional local technicians can be trained in this discipline.

A series of farm management research projects
for agricultural extension training programs should
be organized as soon as possible. Specific cost-of-
production data and other information needed for the
administration of government price-support programs
should also be included in the farm management research project.

A second important area of activity is the development of facilities for improving the preparation
of products for marketing and improving the marketing
and distribution services for agricultural products.
This work involves market research, market development, and information services, as well as the institutional structure involved in production and
assembly, classification, uniform packing, transportation, and storage of agricultural products. Several
segments of this work could be separated for specific
project activities as follows:

1. University-level courses to provide training
in marketing aspects.

2. Specific projects to assist particular groups
of producers to develop assembly, classification, and
uniform packing facilities to permit larger scale
handling of products shipped to the larger consuming
centers. This activity is particularly important

for fruits and vegetables, and was almost completely
lacking in 1966.

3. The projected development of a network of
integrated animal slaughter and meat-processing plants
will provide a basis for drastic change in the market
outlets for beef and pork. However, sufficient consideration has not been given to public livestock
markets, including their operational base, financing,
and management, in connection with these new slaughter
facilities. An urgent need exists for advance planning for the institutional organization necessary to
initiate the development of public livestock markets.

4. The institutional services involved in the
marketing of agricultural products are complex and
show a lack of organization. Continuous efforts to
improve these services are needed, and several other
specific project items are indicated in the extensive
list following Table 91 that serve as reference to the
type of activities that should be undertaken.

Educational improvements for the rural sector,
including adjustment of curriculums and regulations
for primary schools, removal of the institutional
obstacle that prevents agricultural practical school
graduates from participating in higher educational
facilities, and greater financial and technical support for the agricultural research and extension activities of the Ministry of Agriculture and Livestock
need early attention.

A civil service law should be passed so that more
dedicated career technicians will be attracted to
public service and will have some career protection
from frequent changes due to the rapid turnover of
politically appointed program administrators.

Adjustments in the organizational structure and
increased supplies of agricultural credit are urgently needed. For example, price support and storage
activities should be separated from the BAP and handled by a specialized agency so that the administrative facilities of the BAP will not be overtaxed.

Also, integrated credit services for farmers
should be established so that, in addition to the
present supplies of annual operating credit, adequate
funds will be available for farm structural reorganization and development on a medium- or long-term
repayment basis.

Administrative business procedures should be
tightened up so that more businesslike records of
loans collected can be maintained by Venezuelan
Government credit agencies.

Finally, a general law should be enacted authorizing broader use of crop and chattel mortgages, including use by private lenders.

Adjustments in irrigation project planning and
operation should be started as soon as possible. The
size of farm units in projects related to the agrarian
reform program should be adjusted in an effort to improve the utilization of land, labor, and capital.

The utilization, management, and control of land
and other natural resources need more attention. A
permanent staff should be established in an appropriate government agency to scientifically and systematically describe, evaluate, and map Venezuela's basic
natural resources and ecological conditions.

In addition, an effective and more rapid means of
completing a cadastral survey should be developed and
an appropriate land registry system should be established for Venezuela.

Lastly, institutions regulating the conservation
and control of natural resources, wildlife, and
recreational facilities based on natural or historical sites should be strengthened. This phase of work
probably should be given higher priority than indicated here. However, because of the present shortage
of adequate numbers of natural resource technicians
and the long period required for the public to develop the necessary consciousness to support and demand more rational use of natural resources, this
work will be slow to develop.

More clearly stated program objectives and measurable goals should be developed for most of the
institutional service agencies, in order to make possible improvements in administrative effectivensss.
This activity has not been given higher priority
because successful completion of this important task
is dependent on the training of technicians, as well
as successful passage of an effective civil service
law. The development of administrative and technical skills in management is a critical necessity.
Clear-cut statements of measurable goals should be
forthcoming from each agency involved in agricultural
development. Such goals should be periodically reviewed so that progress can be measured and responsibility for lack of progress or misuse of resources
definitely determined.

There are, of course, many other means of removing
important obstacles to greater agricultural development in Venezuela. However, it is believed that if
these key improvements were achieved, the greatest
results in increasing Venezuela's rate of agricultural development would be achieved.

NOTES

1. One proposal was made and documented in a
special study by Vincencio Baez Finol entitled El
Impuesto Predial Rural--Su Institución en Venezuela
(Caracas: Consejo de Bienestar Rural, 1961). Also,
the Agrarian Reform Law in Article 20, paragraph
unico provides authorization for a progressive land
tax in certain circumstances.

2. Ernest Maes, Adviser to the Creole Foundation in Caracas, was instrumental in establishing
the program in Chile and can provide details of that
work.

APPENDIXES

TABLE 1

Land Use on Farms in Selected Regions[a] of Venezuela, 1961
(1,000 Has.)

Land Use Category	Andes	Western	West Central	Central	Western Plains	Eastern & Southern Plains	Eastern
Permanent crops	187	43	105	118	50	58	92
Annual and semi-permanent crops	203	69	182	110	193	168	101
Cultivated pastures	520	779	601	115	176	488	69
Natural pastures	237	100	352	558	2,486	7,838	2,387
Idle crop land	102	82	138	74	134	212	52
Abandoned crop land in brush	205	149	353	174	185	481	106
Forest land	380	594	330	414	712	1,652	392
Other land	85	42	120	78	117	347	119
Total land in farms	1,919	1,858	2,181	1,641	4,054	11,244	3,318
Number of farm units (1,000)	78.9	15.0	50.0	41.5	35.7	52.4	41.7

[a]Regions are divided according to federal entity boundaries as follows: Andes: Mérida, Táchira, and Trujillo; Western: Zulia; West Central: Falcón, Lara, and Yaracuy; Central: Federal District, Aragua, Carabobo, and Miranda; Western Plains: Barinas, Cojedes, and Portuguesa; Eastern and Southern Plains: Anzoátegui, Apure, Guárico, and Monagas; Eastern: Bolívar, Nueva Esparta, Sucre, Delta Amacuro territory, and Amazon territory.

Source: Data from 1961 agricultural census.

FRUIT PRODUCTION IN VENEZUELA

The official statistics of the Ministry of
Agriculture and Livestock, which are utilized by
the Central Bank of Venezuela in calculating total
agricultural product, include only very general
categories for fruit production. The Fruit Development Fund, which has been operating in Venezuela
since 1962, has created considerable interest in
fruit culture. The Fund has collected data on fruit-
producing areas that vary considerably from the data
utilized in official statistics. This activity has
gained more importance than is adequately reflected
in the general statistical reports of the Ministry
of Agriculture and Livestock. Consequently, this
special appendix item has been added.

The estimates of areas devoted to production
of plantain and bananas correspond somewhat with
the official statistics. However, the total hectares
utilized in the production of all other fruits amounts
to 58,924 hectares, which is about eight times the
area shown in the figures used in the official reports
(7,800 hectares). One of the projects of the Fruit
Development Fund is to carry out an accurate census
of fruit-growing areas, which should provide a better
basis for data on this industry.

TABLE 2

Estimates of 1965 Fruit Production in Venezuela

Fruit Crop	Hectares in Production	Production (1,000 Metric Tons)	Value of Production (Million Bs.)
Plantain	99,967	412.9	206.5
Banana	58,317	251.0	153.7
Orange and tangerine	21,844	264.0	93.8
Pineapple	4,279	40.0	20.0
Avocado	12,264	34.5	34.5
Mango	8,470	78.8	23.6
Papaya	2,500	100.0	25.0
Grapefruit	710	3.6	1.1
Soursop (guanábana)	500	2.5	2.5
Guava	2,457	14.7	7.3
Peach	100	1.3	1.6
Lime	1,600	16.0	3.2
Sapodilla (níspero)	500	1.0	2.0
Fig	300	0.9	1.4
Coco plum (hicaco)	300	1.2	1.2
Passion fruit	300	3.6	2.2
Giant granadilla	100	1.0	1.0
Watermelon	1,500	30.0	7.5
Other melons	600	6.0	3.0
Strawberry	50	0.3	1.2
Grape	50	0.5	1.0
Other fruits	500	2.5	2.5
Total	217,208	1,266.3	595.8

Source: Information supplied by Ricardo Araque of the Consejo de Bienestar Rural, a member of the Board of Directors of the Fruit Development Fund of Venezuela.

307

TABLE 3

Changes in Amount of Land Harvested and in Total Production
of Important Crops in Venezuela, 1961-65

Crop	Area Harvested (1,000 Ha.)			Total Production (1,000 Metric Tons)		
	1961	1965	Per Cent Change	1961	1965	Per Cent Change
Cereals						
Rice (paddy)	58.4	105.1	80	80.7	199.9	148
Corn	388.7	461.8	19	419.5	521.0	24
Wheat	2.3	2.3	0	1.2	1.3	8
Legumes						
Black beans	64.6	65.2	1	31.0	26.1	-16
Other beans	24.9	28.9	16	13.0	16.2	25
Peas and pigeon peas	7.1	14.1	99	3.6	6.9	92
Roots and tubers						
Yams	5.1	8.5	67	41.9	71.5	71
Taro root	6.6	10.5	59	51.7	96.6	87
Mandioc	25.7	24.5	-5	344.2	301.4	-12
Potatoes	9.3	16.2	74	74.1	135.9	83
Other roots and tubers	4.9	9.9	102	32.3	64.7	100

Fibers and oilseed crops

Sesame	53.9	87.1	62	24.9	54.1	117
Cotton (unginned)	50.3	45.9	- 9	36.4	44.6	23
Coconut (copra)	25.8	25.4	- 2	10.8	15.3	42
Peanuts	1.1	1.9	73	1.2	1.8	50
Sisal fiber	10.5	11.0	5	8.4	13.3	58
Fruits and vegetables						
Bananas	46.7	58.3	25	341.4	418.1	22
Other fruits	6.5	7.8	12	83.2	106.9	28
Onions	1.7	1.9	12	23.3	34.9	50
Tomatoes	4.3	4.7	9	65.9	72.1	9
Other vegetables	1.7	1.9	12	41.8	47.2	13
Coffee, cocoa, and others						
Cocoa	72.0	70.0	- 3	13.1	20.4	56
Coffee	316.6	340.0	7	53.7	54.1	1
Sugar cane	51.6	63.6	23	3,242.1	3,520.0	9
Plantains	60.1	100.0	66	223.7	547.1	144
Tobacco	7.5	6.5	-13	10.4	9.0	-13
Total	1,307.9	1,502.0	15	-	-	-

309

Source: Calculated from data in Table 45.

TABLE 4

Changes in Production of Livestock, Fish, and Forest
Products in Venezuela, 1961-65

Product	Unit	Production 1961	Production 1965	Per Cent Change
Livestock products				
Milk	million liters	444.6	646.1	45
Cattle	1,000 head	863.8	1,070.8	24
Hogs	1,000 head	694.3	779.5	12
Goats	1,000 head	375.8	378.8	1
Sheep	1,000 head	46.3	45.2	- 2
Poultry	million head	25.8	38.3	48
Eggs	million units	273.2	507.8	86
Fish	1,000 metric tons fresh equivalent	83.6	119.2	43
Forest products				
Lumber	1,000 cubic meters	268.2	410.2	53
Fine	1,000 cubic meters	74.4	55.0	-26
Hard	1,000 cubic meters	37.9	65.2	72
Soft	1,000 cubic meters	155.9	290.0	86
Latex	metric tons	229.0	171.0	-25
Charcoal	metric tons	8,646.0	10,200.0	18
Firewood	metric tons	1,957.0	450.0	130
Chicle	metric tons	126.0	203.0	61

Source: Data in Table 48.

310

The following eight tables provide supplemental statistical information for nine tables included in the text. Some data with regard to the Venezuelan economy and Venezuelan agricultural production have become available for the years 1966 and 1967 and are presented in this appendix in an effort to provide up-to-date information on some of the key factors used in this analysis. The tables in this appendix are generally prepared in the same format as the preceding tables so that continuing trends can be easily observed.

The general economy of Venezuela suffered a slight recession in 1966 and growth rates in most of the sectors of the economy were reduced below those existing during 1961-65. However, recovery was evident in 1967 and has continued into 1968. Consequently, the major conclusions and suggestions regarding possibilities for agricultural development in Venezuela included in this study have not taken into consideration the economic changes that occurred during 1966 and 1967, subsequent to the completion of the study.

TABLE 5

Gross Territorial Product of Venezuela by Principal Economic Sectors, 1966-67

Sector	Gross Territorial Product (Million Bs. at 1957 Prices)		Percentage Distribution of GTP	
	1966	1967[b]	1966	1967
Primary sector	11,606	12,196	33.4	33.9
Agriculture	2,526	2,602	7.3	7.3
Mining	427	409	1.3	1.1
Petroleum	8,653	9,085	24.9	25.5
Secondary sector	7,516	7,814	21.6	21.7
Manufacturing[a]	5,073	5,240	14.6	14.6
Construction	1,635	1,695	4.7	4.8
Water and electricity	808	879	2.3	2.3
Tertiary sector	15,664	15,958	45.0	44.4
Transportation and communication	1,300	1,310	3.7	3.6
Commerce	5,616	5,897	16.1	16.4
Other services	8,748	8,751	25.2	24.4
Total GTP	34,786	35,968	100.0	100.0
Total per capita production	3,836	3,767		
Agricultural sector	945	960		

aIncludes oil-refining industries.
bPreliminary figures, subject to revision.
Source: Annual reports of the Central Bank of Venezuela; figures for 1967 are preliminary.

TABLE 6

Distribution of Venezuela's Gross National Income
According to Contribution of Agricultural and
Other Sectors, 1966-67
(Million Bs. at 1957 Prices)

| Year | Gross National Income | Per Cent of Total | |
		Agricultural Sector	Other Sectors
1966	24,300	8.2	91.8
1967	25,357	8.3	91.7

Source: Annual reports of the Central Bank of Venezuela; figures for
1967 are preliminary. (Adjusted to 1957 base period by the
General Wholesale Price Index from the same source.)

TABLE 7

Fixed Capital in the Agricultural and Other Sectors
of the Venezuelan Economy, 1966-67
(1957 Prices)

Year	Fixed Capital in the Agricultural Sector[a]			Fixed Capital in Other Sectors			Total Fixed Capital	
	Total (Million Bs.)	Amount per Economically Active Person (1,000 Bs.)	Per Cent of Total	Total (Million Bs.)	Amount per Economically Active Person (1,000 Bs.)	Per Cent of Total	Total (Million Bs.)	Amount per Economically Active Person (1,000 Bs.)
1966	10,673	10.5	16.2	55,010	31.0	83.8	65,683	23.5
1967	11,200	10.7	16.3	57,200	31.1	83.7	68,400	23.7

[a]Does not include value of land.

Source: Annual reports of the Central Bank of Venezuela; figures for 1967 are preliminary.

314

TABLE 8

Foreign-Exchange Balances and Level of International
Reserves in Venezuela, 1966-67
(Millions of Dollars)

Year	Foreign-Exchange Balance	International Reserves at End of Year
1966	- 51	772
1967	95	867

Source: Annual reports of the Central Bank of Venezuela; figures for 1967 are preliminary.

315

TABLE 9

Area Harvested, Amount and Value of Total Production, and
Yields of Important Crops in Venezuela, 1966-67

Crop	Area Harvested (1,000 Has.)		Production (1,000 Metric Tons)		Value of Production at 1957 Prices (1,000 Bs.)		Yield per Hectare (Kgs.)	
	1966	1967	1966	1967	1966	1967	1966	1967
Cereals								
Rice (paddy)	103.8	138.9	210.0	292.2	96,810	134,726	2,022	2,104
Corn	466.9	488.5	557.5	604.3	117,626	127,507	1,194	1,237
Wheat	2.8	3.0	1.4	1.6	642	700	500	515
Legumes								
Black beans	69.3	72.0	29.8	31.8	22,103	23,561	430	441
Other beans	29.8	31.8	17.3	18.7	12,705	13,713	580	587
Peas and pigeon peas	15.1	16.1	7.8	8.6	4,685	5,148	520	534
Roots and tubers								
Yams	8.6	8.7	72.4	73.4	34,469	34,917	8,402	8,433
Taro root	11.2	11.9	103.2	110.1	51,172	54,600	9,200	9,275
Mandioc	25.6	25.8	320.0	327.7	71,360	73,073	12,500	12,720
Potatoes	16.5	17.3	142.7	151.0	59,934	63,437	8,651	8,715
Other roots and tubers	10.6	11.2	70.4	75.6	33,870	36,372	6,641	6,750
Fibers and oilseed crops								
Sesame	94.6	133.3	60.0	80.5	56,100	75,307	634	604
Cotton (unginned)	49.1	49.6	46.0	47.8	46,920	48,797	936	964
Coconut (copra)	23.0	23.0	13.8	14.2	11,896	12,254	600	617
Peanuts	2.3	4.7	1.8	4.6	2,150	4,260	1,000	976
Sisal fiber	11.2	11.2	13.5	14.2	6,750	7,107	1,210	1,265

Fruits and vegetables							
Bananas	59.3	59.2	427.7	433.7	86,824	88,040	7,215	7,324
Other fruits	7.8	8.0	101.7	104.7	22,266	22,923	12,951	13,004
Onions	1.7	1.8	36.4	38.0	19,657	20,502	20,968	20,735
Tomatoes	5.2	5.3	72.3	73.5	27,551	27,992	14,025	14,814
Other vegetables	1.9	2.0	47.6	50.0	29,076	30,573	25,006	25,132
Coffee, cocoa, and others								
Cocoa	71.6	71.6	22.9	24.1	63,058	66,147	320	336
Coffee	303.1	303.1	61.0	61.9	258,579	262,072	201	204
Sugar cane	64.0	62.4	4,183.6	4,104.7	157,500	151,912	64,601	65,000
Plantains	107.2	109.3	590.9	595.5	86,862	87,540	5,510	5,447
Tobacco	6.7	6.8	9.8	10.2	54,863	57,058	1,471	1,493
Total	1,569.2	1,678.3			1,435,422	1,531,231		

Source: <u>Agricultural Statistics Annual</u>, 1967, Ministry of Agriculture and Livestock.

TABLE 10

Production and Value of Livestock, Fish, and Forest Products in Venezuela, 1966-67

Product	Production		Value of Production (1,000 Bs. at 1957 Prices)	
	1966	1967	1966	1967
Livestock and products			915,762	978,692
Milk (million liters)	673.7	715.5	305,186	324,119
Cattle (1,000 head)	1,061.8	1,183.1	300,497	334,812
Hogs (1,000 head)	792.8	799.5	61,837	62,359
Goats (1,000 head)	380.2	385.2	3,802	3,852
Sheep (1,000 head)	45.4	43.8	454	437
Poultry (million head)	41.5	45.3	130,671	142,698
Eggs (million units)	584.7	569.4	113,314	110,354
Fish				
Fish (1,000 metric tons, fresh equivalent)	128.8	113.2	70,199	61,708
Forest products			101,791	102,052
Lumber (1,000 cubic meters)			98,730	97,377
Fine	57.0	56.5	21,090	20,909
Hard	77.0	89.8	28,654	33,390
Soft	342.6	301.2	48,986	43,078
Latex (metric tons)	223.0	54.0	535	130
Charcoal (metric tons)	10,771.0	16,753.0	2,074	3,229
Firewood (metric tons)	8,425.0	25,702.0	421	1,285
Chicle (metric tons)	30.0	32.0	30	32

Source: Agricultural Statistics Annual, 1966-67 Ministry of Agriculture and Livestock

TABLE 11

Graduates of Practical and Specialized Schools for Agriculture
in Venezuela, 1934-67

Years	Agricultural Technical Aids (Peritos)	Forestry Technical Aids (Peritos)	Farm Home Demonstration Agents	Coffee Culturists	Cocoa Culturists	Tractor Operators
1934-65	1,322	–	–	–	–	–
1939-65	–	–	953	–	–	–
1948-65	–	320	–	271	229	476
1966	211	18	157	37	52	52
1967	236	ND	122	0	0	80
Total	1,769	338[a]	1,232	308	281	608

[a]Total to 1966 only.

Source: Agricultural Statistics Annual, 1966, Ministry of Agriculture and Livestock; a preliminary annual report of the Central Bank of Venezuela was source of 1967 figures. Totals to 1965 were changed from previous reports in the 1966 publication.

319

TABLE 12

Graduates of Agricultural and Forestry Universities in Venezuela, 1940-66

Years	Agronomic Engineers	Veterinarians	Foresters
1940–65	–	296	–
1942–65	557	–	–
1952–65	–	–	161
1966	80	22	21
Total	637	318	182

Source: _Agricultural Statistics Annual_, 1966, Ministry of Agriculture and Livestock.

ABOUT THE AUTHOR

Louis E. Heaton has worked in Latin America since 1952 as an agricultural economist for the American International Association. He has conducted special agricultural studies and has provided technical assistance in rural development activities. From 1952 to 1961, he was Chief of Special Studies for the Rural Welfare Council (Consejo de Bienestar Rural), a Venezuelan private agency established to assist and complement the rural improvement and development work carried out by official agencies in Venezuela. During that time, many pioneering resource and other studies were completed that have been instrumental in the agricultural development of Venezuela. The author had the opportunity to travel to all parts of Venezuela and has acquired a first-hand knowledge of rural conditions that is equaled by few other persons. During recent years, in addition to continuing his work as adviser to the Venezuelan Rural Welfare Council, he has performed technical assistance work in rural development project planning and execution in the countries of Bolivia, Brazil, Colombia, Costa Rica, the Dominican Republic, Guatemala, Nicaragua, Panama, and Peru.

After graduating in 1937 from Utah State University with a B.S. degree in agricultural economics, the author was awarded a research fellowship by the Giannini Foundation of Agricultural Economics at the University of California at Berkeley, affording him a year of postgraduate study. Mr. Heaton then worked for fourteen years for the Farmers Home Administration and its predecessor agency in the U.S. Department of Agriculture in administering agricultural credit programs in California, Arizona, Utah, Nevada, and Hawaii.

338.10987 **Date Due** 94228
H44

DEMCO NO. 295
